DEFEAT AND BEYOND

*An Anthology of French
Wartime Writing, 1940–1945*

DEFEAT
AND
BEYOND

An Anthology of French

Wartime Writing, 1940-1945

GERMAINE BRÉE and

GEORGE BERNAUER, Editors

PANTHEON BOOKS

A Division of Random House, New York

*Acknowledgment is gratefully extended to the following for permission to
translate, and reprint from their works:*

Atheneum Publishers: From *The Proverb and Other Stories*, by Marcel
Aymé, translated by Norman Denny. Copyright © by the Bodley Head Ltd.

Éditions Gallimard: *Solstice de juin*, by Henry de Montherlant. Copy-
right 1943 by Éditions Gallimard. From *Journal (1944–45)* by Pierre
Drieu La Rochelle, in *Récit secret* from the *Journal* and from *Exorde*.
Copyright 1951 by Éditions Gallimard. "Labyrinthe" and "Immense
Voix" in *Épreuves, Exorcismes*, by Henri de Michaux. Copyright
1946 by Éditions Gallimard. From *Caligula* and *Le Malentendu suivi
de Caligula*, by Albert Camus. Copyright 1942 by Éditions Gallimard.
From *L'Étranger* by Albert Camus. Copyright 1942 by Éditions Gallimard.
From "La République du silence" from *Situations*, by Jean-Paul Sartre.
Copyright 1949 by Éditions Gallimard.

Permission to translate an excerpt from *Les Beaux Draps*, by L. F.
Céline, has been granted by Madame Destouches.

Éditions Bernard Grasset: From *Triomphe de la vie*, by Jean Giono.

Harcourt, Brace & World, Inc.: From *Flight to Arras*, by Antoine de
Saint-Exupéry. Copyright 1942 by Harcourt, Brace and World, Inc.

Librairie Lardanchet: From *La Seule France*, by Charles Maurras.

Meredith Press: From *Aragon: Poet of the French Resistance*, edited by
Hannah Josephson and Malcolm Cowley. Copyright 1945 by Duell,
Sloan and Pearce.

Contents

DEFEAT AND BEYOND

An Anthology of French
Wartime Writing, 1940–1945

Introduction

Boundaries and Limitations

THIS IS NOT A LITERARY ANTHOLOGY; though
most of the texts we selected were written by literary men,
their purpose at the time was not, on the whole, literary.
Several poems are included, because the groups of poets
who gathered in various small communities, north and
south, were singularly successful in voicing the moods of
their fellow men; poems, besides, could more easily be
mimeographed for circulation.

The anthology does not propose to give a full account
either of the writers' resistance or of the more general
reaction to the French defeat. These have already been
the subject of many bulky books written by competent
historians.

It is not a political book; we have not taken sides or
passed judgment. That too was done and then undone.
We have attempted to let each person represented speak
for himself, furnishing only the frame of reference that
would recall events and positions now widely known.

Our aim has been to recapture somewhat the complex
moods and patterns of feeling, uncertainty, bafflement, that
underlay the simplistic either-or dialogue of traitor and
patriot in which, retrospectively, we tend to cast the
1940–1944 confrontations. As far as possible we have tried

to give a glimpse of the submerged world of feeling and thought that evolved, took shape, and surfaced in many forms, writing being one of these. Writing itself took many forms: indirect in allegory, black humor, or exemplary tale; direct in inner meditation or factual information.

The material was abundant; some of it is already widely known. We imposed strict limitations on ourselves; we eliminated all texts written or published outside France or, with a few exceptions, outside the date limits of 1940–1944. The exceptions are a few pages from intimate journals, written in France at the time, though published only in later years; they expressed submerged inner dialogues and sometimes a man's ultimate confrontation with defeat and death. All the texts are translations except one: the page in which Drieu La Rochelle—who had opted for collaboration—on the eve of suicide resorted to halting English, so deep was his sense of alienation.

On June 17, 1940, the victorious German Army marched down the Champs-Élysées in a silent, empty Paris. The parade was a temporary climax to two momentous years of conquest: Austria, Czechoslovakia, Poland, Denmark, Norway, Belgium, France. Under the German impact, the countries of Europe had gone down like tenpins. Four years later, on August 19, 1944, as the Allied columns spearheaded by General Leclerc's Free French division bore down on Paris, a people's insurrection, in traditional nineteenth-century style, started the movement that culminated on August 25 in the surrender of the Paris-centered Nazi command.

The war was not over. Indeed, within the broad context of the world-wide operations that characterized World War II, neither the fall nor the liberation of Paris may seem as momentous in retrospect as they did to the Western world at the time they occurred. The facts are well-known, as are also, on the whole, the struggles, the sufferings, the bitter hostilities and myths they engendered. It is not the purpose of this book to retrace once again the events of those four years of occupation, to explain, exonerate, idealize, or blame. For the French in 1940, the defeat of France followed a period of national dissension and debate carried on, for the most part, against a background of tacit common belief. However divided on political and social issues, right or left, the French as a people prided themselves on belonging to a great civilized country, liberal in its inclinations, sure of its values. Beneath party fabric of the country, and beyond the class antagonisms that had surfaced so violently in the thirties, lay a somewhat amorphous common belief concerning the importance and resiliency of France itself, an entity distinct from its government.

Certainly the defeat did not cancel out these antagonisms, although once or twice in the course of those years—in the shock of defeat or the euphoria of liberation —the majority of Frenchmen dreamed of a country unified in feeling and goals. It did, however, place these dissensions in a dramatic perspective, survival. Brutal and inglorious, the facts, however interpreted, made clear the gap that had separated myth and reality. A reappraisal of France's image of itself could hardly be avoided. What image cast in what ethical and ideological mode? Against French failure stood the Nazi triumph outstripping all expectations, an image perhaps to be emulated. Outside France it was possible not to think in apocalyptic terms. Inside France, the disaster was so great that it was difficult at first to think otherwise.

It is with the reactions *inside* France during those years that we are concerned here. Shut in on themselves spiritually, held within the prison of occupation, in their journals, essays, poems, and fictional works French writers debated issues, each one with himself, and with or against one another. We have selected for inclusion in this volume

only such works as were written and—with rare exceptions
—published *inside France during the war years*, elimi-
nating thereby the great mass of literature produced outside. Hence the absence of many well-known names,
among them. Georges Bernanos's calls to resistance, all
General de Gaulle's and André Malraux's not the least
written from outside France, have had to be omitted. We
also most regretfully eliminate the historian Marc Bloch's
Strange Defeat, written in 1940 but published only in
1957, though available since 1949 in English translation
and well known over here. We are not using this book for
any polemical purpose but rather its documentary value,
for what it reveals of the motivations that move men to
act in desperate circumstances. In the forties, as both the
military struggle without and the evidence of Nazi brutality within grew in intensity, issues were simplified,
judgments and condemnations became peremptory. Writers paid, sometimes with their lives, for the positions
they took. But the concept of the "two Frances"—one
heroic, the other treacherous—an ambivalent concept in-
herited from France's revolutionary past, is an obvious
oversimplification.

The texts we have selected establish a more complex
perspective closer to the confused, contradictory moods
that succeeded each other in those four years. They give
a glimpse into the course of a small sector of history in
the making, lived from day to day without benefit of
a posteriori certainties. In the past the "literature of the
Resistance" has quite naturally received the lion's share
of public attention. The outcome of the war had silenced
the collaborationist writers, genuine and disinterested
though some may have been at the time. We have introduced several of these, often hitherto untranslated, none
of whom came out of the war years unscathed, yet all
of whom were, in our opinion, fully and honestly committed to some cherished ideal for the regeneration of

their country. Their options were serious and must be so understood. The validity within what may seem to us distortions in their thinking needs to be carefully assessed. Furthermore, they help make clearer within what context the men who disagreed with them made their decisions, the rejections as well as the assertions involved. Three generations of writers are represented, spanning a half century in age and representative, we think, of varied reactions, though far from exhaustively.

To select appropriate texts is always a hazardous business, to organize them no less. The pattern we have chosen is relatively simple. The four main sections set a few guide-lines, providing central themes within a rough chronological framework and furnishing focal points within the main areas of confrontation and debate. Part I covers the initial period during which the shock of defeat was followed by the maze of existence in a dislocated, German-dominated country under two different regimes, cut by a line of demarcation into two main zones, with two other smaller enclaves of different status in the north of France and Alsace-Lorraine. Part IV, symmetrically, recalls the reversal of that movement in the last crucial stages when, with the Allied victories, the end of the Occupation approached. Parts II and III span the intervening years, recalling the attrition, frustration, anxieties, and ultimate revolts; and beyond these moods, the writers' efforts to make sense of the nightmarish series of events, to establish and maintain a vision of life and an ethic that, under the circumstances, would appear neither spurious nor cheap to other men.

We have limited editorial comment to the minimum, supplying by means of notes and short biographical sketches such essential references as might be needed by nonspecialized readers to situate the men and the values they defended within the historical and ideological framework that by now may have become dim in our memory.

The issues we confront today are different in order and
intensity, and new in many ways; the dilemmas, ideologies,
and antagonisms of the men who attempted to think their
way through the years of occupation in France may appear
irrelevant to our present outlook. But it seems possible
that the confrontation with them may clarify our own way
of conceiving the kind of society in which we find ourselves
and the kind of action we may best engage in at equal
distance from myth, self-righteousness, and cynicism.

We are concerned here almost exclusively with French
writers. Since the Dreyfus Affair, writers in France had
increasingly become involved in the social and political
issues of the hour. Very much a part of the Establishment,
they could no longer be thought of in any way alienated
from society. They enjoyed in fact the high regard of the
community as a whole and were looked upon as the
spiritual and ethical mentors of France, a mission which,
with exceptions, they accepted. The Dadaists, it is true,
had poured scorn on what they considered an outrageous
myth. But beyond them, World War I had raised the
question of the nature of the writer's commitments and of
his responsibility to the community, a question that in
itself points to a change in the writer's position: the
increasing scope of his influence. The 1940 defeat provided
a new and dramatic context for the debate which was to
culminate in Jean-Paul Sartre's postwar call for a literature
of commitment. We have chosen the early meditations of
two very different men on literature and freedom as a brief
prelude to this anthology.

A DUAL HERITAGE

In 1941, the panic of defeat was over. The Armistice, followed by the Montoire interviews, had established France's mode of existence under German occupation and also the patterns of Nazi demands—economic exploitation, application of the Nazi statutes to French Jews, etc. It was becoming clearer that the war was far from over. Various alternatives to despair and resignation began to take shape. In the general uncertainty, writers, often in isolation, examined and attempted to elucidate their position in terms of their convictions and personal integrity.

Henry de Montherlant and Jean Guéhenno were reaching their fifties in 1940, established figures of France's intelligentsia. The first was a novelist and master of a brilliant, trenchant prose style in the great French classical tradition; the second, more effaced, a professor and essayist, was a dedicated antifascist with a passionate allegiance to the ideals of the Enlightenment and the French Revolution.

A self-conscious aristocrat, Montherlant had fashioned for himself in the twenties a neo-Nietzschean ethic of courage, physical prowess, and personal achievement, not unlike the code of the young fascists, but fused in his case with an anarchistic individualism and contempt for the

masses debased by a democratic system that bred mediocrity. For Montherlant the ideal of single-minded devotion
to artistic integrity with its accompanying contempt for
politics, a heritage of Flaubert and Mallarmé handed
down to him via Gide and Valéry, was compatible with
his more egotistic drives toward self-fulfillment. For many
years a semi-expatriate in the Mediterranean ambience of
Spain and North Africa which he favored, he had in fact
adopted the traditional anarchistic posture of the alienated
artist, though, in his own flamboyant style, with a
difference. In the thirties, from beneath the arrogant mask
of contempt for his contemporaries, a real concern for his
country began to surface. He attacked the delusions and
stupid complacency of his countrymen, proposing in contrast a romantically elitist ideal of self-sacrifice without
guarantee of reward or hope of recognition.

Of working-class origin, Jean Guéhenno had maintained
a deep sense of solidarity with his class and its aspirations
and a loyalty to the principles of the Republic. Optimistic,
with a Rousseauist faith in the fundamental goodness of
the individual, he fully believed in the ultimate establishment in France and in Europe of a human order and
culture embodying the "liberty, equality, fraternity" creed
of France's Revolutionary past.

In 1941, both these men raise the question of the
writer's freedom, both assuming that art and freedom
cannot be dissociated and appealing, beyond the present,
to the past and to France's literary heritage. But the
freedom defined is not the same. Montherlant, with the
dexterity of a master ironist, subtly juggles such loaded
elements, under the circumstances, as the word "collaboration" or a Hitler quotation, giving them an ambivalent
resonance. His creed, nonetheless, is unambiguous. Art
cannot become subservient to any political cause, the artist
political in which the artist, as individual, may or may not
recognizing only an inner necessity that transcends the

choose to become involved. Far less detached, Guéhenno
had already taken sides, justifying his stand with the
moral self-righteousness of the man of principle. His image
of the collaborationist writer as traitor and lackey is
simplistic, his rhetoric conventional. But one feels a certain discomfort in the presence of Montherlant's arguments, in his assessment, however ironic, of the advantages
of occupation and the freedom it offered the writer to live
in the private world of his own imagining. It took a certain
self-centeredness and a measure of optimistic blindness
or complicity with Nazi ideology to remain unmindful of
the narrow frontiers reserved to the writer's private freedom under Nazi rule, especially if the writer happened
to be a Jew or opposed to Nazi ideology. Guéhenno,
earnest and naive by comparison, was a prewar antifascist.
He now sensed that the era of dialogue—however acrimo-
nious—was for the moment over. He had the courage to
see that there could be no real distinction, that the two
freedoms, the writer's and the citizen's, were equally under
attack and would have to be either relinquished or fought
for. The curtain had risen on a deep spiritual rift,
heralding a conflict fierce in its intransigent intensity, in
which the embattled opponents, alternately in the position
of winners and losers, appeared successively in each other's
eyes as saviors of or traitors to their calling and their
country.

   For some writers in these years, the endemic conflict
in totalitarian regimes between segments of the intelligentsia and repressive police forces took on a new color.
French civilization became, in their eyes, the standard-
bearer of the values of freedom. A decadent civilization
to be transformed; a civilization, worthy but betrayed, to
be reaffirmed: Montherlant and Guéhenno represent two
poles of a still unresolved debate whose ambiguities under-
lie the divergent meaning the word "revolution" acquired
in those years.

HENRY DE MONTHERLANT

PEACE IN WARTIME

Nowadays anyone talking to an artist—a writer, painter, or musician—invariably asks him, without much conviction: "Can you do any work?" Well, we'll tell them.

You know what René Quinton[1] said: "There is something very peaceful about war: there are no women." There is also something very peaceful for the artist about this war which encircles and still grips France. A writer once said that when he was a child the 1914 war had been a "long holiday" for him. This does not apply only to children. I have a portrait of one ancestor of mine dated June 1794: it took the Terror[2] for him to have time to have his portrait painted.

First there is peace in little things—these important "little things." No noise of radios (at least in the town where I live). Your correspondence is halved since mail has been suspended between the two zones,[3] and more than half the people in your zone don't know who you are. There are no more bores. And restlessness is curbed by transport difficulties.

Let us be objective. There is no market for the arts, therefore an artist no longer wants to earn money by his art. This eliminates the possibility of a career: so there are no more impositions and no more time to waste. Nobody watches the maestro: so there are no more exhibitions or contortions. In a word, there is no more sordid trade between artist and public. The public was undoubtedly a good tuning fork (indispensable for certain artists), but it was also an obstacle between the

SOURCE NOTE: Henry de Montherlant, "La Paix dans la guerre," *Le Solstice de juin* (Paris; Grasset, 1941), pp. 98–101. This text was given as a lecture by Montherlant at Lyons and Limoges in December of 1940.

creator and the creation. It was like those parasites which disturb the radio waves. Henri Matisse, who was severely criticized to start with, told me: "You are much freer when people turn their backs on you. Your path seems inevitable. You tell yourself, 'Go on like that, whatever happens.'" And what is true when people turn their backs on you because they don't understand you is also true when they no longer take an interest in your work because they have too many other things to do.

So it is to the credit of this period that art should return to its apparently most trivial but really most majestic source: that of being no more than the natural function of the artist. I was going to say: The artist produces in order to empty his soul and clean it well before refilling it. But I repudiate that "in order to." The artist doesn't produce "in order to" do anything. He produces his work as the apple tree produces its apple, without aim or responsibility, without worrying about a recipe or the use to be made of it. Naturalists can, if they like, teach us what this fruit is, and if it is edible, and the cooks have every right to cook it their way.

You will say to me: "Writing in a vacuum, without knowing if your work will ever see the light of day!" I reply: "One thing alone matters: it must be written and written as the artist conceives it."

You will say to me: "So you make everything revolve around art!" I say: "Of course, since I'm an artist. The artist must be the center of his own world; he must reject, or skim over, everything that does not concern his creation; he must only accept emotions useful for his art. He is a magician who celebrates his own mysteries, not with an ingredient which nature may offer him, but only with the ones he chooses."

To a Balzac obsessed by the construction of *La Comédie humaine*, to a Tolstoy obsessed by *War and Peace*, what did contemporary turmoil matter as long as it didn't touch them too closely? How self-confident and right they must have felt in rejecting it with such energy! How much more real, more alive, more powerful than the other this inner world must have

been for them! At moments the outer world, with its noisy
events and its show of force, must have seemed almost ridiculous compared to the one inside them. They wanted eternity,
on which they had already laid hands. A lesser intellectual does
not escape from this deformation, which is a necessary deformation. It is said that when Rémy de Gourmont[4] was asked
about the 1914 war, he simply replied: "It doesn't worry me."

Is that very different in meaning from Balzac's famous remark? Balzac was talking to a visitor about the heroes of his
novels. The subject changed to political and other events of
the day. After a pause Balzac suddenly said: "Let's return to
reality," and started talking about his characters again.

And I recall an acute observation by some Persian author. A
certain hero of an Iranian epic, Isphendyar, died after countless
exploits. A poet imagined that a nightingale had sung his death,
and composed its song. The chronicler writes: "The nightingale's lament on Isphendyar's death is all that remains of the
hero."

Maybe these justifications of art are a little suspect coming
from artists. But let us hear a man of action talk, a genuine
man of action. This it what one of them once said:

"Can we sacrifice to art at a time when we are surrounded
by such poverty, misery, distress, and lamentation? Is art not
the luxury of a small minority, while we should be ensuring our
daily bread? Should we, in these times, occupy public opinion
with artistic problems, and would it not be fairer to give them
up and return to them later, when we have overcome the
present political and economic difficulties? To this I say: Art is
not a phenomenon which we can summon, dismiss, and put
aside . . . We cannot temporarily suspend the activity of the
mind without a general regression of culture and definite decadence . . . Never is it more necessary to return to the eternal
qualities of a nation than at a time when political and economic
difficulties make her doubt her mission.

". . . So if art has repercussions and effects more powerful
and lasting than any other human activity, we must devote

ourselves to it all the more at a time when we are depressed and upset by general political and economic difficulties. And nothing can be more calculated to make a nation realize that her political blunders are merely temporary, compared to her perennial greatness.

". . . Even when she has been conquered, a nation which produces immortal works before History becomes the true conqueror of her adversaries."

Such an apology for art cannot be suspect, since it is taken from a speech made by Chancellor Hitler to a National Socialist congress in 1935.

And at the same time—in curious contrast to this high idea which the artist has of his work—when all our canvases, models, or manuscripts are somewhere under the bombs, or almost lost, we discover that basically this doesn't affect us. Is it not surprising that a man who has, for example, embarked on a long, exhausting, and expensive voyage to shelter a part of his essential substance, I mean an important part of his work which he has outlined or started, should only feel indifferent when the hazards of war incur the risk of permanent destruction for his precious treasure, more exposed to danger than it has ever been before? It is our present work which interests us. We need to create, not to have created. And here I have said the right words: creation, a need.

By *necessary* work I mean that given to a writer by an inner necessity; that which he knows he is made to write, and which he alone can write; that of which he says, "I mustn't die before writing that." Of course, we have so spoken of a writer the *necessary* aspect of whose work has nothing to do with reality. But the necessary aspects of his work can also coincide with reality, and that is all to the best.

He may also want to serve a purpose by consecrating his talent to reality in some work which is not necessary, but which he considers it his duty to write. I spoke of this in a lecture I gave five years ago and which has been printed in *Service inutile*:[5]

"At a time when one's country is threatened from without or within, the writer, whose essential duty is alien to politics, and who fades into and confines himself in this essential duty, prepares remorse for himself. The day when the crisis is over, what he loved will have been lost or saved without him. He is going to benefit from a system which others have prepared for him, with their pain, blood, or even their life. Or he is to suffer from a system which he might have prevented if he had added what little force he possessed to other forces which agreed with him. By abstaining he betrayed not only his compatriots but also, to a certain extent, his work, in whose name he betrayed them. For a writer's authority, whether just or not, will always be in relation to the authority of his country in the world. All this is worth nothing for his peace of mind. He should have collaborated. I mean: collaborated like a soldier who picks up his knapsack when the alarm rings, but who knows that his duty lies elsewhere, with the plow or the factory, and that he will return to it when peace has been restored. But the public above all must be reminded of the provisional nature of a writer's national or social service, when the writer is in question whose essential duty is elsewhere. The public should remember that a great writer serves his country by his work, far more than by the action which he can perform, and that it is unreasonable to ask a man to work in quicksand when, if left to it, he could work in bronze. The public is also invited to survey the tissues of stupidity that constitute the political activity of most great writers, so as to realize that it is by being spared as much of this activity as possible that a writer will best serve his country."

ALASTAIR HAMILTON

NOTES

1. *René Quinton*: French physiologist (1867–1925) in the Darwinian tradition, often quoted with approval by the fascists as a proponent of the "survival of the fittest" ethic.

2. *the Terror*: period of the French Revolution between May 31, 1793, and July 27, 1794. During the final two months of this

period, Robespierre became the dominant personality and nearly 1,400 people were guillotined.

3. *the two zones*: after the Armistice, France was divided into four zones, the two main ones being the so-called "occupied zone" in the north and the "free zone" of the south. All of France was to become occupied after the American landing in Morocco in November 1942.

4. *Rémy de Gourmont*: French essayist and critic (1858–1915) connected with the symbolist movement in literature; a critic in the impressionistic vein.

5. *Service inutile*: collection of essays written in 1935, the first of Montherlant's "civic" works.

JEAN GUÉHENNO

1941

NOVEMBER 1941

On the whole the republic of letters is behaving well. The "collaborators" are rare: a few dissatisfied old buffoons, always in need of fame or money, all the more eager to hear their names murmured once more because they feel so close to the spadeful of earth which will block their ears for good; a few newly fledged young failures, keen despite the tragedy and silence of France to make the name for themselves which they think she refused them when she was free; finally a few pathetic bumpkins, incapable of keeping quiet.

Voltaire coined the term "man of letters" to designate a new function and a new honor. As there had been men of arms, men of the robe to lead the social ceremonies in other centuries, from then on there were to be men of letters, free men, the makers of free men, and liberty would be their weapon and their honor.

SOURCE NOTE: Jean Guéhenno (pseud. Cévennes), *Dans la prison* (Paris, 1944), pp. 41–43. Published by the clandestine Éditions de Minuit.

One is free or a slave according to one's heart. A true man of letters is not a supplier of petty pleasures. His liberty is not his idleness or his dreams. Vain self-confidence is not enough for him, any more than the subtle games of his intellect. For every true man liberty is still more than his own liberty: it is the liberty of others. He cannot feel free when two million of his countrymen are hostages in a conqueror's prisons and forty million men around him only save what dignity they have left by silence and cunning.

ALASTAIR HAMILTON

PART ONE

CONFRONTATION WITH DEFEAT

THE MILITARY DEFEAT

THE FOCAL POINT of the period was the military defeat in mid-June 1940. Both Montherlant and Louis Aragon—a militant Communist since the early thirties and a highly talented poet and novelist—witnessed the debacle from within the ranks of the Army. Putting aside all ideological concerns, Aragon, in haunting lyrical poems, expressed his immediate moods, the heartache, the dismay, the passionate love for the beauty of the countryside that is France, the deep concern for the misery of its fleeing, bewildered population. How widely these emotions were shared by his countrymen can be judged from the popularity of poems such as "Richard II Forty." The plaint of the abandoned king, the image of the kingdom lost, the balladlike form and pathos, were attuned to simple, deep-lying emotions, as was also the barely suggested theme of hope introduced with the figure of the young, unknown Joan of Arc setting off on her mission at Vaucouleurs.

There is no doubt at all that Montherlant witnessed the triumph of the Nazi armies with an enthusiasm born of admiration. The vigorous German youths, rolling over France like a tide under the solar sign of the swastika, were symbolic in his eyes of the kind of heroic ethic he had dreamed might regenerate France. There is no ques-

tion at all, either, as to his own concern with the fate of his
country, his desire to mitigate the crushing impact of
defeat by placing it in a vast historical perspective. He is
singularly exempt from any form of illusion as to the true
relation of victor to vanquished; in conquest, might under
whatever mask means right. But he molds the event and
interprets it according to a grandiose comprehensive vision
of cosmic proportions in which everything falls into place.
His vision blends the Nietzschean myth of the "eternal
return" and the related cyclic Spenglerian view of the rise,
decline, and fall of civilizations with Montherlant's own
dramatic concept of life as perpetually alternating between
two poles—the sensuous and the ascetic, the aesthetic and
the moral, the natural and the spiritual, the pagan and the
Christian. The cosmic "Solar Wheel"—the swastika—
reaches its zenith in the June solstice, there to reign until
the September equinox and its wane in the "fall" of the
year. The ambivalence of each phase, binding rise and fall,
death and rebirth, is symbolized in the myth of Adonis,
for whom, as for France, the June solstice is a period
of mourning yet a presage of rebirth. In a vast, visionary
historical context Montherlant sees the French defeat as
a cataclysmic event, a vast revolution, the end of an era
that had originated in 323 with the September equinox
and the waning of a disintegrating pagan civilization at
the time of the victory of the Christian emperor Constantine over the pagan Licinius. In June 1940, history has come
full circle, as the disintegrating Christian civilization, of
which France had been the center, is superseded by the
flowering of a new paganism.

There is obviously more than a touch of megalomania
in this view, though in no sense does Montherlant identify
with that paganism. But he does see it as a rising creative
force which France must assimilate if she is to prepare
her own rebirth. The concrete immediacy of defeat is
absorbed in the grandiose romantic elaboration of a myth

that elides the harsh facts of the situation, poeticizing the struggle and the victor, while yet the first French victims were joining others, Germans, Poles, Czechs, Dutchmen— Jews mostly, but also Christians—in the ugly reality of the concentration camps.

Céline's reaction, in contrast, in one of its facets is brutally realistic, based on a violent dislike for the unctuous rhetoric that emanated from the Vichy radio extolling the virtues of discipline, calling upon the French civilians to recognize their guilt and atone for their past irresponsibility, masking the ugly facts. Céline too had witnessed the rout of the French Army, as a doctor evacuating patients from a Paris clinic. He shouts his contempt, with the maniacal single-mindedness of hatred, impervious to its psychic effect and heedless of the practical aid he was furnishing the Nazi occupier. Rage, excess, fear, despair: Céline, regardless of circumstance, was obsessively continuing his pre-1939 one-man campaign against the suicidal treachery of the Jewish, capitalist-communistic-warmongering, murderous Establishment that, in his eyes, was steering the Western world down the path of degeneracy and waste to its ultimate destruction. A genius, half mad, yet one who in his own strange way shared the agony of the nation.

Jean Giono had long since been a pacifist. World War I in which he had served in the infantry for four years, had inspired in him a bitter hatred for the mechanical "progress" that had culminated in so savage a waste of human life and natural resources. During the interwar years, from the village of Manosque in Upper Provence, he had advocated in novels and essays a return to natural rhythms of life in small, self-sufficient peasant communities, a highly utopian form of anarchism. In 1939 he was briefly imprisoned for his pacifism, and in 1945 he spent six months in an internment camp on an unfounded charge of collaboration. He wrote his rather rambling essay—*The*

Triumph of Life—in 1940, once again proposing as the cure for the ills of the time the peaceful, idealized life of the isolated village. But a note of anxiety can be detected in the book: Giono seems to realize that his vision of innocence is a thing of the past. Nonetheless, his views seemed to coincide with Marshal Pétain's "back to the land" policy; and in fact, in the next years, many people lived in reality the life Giono had described, and found it did not quite tally with the ideal.

LOUIS ARAGON

Carcassonne, September 1940

RICHARD II FORTY

> *You may my glories and my state depose,*
> *But not my griefs; still am I king of those.*
> Richard II, Act IV, Scene 1

My country is a bark adrift
Abandoned by her one-time crew
And I am not unlike that king
Left friendless when his luck turned ill
But monarch of his sorrows still

To live takes cunning now, no more
Winds cannot dry the tears I spill
Now must I hate what I adore
And what I lost must give away
While monarch of my sorrows still

The heart can almost cease to beat
The blood may run, though slow and chill
No longer two and two be four
When robbers play at blind man's buff
I am monarch of my sorrows still

SOURCE NOTE: Louis Aragon, "Richard II Quarante," *Le Crève-coeur* (Paris, Gallimard, 1941), pp. 50–51. The poem takes its title from the Shakespearean tragedy *Richard the Second*, which focuses on the anguish of the English king in the midst of overwhelming military defeat. Richard II, a weak king, was forced to abdicate in 1399.

Whether at sunset or at dawn
The skies are colorless and wan
Spring dies among the flower stalls
Bright Paris of my youth, farewell
I am monarch of my sorrows still

Forsake the fountains and the woods
Hide away, chattering birds, be still
Your songs are put in quarantine
The days have come when fowlers reign
I am monarch of my sorrows still

There is a time for suffering
Cut France in pieces if you will
When the Maid came to Vaucouleurs
The morning had this pallor too
I am monarch of my sorrows still.

MALCOLM COWLEY

RICHARD II QUARANTE

Ma patrie est comme une barque
Qu'abandonnèrent ses haleurs
Et je ressemble à ce monarque
Plus malheureux que le malheur
Qui restait roi de ses douleurs

Vivre n'est plus qu'un stratagème
Le vent sait mal sécher les pleurs
Il faut haïr tout ce que j'aime
Ce que je n'ai plus donnez-leur
Je reste roi de mes douleurs

Le coeur peut s'arrêter de battre
Le sang peut couler sans chaleur
Deux et deux ne fassent plus quatre
Au Pigeon-Vole[1] des voleurs
Je reste roi de mes douleurs

Que le soleil meure ou renaisse
Le ciel a perdu ses couleurs
Tendre Paris de ma jeunesse
Adieu printemps du Quai-aux-Fleurs[2]
Je reste roi de mes douleurs

Fuyez les bois et les fontaines
Taisez-vous oiseaux querelleurs
Vos chants sont mis en quarantaine
C'est le règne de l'oiseleur
Je reste roi de mes douleurs

Il est un temps pour la souffrance
Quand Jeanne vint à Vaucouleurs[3]
Ah coupez en morceaux la France
Le jour avait cette pâleur
Je reste roi de mes douleurs

NOTES

1. *Pigeon-Vole*: French children's game of forfeits.
2. *Quai-aux-Fleurs*: site of the Paris flower market.
3. *Vaucouleurs*: it was to the captain of Vaucouleurs, Robert de Baudricourt, that Joan of Arc first spoke of her plan to aid Charles VII.

HENRY DE MONTHERLANT
Marseilles, July 1940

THE JUNE SOLSTICE

Heathendom unfolded on our heels, its helmets crowned with branches: "They call the secret of the woods their god."

Thousands of tanks rolled like the sea. Towns fell to ten cyclists, ten scruffy lads, dripping with sweat, a gun slung over their shoulders, laughing heartily. And I thought that heathendom had won its land forever, that the belfries burned down by its fires would never be rebuilt, and one day I would see the standard of the Solar Wheel[1] flying on the towers of Notre-Dame de Paris. The city was no longer the city of Geneviève,[2] but of Julian.[3] The country was no longer the country of the saints, but of the Emperor. By will or by force France had been wrenched from her picture-postcard image[4] of herself. If she wanted to survive she would have to invent a new form of creativity.

One evening, in the domain of Caumont, I saw the vanguard of our Christian army march along the edge of a great quarry. The color and strata of the quarry resembled the high tiers of a Roman circus, and I recalled an image engraved in my mind. During Constantine's reign the amphitheater of Vespasian[5] was closed on the anniversary of the foundation of the Secular Games,[6] either on the Emperor's orders or for fear of displeasing him, and on the hills above, a synod was celebrated by nineteen bishops. The empty circus had remained in my heart since I was twelve, like a deserted, dilapidated family seat awaiting the return of the son to cheer it.

In 323 two Emperors had tossed for the religion of the civilized world—Constantine and Licinius,[7] two emperor sharks (but the Christian shark was the better swimmer). Two Emperors who knew what they wanted—each one wanted to triumph over the other—and behind them marched their two armies, which fought without knowing why: that is a very old tradition. Two armies of scoundrels—but Licinius' troops, who were Orientals, were the greater scoundrels. A war of ambitions which had the same results as a war of ideologies and was presented as such. On the morning of the battle Constantine prepared himself by acts of piety and prayer (he had a chapel

SOURCE NOTE: Henry de Montherlant, "Le Solstice de juin," *Le Solstice de juin* (Paris, Grasset, 1941), pp. 303–10.

served by Christian priests, just as each regiment had its chapel and its almoner). At the same time Licinius sacrificed to the gods and told his men: "Here are our gods and those of our fathers. Our enemy has abandoned them to follow a god we do not know. Today we will see which of us is wrong and whom we should worship." Licinius' ensigns bore the device SPQR[8] and Constantine's the monogram of Christ. Defeated near Andrianopolis, Licinius fled across the Bosphorus. Like a hunted boar he finally turned and faced his enemies on the far point of the Orient, on the banks of Asia. The defender of the ancient religion of Rome[9] fought from the East; and Constantine, who represented the religion of the Jews, was backed by the West. It was the September equinox (September 23): even the cosmic signs participated. Licinius was vanquished a second time and surrendered. His soldiers deserted to the stronger army: all was for the best. That evening the loser dined at the victor's table; conversation must have been difficult, but there have been a number of difficult conversations since. Constantine solemnly promised to save his enemy's life. The next year he had him put to death with his twelve-year-old son —a splendid Christian exploit. One world had ended, another began. Impurity replaced impurity.

Today it is as though France and Germany, united under the emblem of the Solar Wheel, wanted to bury the season of Constantine, for a season or two, and put Christianity to sleep.

* * * * *

The June solstice was an ambiguous moment—a sort of lie, exciting, perturbing, pleasing. For a few more months the year still appeared to be charging toward its zenith of heat and splendor, and yet it was over. The days had begun to grow shorter. The sun sank and died. Adonis died, leaving only the rose.[10] At the doors of the houses there were the terracotta or metal images of the young god lying on his bed, half naked, surrounded by flowers which wither fast and for this reason are named after Adonis. Women wept and beat their chests to the sound of the Phoenician flute. But this feast was ambiguous: the women's tears contained a secret joy because they knew that Adonis would arise with the winter solstice. They wept, towns wept, whole nations wept. Absurd as it may seem, it was as though the whole of the old world were weeping through the ages for little France, for the French Army which has withered in a few days like the flowers of Adonis. I too am weeping for France's death, but, like the Alexandrian women, I know that what I weep for will somehow rise again. The victory of the Solar Wheel is not only the victory of the Sun, the victory of heathendom. It is the victory of the solar principle —everything rotates ("the wheel rotates," they say). One day I shall witness the triumph of that principle with which I am imbued, which I have sung, which I can see ruling my whole life.

Alternation. All things alternate. Whoever understands this has understood everything. The ancient Greeks were full of it. And that is why ancient China chose the dragon with an *undulous* tail as her emblem. Nature advances from pole to pole. The pleasure which we feel in "repudiating ourselves" is the pleasure of revealing those parts of us which we have tried to conceal, the pleasure of feeling in harmony with the order of things.

"Remain yourself and become someone else! Become another self!" (*Pasiphaé*)[11]

Nations are subject to motion: victory, defeat, republic, dictatorship. France has flowered, if you can call that flowering. She must now flower again, but it is a different part of herself which must flower—a part which seems in opposition to her other self.

In a new system France must take the place which she had promised to take before the trial of force: defeat was only one signal, among many less obvious ones. She must realize that the victor's rights over the vanquished are limited only by the victor's interests. Before the modern era not even the purest voice protested against the victor's rights, any more than against war itself. She must realize that Franco-German relations can only flourish if they exist in that same revolutionary climate in which Nazi Germany was born. What we have experienced and suffered, what we are to experience and suffer, only has a meaning in terms of the real revolution at stake in this war. Finally, France must learn from the many lessons which her victor could give her. But I only mention this for the sake of posterity. I fear that it will never occur.

ALASTAIR HAMILTON

NOTES

1. *Solar Wheel*: the swastika, the Nazi emblem, a cross with gamma-shaped branches; an ancient pagan emblem of the rotating sun.

2. *Geneviève*: patron saint of Paris (c. 422–c. 512), who successfully promised the citizens of the city immunity against the attacks of Attila.

3. *Julian*: Julian the Apostate, nephew of the Christian emperor Constantine the Great and himself Emperor of Rome from 361 to 363. He renounced Christianity and attempted to reimpose pagan religion on the Empire.

4. *picture-postcard image* (*image d'Épinal*): Épinal, a city of the French Vosges, famous for its illustrated children's books, ancestors of the comic strips, in which the story was presented in simply designed, vividly colored scenes accompanied by single captions.

5. *Amphitheater of Vespasian*: the Coliseum in Rome.

6. *Secular Games*: games held by the Romans with great festivity every hundred years.

7. *Constantine and Licinius*: Licinius, a Roman emperor, rival to Constantine, strongly repressed the Christian Church, perhaps as an attempt to counteract the influence of Constantine in the East. In a second war between the two emperors at Adrianopolis and then on the Asiatic coast, Licinius was defeated by Constantine, thus putting an end to the former's repressive measures against the Church and assuring the future role of the Church in the history of Western civilization, according to Montherlant.

8. *SPQR*: Senatus Populusque Romanus (the Roman People and Senate), the motto of the Roman Empire.

9. *religion of Rome*: Quirites, name of Roman citizens residing in Rome as opposed to those engaged in the Army.

10. *Adonis*: in Greek mythology, a beautiful youth beloved by

Aphrodite. Slain by a boar, he was subsequently allowed to pass half the year on earth, half in the underworld. His death and resurrection, symbolizing the vegetation cycle, were widely celebrated in Greece in the midsummer festival Adonia.

the rose: where Adonis' blood fell on the earth, it was changed by Aphrodite to an anemone, sometimes called a rose.

11. *Pasiphaé*: a play by Montherlant, first produced in 1938, again in 1949; published in Tunis in 1936, then by Grasset in 1938.

LOUIS-FERDINAND CÉLINE

1941

A FINE KETTLE OF FISH

> *Hey! What did you do with your rifle?*
> *It's left on the Field of Honor!*

Y'know, it makes ya wonder, about soldiers I mean, when they don't wanta die no more. Somethin' funny's goin' on. They got no spirit. Get a load of those sweet little officers hightailing it with their packs . . . moving their most precious property . . . their girlfriends . . . in sporty convertibles with travel priority . . . You won't see them again too soon . . . the great day they give out the medals . . . A day of glory like the others . . . The earth is turning around just like always, God damn it! . . . They'll repeat it for us at the movies! . . . The World Champions of War . . . They'll run it all backwards! . . . You know, the pretty girl who somersaults back to the diving board . . . springs back up there in reverse order . . . They'll do that trick again for the French Army . . . From Saint-Jean-Pied-de-Port to Narvick . . . Backwards! . . . And it'll come off perfectly! And everyone will be very happy. The losers

SOURCE NOTE: Louis-Ferdinand Céline (real name Louis-Ferdinand Destouches), *Les Beaux Draps* (Paris, Nouvelles Éditions Françaises, 1941), pp. 12–14, 16–24.

will be on the other side . . . It's all anyone could want . . .
It's already been done . . .

Haven't you seen a little bit of it? . . . all the prisoners they
parade around? . . . who pass by in trucks? . . .

—Nothing but meat! I'm telling you! Wretches! Cattle!

Wit is on our side! . . . That's the main thing!

It's a funny thing, but these days it's fashionable to dump on
civilians every chance you get, they're the stinkers, they're the
ones with mange, they're the evil-smelling cause of it all, the
yellow-bellied carrion crows of disaster. It's them, it's them,
and nobody else was in on the deal. Let *them* account for
themselves! Let *them* clear their names! Why were *they* scared
like that? . . . Why weren't *they* heroic? . . .

Maybe we better get a few things straight right away . . .
Who is it who's supposed to defend France? The civilians or
the military? The twenty-ton tanks or the old men? Village
idiots, great big guys who go to nursery school, snot-nosed brats,
pussyfooting, prancing pansies, or machine-gun regiments? God,
it's hard to express things clearly with words . . . We're not
really understanding each other. There's confusion, ambiguity,
we're not telling the whole truth . . .

The French Army cost a lot, 400 billion francs, for running
away, for eight months of poker and one month of rout . . .
It began to seem like we'd never be done paying taxes . . . The
civilians were right to pull out any way they could. They
didn't want to die either. They couldn't have done anything
at the front lines except bog down the fighting, if there had
been any fighting . . . It was the soldiers' job to be up there,
to slow down the invaders, to stay and die there at their posts,
thrusting out their chests at the Huns, not their asses as they
fled. If they'd been a bit slower, the traffic jam wouldn't have
been so bad. A man can figure these things out for himself,
without a degree from the École de Guerre. An army in flight
is inconvenient, it stirs up winds of panic. From the Meuse to
the Loire, the whole place was putt-putting away, it was a
nationwide farce. Who was it had the worst case of diarrhea?

The civilians or the military? Is that any reason to celebrate,
to put on airs, Mr. Scipio-shitbreeches-runaway-judge? Everybody was sick, sick of phoniness, sick of bragging, sick of the
fear of death. Those monuments to the dead you see everywhere are unfair to the memory of the war. An entire country
turned ham-actor, farmer-Punches, tankriding-Judys, who didn't
want to die on stage. Drop by the theater hoping for a part-time
job, yes! A chance to shine? Ready and willing! Stay with a role
to the end of the run? . . . Sorry! Misdeal! . . . All the ballerinas
who dance badly claim it's their tutu. All the soldiers whose
knees knock always bawl that they've been betrayed. It's their
hearts that have done the betraying, there's never anything else
that betrays a man. They all really wanted to act in a play, to
pass under the Arches of Brandenburg, be carried aloft in triumphal parades, to cut off the villain's mustache, but not to
croak for the Nation. They know the Nation well. It's all
horseshit and gentlemen's agreements. It's all personal enemies!
Excuse me—and after the war? Who's going to enjoy it if we
don't? The chiseling riffraff! Only dumb sons of bitches are
whimpering! That's the best time, after the war! Everyone
wants a hand in it. No one wants sacrifices. Everyone wants
benefits. Pure milk chocolate. Sure, there were deaths anyway!
Real victims of indiscretion. That's nothing compared to the
millions, the absolute martyrs in the other war, the ironhearted
men who cashed in their chips between '14 and '18. Shit! You
could say they've been had! Like the old nags with lousy luck
that we should regret, completely ashamed of the 800,000 we
got bumped off.

All in all, the situation is brilliant . . . Here we are in a
very tight spot . . . Yet you can't say we were short on opti-
mism. We had tremendous orgies of it, avalanches, real cyclones, and the best kind of optimists were on our side,
thundering on every radio station, ecstatic in the papers, cooing
sweet songs at us, fulminating from the Bench.

If the power of words could do it, we'd certainly be the

Kings of the World. No one could outdo us in bravado. World champions at braggadocio, befuddled by publicity, by stupefying fatuity, Herculean boasters.

On the side of what's solid: the Maginot! Our Guarantee: the Genius of the Race! Cock-a-doodle-doo! Cock-a-doodle-doo! The wine blazes! We aren't sloshed but we are cocky! Four abreast! Let it start all over again!

All the same there's a big difference between '14 and today. In those days men were still on the level, now they're all crooked. The buck private with his mustachio used to play the game "with cash on the line"; now he's slipperier than a jailbird, a shifty confidence man and sly and mean, he's a phony, he sends out challenges, he pisses off the whole world, he acts like a big shot, but when it's time to shell out he's gone. Faced with his IOU's he loses his spunk. He's a ventriloquist, it's all hot air. He's a swindler like everyone else. He's a bum and born that way, he's a proletarian two-face, the shittiest, worst kind, the flower of civilization. He plays the poor wretch, he isn't one any more, he's a whore and a pimp, a gladhanding idler, a hypocrite. He sponges off his brother, the bourgeois. He's leery of every sort of swindle, someone told him the theory, he doesn't know the details yet, but he knows that everything stinks, that there's no point in looking too closely at himself, that he will never be base enough to trump his leader in that department, that he will always be stuffing himself a little later than so many others. It's the opportunism of a guttersnipe, of the guy who's all take and no give. Small-time anarchy. It's good old-fashioned normal villainy, the kind that sends others to war, that makes the battalions retreat, that considers its navel the center of the world, that makes a joke out of old-age retirement and calls poison gas a blessing for all.

What cause would inspire the combat soldier to get himself bumped off? Really he still wants to play the fool, he has a passion for the stage, the bravos at the circus, like all degenerates, but when it comes to dying, then beg your pardon! he

absolutely refuses! It's not in his freedman's contract. The
gentleman takes off at tremendous speed. Let the theater burn,
he flees the scene! It's none of his business!

And then right from the start it's universal, the leaders don't
want to die either. You will notice that the great despots, the
presidents, the powerful tenors, the kings, the princesses, that
whole crowd splits, dives for cover as soon as the adventure
turns sour, wobbles . . . They bolt like lightning. Not one pays
with his life. Saving your skin is the supreme form of sentry
duty. During their wildest exhortations, when they're dashing
into the slaughter, their eyes never leave their "Shell." It's their
true Madonna!

Only an ass gets himself laid out!

Promises! Microphones! They're all part of the great game!
Whatever anyone will want! Perfect lines! However much it
will amount to! Everything is theater for them too . . . From
Ras Tafari to Reynaud it's a snappy troupe . . . How many of
them felt a bit pale when the time came to pay the bill? Count
them up for a second on your little fingers. Probably that's not
the end of it.

It's a nonstop performance . . . Who do you want to believe?
Which medicine show?

Think for a minute what it would have been like in our
country if Reynaud had chatted with us in this charming way:

"We will conquer! beloved fellow citizens, I'm sure as hell
of that! because we, we are stronger! Drum! Drum! Brothel
blood! I'm so convinced of it that I'm staying right with you,
my loves! We will defend her, the land of France! With all
our bones if necessary! This country is the most marvelous, the
most super-duper, the most etcetera and all that! Not one
dumbbell trembling! It's conquer or die! We kiss! We get into
gear some way or other! And everyone knows! I'm the boss!
I set the example! My blood is the blood of Achilles! I make
your hearts beat faster! Rally to my microphone! If one of
you retreats ten inches from the Somme to the Rhine, I'll
blow my brains out! Pronto! Right here by my Louis Quatorze!
I won't survive the shame! I'll go down with my desk! God

damn it, you'll all hear about it! Every one of you will return over my corpse! It's not worth living any more when France has rotten soldiers! Dogs with their tails between their legs! shitting in their pants! filthy! hiding under skirts everywhere! . . . I don't want any more of this! I have spoken! I, the Minister of War! And for once I'm not kidding! Sound the bugles! Beat the drums!"

That's how Currier & Ives would do it! Inspirational frescos to pump some life back into Heroism! The textbook people would be delighted! . . .

Ah well, today's crusaders don't talk that way any more!

"Shell and Safety!" . . . and "Safety first!"

RAYMOND A. SOKOLOV

JEAN GIONO

1941

From *THE TRIUMPH OF LIFE*

Much was said about culture in the years of perturbations, those sterile and flat years between 1934 and 1939, when winds ever more violent blew over desolate spaces. I'm not saying that all these appeals to culture were sincere and that some bad forces did not hypocritically make use of that huge human aspiration for selfish and mediocre ends. I am saying only that at the approach of monstrous catastrophes, which were already looming over the horizon like thunderheads reddening the sky with their frightful dawn, the quick natural appeal to culture certainly indicated that, in every mind, culture was the essential remedy, the safeguard and hope. (I use the word culture in a very particular sense; what I mean is: Who, in the last six years,

SOURCE NOTE: Jean Giono, *Ides et calendes* (Paris, Grasset, 1942), pp. 28, 31, 61. First published in Neuchâtel in 1941.

can have read the *Georgics* or *Works and Days*[1] without feeling like Adam, banished from the earthly paradise: naked,
frozen, lost, looking wildly back at the ashes of his splendor?)
Freshness, ingenuity, good faith, peace, all the things that
foster joy, were lost. The "professorate" that had governed and
directed human souls since the end of the Renaissance had
guided them along false paths and instilled the fear of ever
turning back. So much confidence in oneself killed the natural
world at every step. The human future was represented as a
straight line, inflexibly traveling toward some unknown summit
without air or light, and whoever had the presumption to look
humbly at the flowers of this earth was considered as the
assassin of the real glories of humankind.

*   *   *   *   *

Here, we live in the mountains, and as soon as winter comes,
the roads are blocked by snowdrifts nine to twelve feet high.
This takes place every winter, so we have had to live not "in
spite of" but "with" it. It lasts from four to five months; the
rest of the year is seven months at most and requires only a
simple common-sense organization. It becomes a fully rounded
year where life moves without abrupt shocks, in complete
harmony with the condition of the earth. And that common-
sense organization, I can see it with my eyes and feel it with
my soul as it was that evening in 1937 which I recall so exactly
today, in 1940, that it is here whole, in front of me. At this
hour beautiful grey horses were returning to the village, drawing muddy plows and harrows. No need to climb up the hills
to understand the vast country. All you had to do was to go
to the start of a street, where the last houses bordered the fields.
The peasant land began there. I speak for the nonsophisticated,
for those who can still imagine that there are peasants and non-
peasants. In fact the fields, meadows, woods, pasture lands,
ponds, springs, hills, valleys, were freely at ease in the little
town and no wall prevented them from spreading and occupy-
ing the eminent place which is theirs. No wall in the mind

either held behind it minds cut off from the world, but within the carpenter, the wheelwright, the weaver, within all the artisans of the village, the fields were plowed, sown, planted, harvested; and the organization of life did not separate men into categories, but they were all engaged in living on this earth as a single community. . . . The real human condition turns with the seasons, and the earth's wallowings in its bed of stars governs our body and soul more surely than the intrigues of politics. . . .

*   *   *   *   *

I stop a moment to imagine all the births at each second on the earth. As I count one, then two, then three, counting the seconds or the beating of my own heart, thousands of children of all colors are being born on the whole surface of the earth, in towns, villages, farms, forests, in ice huts on the polar circle, straw huts on the equator, everywhere, even on the ocean, even under the bombs . . . and the triumph I witness now in myself, tonight, as I count one, then two, then three and little by little, one after the other the numbers that carry me beyond the tens and tens, then the hundreds and hundreds, then the thousands and millions and billions of seconds without end . . . is the triumph of life. . . .

And at the exact moment when the vision has been lighted up within us, we have to come back abruptly to these times where they want to sell a man's skin before they kill him.

GERMAINE BRÉE

NOTE

1. *Works and Days*: the most famous poem by Hesiod (fl. eighth century B.C.), often called the father of Greek didactic poetry. This work embodies the daily experiences of peasant life. *Georgics*: poem by Vergil (Publius Vergilius Maro, fl. 70–19 B.C.). In this poem, which he composed in 37–30 B.C., he contrasts the simplicity, security, and sanctity of the Italian yeoman's life with the luxury and lawless passions of the great world.

CHOOSING SIDES

THE PAST REASSESSED: POINTS OF VIEW

WHEN ROBERT BRASILLACH was called up in
1939, he was sure he was going to witness the end of an
epoch. On the Maginot Line throughout the "phony war"
and in an officers' prisoner-of-war camp after June 1940,
he set out to record what he saw in a journal of the prewar
years. It was published in 1941 when he was released and
came back to Paris. "Our prewar years" are distinctly not
everybody's. For Brasillach, the interwar years had been
"a succession of sentimental and intellectual educations,"
the education of a young fascist and he speaks from that
premise. With obvious relish, he portrays the march of
events in Europe and the atmosphere of France in the
twenties and thirties as a tissue of inept and dissolute
absurdity. The sense of aberration and futility alienated
the young who dissociated themselves from the fiascos of a
pseudo-democracy, mystified, Brasillach considers, by the
pseudo-ideals of international communism. In contrast,
he presents his own mystique with the fervor of anticipated victory: the emergence of a "new man," fascist
man, awakening in country after country the national
loyalties and creative energies that had fashioned the
great past of Western civilization. Fantasy, romantic
idealism, Nietzschean overtones, disenchantment with the

political scene, are inextricably woven into Brasillach's
recording of the past. He often indulges in facile, corrosive
persiflage, unsubstantiated allegation, overt anti-Semitism,
latent antifeminism, and a callous indifference to the plight,
in 1941, of such political opponents as Léon Blum, pitilessly lampooned. When he spoke of "our" prewar past,
Brasillach was not speaking for all his compatriots. "His"
France excluded the democratic France of the republican
left. Defeat had passed final judgment on the democratic
way of life. It was now his turn.

One can understand to a certain extent the disaffection
that young intellectuals like Brasillach felt toward the
Establishment during the interwar years. They were eager
for a new world, an inspiring, magnificent, past-centered
world in which all Frenchmen would be reconciled.
Guéhenno's hesitant, apologetic defense of the practical
and social way of life under attack can hardly counter-
balance Brasillach's views. He presents a nostalgic, senti-
mentalized picture, touching in its simplicity and partial
truth, of the "little man's" dream of happiness in France,
made accessible by a hundred and fifty years of the Republic. Even the sprawling chaos of the modern city is
idealized as a sign of the anarchistic individualism which,
traditionally, he sees as a form of nobility, whereas
Brasillach saw it as self-centered weakness.

More complex, moralistic, and abstract, François Mauriac's meditation ranges over past and present, restating his
allegiance to the traditional humanistic creed of France as
embodied in the principles of the French Revolution. For
him what is in question is not so much the political and
historical future of France but rather a conception, essen-
tialist in kind, of individual and national morality, the
ethical basis of society. Combined with a revulsion against
the inhuman acts of Nazi rule, it was a firm ground of
principled opposition to the Nazi occupier and to any
form of collaboration with him. Failure there had been in
the past, and national guilt. Regeneration, then, and

atonement must arise from a reaffirmation of Christian, moral, democratic principles over the Machiavellian cult of efficacy, the basic principle of the fascist credo. Thus the battle with Nazi Germany becomes for Mauriac the age-old combat of right against might, good against evil, freedom against slavery, in what he sees as the high tradition of the French nation.

In the thirties Guéhenno, a non-Communist socialist, had been a sharp critic of social injustice under the Third Republic and a proponent of far-reaching social change. Under the impact of Nazi and Vichy rule, the Third Republic was becoming in retrospect a kind of golden age. The republican mystique and patriotism had coalesced. But to what extent were the policies of the Third Republic, responsible for the defeat, as Brasillach believed? And if they were, did it mean that the principles of French democracy had been disproved? To what extent was the picture of decadence drawn by Montherlant and Brasillach true? And was the disaster in fact a matter of ethics? The principles of efficacy and morality in government were presented by all three men as inseparable. Corrupt and inefficient was Brasillach's diagnostic of a regime that Guéhenno saw as basically sound and successful and Mauriac as ultimately good because it was basically moral.

ROBERT BRASILLACH

1939

From OUR PREWAR YEARS

The postwar period was dying a slow death. The Wall Street crash of 1929 had no immediate effect in France and the Tardieu[1] ministry seemed wreathed in the prettiest promises.

Industry, however, gradually began to feel the repercussions of the crisis, and everywhere the world grew dumb, padded, and shifty. Ever so quietly and methodically communism was getting organized, but people pretended not to believe it. In 1931[2] the Spanish monarchy was overthrown by a conspiracy of freemasons, priests, and revolutionaries, and Pierre Gaxotte[3] exclaimed in *Je suis partout*:[4] "This time it's at our doorstep." Germany was rearming no less methodically, and every season there was some false alarm from across the Rhine. But Herr Brüning[5] came to Paris and went to mass at Notre-Dame-des-Victoires. The ladies and the intellectuals raved about a German, Monsieur Frédéric Sieburg,[6] who published a book called *Is God French?* We were very much afraid of the Stahlhelm[7] and very much afraid of Herr Treviranus.[8] Who can remember him now? As for the "agitator" called Hitler, Monsieur Blum, leader of the Socialist Party, claimed at each of Hitler's successes that he had not the slightest hope of coming to power. That was one of his most famous prophecies. All our hopes were based on a strange champion of democracy and liberalism —the old Marshal Hindenburg, a rampart against Hitler's nationalism. Pacifism was in its heyday. German war books were all the rage—*All Quiet on the Western Front, Class 22*,[9] and then there were the films based on these books, like Pabst's *Four from the Infantry*, full of gray and gloomy images of the horrors of war. In short, we fell asleep. Sleep is the fundamental characteristic of those three or four years between the evacuation of Mainz[10] and the National Socialist rise to power.

Nevertheless there were notes of warning worthy of more attention. Monsieur Briand[11] had vanished, beaten by a good old republican, Paul Doumer.[12] But a year after his nomination the thirteenth President of the Republic was assassinated by a crazy and shady Russian, Gorgulov, whose motives and accomplices were never very closely investigated. In the 1932 elections, even if the Communists did not have the success they expected,

SOURCE NOTE: Robert Brasillach, *Notre Avant-guerre* (Paris, Plon, 1941), pp. 99–101, 180–90, 234–37.

Monsieur Tardieu was turned out and the field left clear for
radical and opportunist ministries, and for deeper sleep. Apart
from *L'Action française*[13] the national newspapers were drab.
A megalomanic perfumer, François Coty,[14] had started to publish *L'Ami du peuple* for two sous instead of five, and it might
have been a powerful weapon. But he sank into incoherence,
after quarreling with everybody. The Socialists had always been
against military credit; together with several left-wingers they
had voted in the Chamber against the fortifications in the East
and on the Maginot Line; people still believed in the League
of Nations, those doves of the Lake of Geneva with their
"cellolike" cooings, and they closed their eyes. In January 1932
Maginot[15] died a strange death. The defendants of the Oustric
case[16] were acquitted. We danced to new tunes; we lived in
an intermediate period between the miaowing of the Hawaiian
guitar and the miaowing of West Indian dances; jazz became
more brutal, richer in quality, more anarchical, and finally gave
way to hot jazz. By the beaches, in the bars, we saw the first
Russian billiard tables; at Saint-Tropez a magic top at the end
of a string, the yoyo, was introduced . . . We talked about
eroticism and raved about Lawrence's *Lady Chatterley's Lover*.
France needed dreams: she occasionally awoke with a start
before a nightmare, but went straight back to sleep again. It
was a period of sleep.

*   *   *   *   *

The fifteen or twenty months after 1936 are one of the
weirdest periods France has ever known—one of the most harm-
ful periods, too: we are still suffering from the consequences
at home and abroad. But it was also one of the most ridiculous
periods. Never have stupidity, pedantry, bombast, pretension,
and triumphant mediocrity been so arrogant. Time passes
quickly and these extravagant weeks have not yet been fully
described; but what has been recorded of them will one day
fill historians with amazement, shame, and mirth. Read Alain

Laubreaux's[17] *La Terreur rose*, the account of dusty meetings where everyone is called "Monsieur le président"; read those incredible stories: an old woman sued for keeping a German machine gun brought back by her son who was killed in the war; an attendant letting a patient die in the hospital because his working day was over. And remember the death of four-year-old Paul Gignoux, killed by the other children at Lyons because he had some tickets for a charity sale, and that meant he was a little fascist. The incredible period which we have just witnessed is a combination of the odious and the grotesque.

Strikes everywhere. In the Rue Vaugirard, where we were still living, we used to bump into the alms collectors. The windows were strung with red flags bearing hammers and sickles, or stars, or even—out of decency—the national shield. As a reaction Colonel de La Rocque[18] persuaded the patriots all over France to deck their houses with the French flag. The factories were occupied periodically. The director and the engineers were locked in and the workers would not leave the premises: that was called the "sit-down strike." On the gates hung a blackboard where the days of strike were written up, while in the factory the workers formed very photogenic groups with accordion players, such as you see in Russian films. Prime Minister since January, Monsieur Blum[19] complained and sniveled twice a month on the radio, and languidly gave satisfactory assurances to everybody. His false prophecies and innumerable blunders were printed and reprinted, and references were made to the books of his youth and his dated, obscene aestheticism. At the same time, on July 18, in a Spain enfeebled by a still more damaging Popular Front,[20] a generals' rebellion broke out which was to become a civil war and a nationalist revolution. The Communists demonstrated in favor of sending cannons and planes to Madrid, to quell "facism." They organized the transport of arms and men and shouted "Blum into action!" thus satisfying their desire for war abroad and devitalization at home.

The Revolutionary Writers' and Artists' Association had had

its heyday. Covered in honors, its members used to go around with their Légion d'honneur ribbons under their lapels: that was their way of proving their independence of the regime. In May 1936 these scrupulous consciences were liberated and, by a divine grace, promotions began to rain down. The Maison de la Culture[21] was there. It had a real house all of its own in the Rue de Navarin, and in the face of the "reactionary vigilance," distinguished by the professors Langevin, Perrin, and Joliot-Curie.[22] Nearly all the literature of the period ended up there, and with the Red marchionesses' money an astonishing paper, Vendredi,[23] was founded.

Vendredi, which did not survive Franco's victory in Spain and the disappearance of the Popular Front, was directed by Jean Guéhenno and André Chamson. It started by claiming it grouped "free men" from André Gide to Jacques Maritain. The latter, credulous by nature, withdrew immediately. As for Gide, after having contributed to it for some time he went to Russia, and when he returned he published his Retour de l'U.R.S.S. He had been ingenuous enough to have been a Communist for a couple of years, and now that he reappeared disgusted by Stalin, he had the courage to say so. He was dismissed out of hand, for Monsieur Chamson still believed in the holy fatherland of the revolution. From time to time Monsieur Guéhenno was still allowed to shed a tear for the Trotskyites and for the Moscow trials, where so many "right-wingers" and "deviationists" admitted their crimes to the amazement of the whole world—this was how Vendredi retained a tinge of liberalism. Its real aim was to support the Spanish revolutionaries, but it was very boring and school-masterish—typical of those years.

The false revolution of 1936 was an intellectual revolution. Showered with grants, all the intellectuals could produce were reports and theses. Even the humorists had lost their sense of humor. The old anarchist paper which we all used to read, Le Canard enchaîné, dismissed most of its contributors, who were guilty of irreverence, and became strictly Popular Front, flirting overtly with the Stalinists. Immense sums were spent at the Exhibition of 1937[24] in order to produce the most extraordinary collective spectacles: J.-R. Bloch's *Naissance d'une cité*, where there were more actors than spectators; *Liberté*, written by twelve writers who dealt with an episode in French history, each one in his own way—after a farcical Joan of Arc and a scholarly discussion between Pascal and Descartes about the heart and reason, it all ended in an apotheosis of the oath of July 1935 for the "defense of democratic liberties." That was what history amounted to.

Some talented writers took part in the game. The most obvious was André Malraux, whose somber, misty, tough novels we used to read, justification of suffering and intellectual sadism, filled with Chinese tortures and machine-gun fire—*Les Conquérants* [*The Conquerors*] and *La Condition humaine* [*Man's Fate*]. He recruited officially for Red Spain, and even became lieutenant colonel in command of the España squadron. Malraux's glory put the other firebrands in the shade, but they had found an aim in life; they thought they were entering into action, going out to the people, by raising their fists at meetings. A little later sincere, inexperienced Jean Guéhenno wrote a few almost repentant pages about it. This was when a painter would be booed at an artists' congress if he said that he was a Communist and went on strike when he had to, but that he preferred to paint his wife and daughter rather than exalt class consciousness. It was when Aragon and Jean Cassou deplored the fact that one couldn't tell if a canvas had been painted before or after February 6 (they really did say and think these things!) and explained that the decadence of art was due to the "two hundred families."[25]

Because France was governed by an oligarchy of "two hundred families." At the Métro stations newspaper vendors used to cry out:

"Buy the complete official list of the two hundred families!"

Nobody was surprised by this grotesque announcement. The bourgeoisie paled: they thought they would be saved either by

the PSF[26] or by the radicals, and gave money to the Red alms
collectors. They were accosted by them in the street and used
to get pretty scared. Few of them came to blows with the
strikers: there were some, though, and nobody dared touch
them. Others were more prepared for the revolutions, which, it
must be said, were not always unjustifiable. In a firm I know
word got around that the Reds were going to "attack" on a
Saturday afternoon. It was in summer; the boss was on his
yacht. He telephoned to say he was coming and to tell some
of his staff to be ready to defend capitalism. A few friends
came along with a small arsenal and stayed all afternoon. No
assailants. No boss either. He appeared next Monday and said,
smiling:

"So you were in a loyal state of emergency on Saturday, were
you?"

It is not surprising if, caught between social conservatism
and Marxist rabble, many of the young hesitated. The triumphs
of 1936 showed up the appalling state of injustice, helped
people to understand certain situations, and made us hope for
some necessary reforms. Not all the strikes were unjustified,
especially in the beginning when there was a feeling of joy,
freedom, and hope. We knew perfectly well that *no* workers'
request has ever been complied with willingly, and that the
owners groaned they were going to be ruined when the eleven-
hour day was introduced under Louis-Philippe[27] and children
under twelve were forbidden to work at night. We knew perfectly well that nothing had been accomplished without a
struggle, blood, and sacrifice. We had no interest in capitalism,
and we were not totally opposed to the "breeze of May 1936."
Alas! The reforms announced were performed in an unimaginable atmosphere of intrigue, excess, demagogy, and baseness.
That is how fascism starts.

Fascism started. We saw it start. We used to watch those
incredible processions in 1936, those vast crowds trudging from
the Place de la République to the Place de la Nation. Enthusiasm? I'm not sure. But there was an extraordinary docility.

French destiny led toward a red, mysterious goal, and the passers-by raised their fists and rallied behind the free-thinking bigophonists, the antifascist anglers, and marched to the Place du Trône where the columns were draped in huge banners. Little puppets were on sale: Colonel de La Rocque. Giant portraits were carried around, as in Russia: the liberators of thought, Descartes, Voltaire, Karl Marx, Henri Barbusse.[28] It was farcical and dusty; the intellect had become the master. And yet if you told the alms collectors of July 1936, "No, comrade, I'm a fascist," nobody minded. The Roman salute grew quite common, not out of conviction, but as a reply when the Communists marched past pointing their fists at the Arc de Triomphe. We raised our arms and sang *La Marseillaise*. The nationalist spirit demanded its rites, and the Moscovites tried to nip them off it by singing the *Marseillaise* too, by flying the French flag and saying they were struggling against the threat of fascism, fighting for the liberty of France. This is what Maurice Thorez[29] said, a Communist deputy who has since deserted. An odd period.

* * * * *

The International Exhibition of 1937 will for long remain one of the strangest of these manifestations. What with the strikes and the compromises everybody knew that it would not be ready in time. Monsieur Blum beseeched the workers to work. He spoke under banners which proclaimed that "the opening of the Exhibition on May 1 would be a victory against fascism." Despite the presence of Italy and Germany. On May 15, I think, a phantom exhibition was inaugurated among the debris. The fountains were replaced by fire hoses covered with patches of lawn—a historic detail. Lucien Rebatet[30] described the preposterous ceremony, worthy of Father Ubu,[31] in *Je suis partout*. "To the call of ten names dishonored by illustrious trials," the country's rulers advanced. When Monsieur Blum, Monsieur Zay, Monsieur Abraham, Monsieur Cahen-Salvador, and Mon-

sieur Moch[32] appeared, the band struck up with *Fiers Gaulois
à tête ronde* . . . Then the gates were closed and the public was
only admitted to the building site a month later. The Mexican
pavilion was not even ready when the fair ended in November.

It was a financial failure, of course, while the Colonial Exhibition in 1931 had been a success. But it had been talked about
so much and given such publicity that many people went there.
It was situated in the real center of Paris. The royal banks of
the Seine were taken up by ramshackle buildings, which had
still not been entirely demolished by the 1939 war. Nevertheless
there were some pretty things: the river at night, the children's
gardens looking like toys, a country house or a wooden palace.
The old Trocadéro Palace, bulging between its two towers,
which had dominated the banks of the Seine since the Second
Empire, disappeared. It had in fact only been camouflaged and
replaced by a semicircular building with a gap in the middle
revealing some hideous scaffolding. It was inscribed with slightly
insidious, slightly ridiculous expressions which current opinion
attributed to Paul Valéry. But the steps of Chaillot had a
certain grace, and from up there one could see the old Eiffel
Tower—the queen and torch of this new Exhibition—and
Paris. On the square of the foreign pavilions, the Soviet pavilion,
surmounted by a giant pendulum, faced the German pavilion,
decorated with an eagle. We smiled to see the two red flags,
one with a swastika, the other with a hammer and sickle.

But when we left[33] we found the Popular Front again. I
happened to travel a little in those years. I gave some lectures
in the provinces, in Tunisia and Morocco. I stopped in Switzerland, Italy, and Belgium. Everywhere I went I realized what
permanent and insane damage had been done by this mediocre
revolution, this victory of baseness. In North Africa, where
there were some demented plans to undermine French influence, the settlers and the conquerors were beginning to organize
a resistance, and it was here that the true nature of France
was brought back to me and I found some consolation. In the
meantime, in Paris, the extraordinary saraband continued to

ruin the state and the individual, and above all to destroy the spirit of the workers by gradually spreading the conviction that there was no need to work any more, that everything would turn out all right, thanks to the government. After a press campaign the Home Secretary, Roger Salengro, committed suicide for no apparent reason. His name was given to streets, student organizations were christened Karl Marx, Lenin stadiums were built, squares were named after Marty[34] or Barbusse. To flatter feminism Léon Blum had taken some women into his cabinet: a large authoritarian Jewess, Madame Brunschvigg, and a thin, sly-looking little schoolmistress. People made fun of them. With a fringed idiot in their midst, pictures of the Ministry presented an unforgettable sight.

We must not be surprised if people sometimes reacted violently and ideas sprang up in France which were far from the tepid liberalism so fashionable after the war. Blum's ascent to power revived a movement almost unknown in France since the Dreyfus Affair[35]—anti-Semitism. The French are instinctively anti-Semitic, of course, but they don't like to be seen persecuting innocent people just because of the color of their skin. Monsieur Blum taught them that anti-Semitism was quite different. In the Chamber the deputy Xavier Vallat ironically hailed the day when, for the first time, a Jew had been elected to head an old "Gallo-Roman country." There were some incidents: after a Breton deputy, Monsieur Ihuel, had alluded to the chosen people, the minister Max Dormoy shouted: "A Jew is worth a Breton." An uproar ensued. The town councilor Darquier de Pellepoix, who directed an extremely violent review, *La France enchaînée*, seriously proposed that a street be named after Drumont as compensation. *Gringoire*[36] published an impressive list of Jewish ministers, cabinet attachés, and departmental managers of the Popular Front. By a curiously sadistic coincidence, the ministry of education was given to a notorious antimilitarist, who has since become a warmonger and has distinguished himself by writing offensive articles about his country. The cinema was virtually

closed to Aryans. The radio had a Yiddish accent. The most
peaceable people began to look askance at the curly hair and
hooked noses which they saw everywhere. This is not polemical,
this is true.

In April 1938 *Je suis partout* printed a special number on
the Jews in the world, and in February 1939 a further one on
the Jews in France—a collection of documents gathered by
Lucien Rebatet in an attempt to compile a reasonable Jewish
constitution. It was a great success, but it also caused an outcry.
At the same time instinctive anti-Semitism found its prophet
in Louis-Ferdinand Céline, the author of *Voyage au bout de la
nuit*. His torrential, joyously ferocious pamphlet *Bagatelles pour
un massacre* was splendidly energetic, even if it went too far.
There was no attempt at rationalization, simply the "revolt of
the natives." It was all the rage.

The notes of warning continued to sound, however. In March
1936 Chancellor Hitler reoccupied the area demilitarized since
the Treaty of Versailles. I don't know whether the French Army
was ready or not; I only know that the elections were close at
hand and that one can't impose a military expedition on a
republic a few months before the vote. Monsieur Flandin,
who was then a minister, later revealed that he had asked the
English their advice and that they had been against any retaliation. There were some empty speeches and from then on we
were sure that war was inevitable. On the other side of the
Rhine the Germans set to work gaily: they offered friendship
to France and to the whole world, and patiently continued to
build the sumptuous, hard machines of the Third Reich. In
March 1938, fulfilling his life's desire, Hitler entered Vienna
without firing a shot and the Austro-German *Anschluss* took
place—it had been on the program of every German party,
approved by the French Marxists, and when the Nazis accomplished it France, as if by chance, was having a ministerial
crisis. Italy, who had sent troops to the Brenner in 1934, no
longer budged, antagonized as she was by the criminal sanctions policy.[37] France was just beginning to wake up.

*   *   *   *   *

From now on we are far from those vague promises made to us in Geneva in 1925[38]—the architects of clouds and illusions. Ten years later the French youth may still have had illusions. But their dreams had another color, and this color is the most difficult thing to grasp in all its shades if one wants to describe the intellectual adventure before the war. It was a time when everyone turned toward foreign countries and searched for— and frequently rejected—warnings and lessons. It was a time when, faced with other forms of nationalism, French nationalism developed a greater self-awareness, but it was also a time when the French nationalists listened more attentively than ever to what was going on beyond their frontiers. A state of mind was formed which paved the way for what one might call French "fascism." It was the last adventure attempted by a part of prewar youth, and the one which has been least recorded.

From now on, when a leader, friend, or enemy turns to our comrades in the Empire and overseas, when we see the hard bloom of nationalist youth[39] flowering on silver screens, we must take a stand: it is not only the men within dictatorial frontiers who feel their hearts leap, but all those throughout the universe who still believe in the nation, in the race, in history, and who, with emotion or fanaticism, view the past and present of their country and ask: "Why not us?"

Thanks to the fortunes which have carried millions of men to power or toward power in some countries, thanks to the lines of chance devised by the prophets, we have now been able to witness for twenty years the birth of a new human species as differentiated and astonishing as the Cartesian hero,[40] or the sensitive Encyclopedist intellectual[41] of the eighteenth century, or the Jacobin "patriot."[42] We have witnessed the birth of the fascist. Since science distinguishes between *Homo faber*[43] and *Homo sapiens*,[44] we should perhaps submit this *Homo fascista*[45]

to the classifiers and label lovers. For, although born in Italy,
he too can now claim the universal designation of Latin
etymology. Even those who do not accept his domination need
to know him, if only to combat him, because he stands before
them as the Christian knight stood in other times, leaning on
his sword and his cross, or the pale revolutionary conspirator
in his secret printing presses and smoky cafés—one of the most
definite incarnations of his epoch.

If we were writing history rather than presenting a collection
of images we would say that just as the sensitive young demo-
crat formed by the Encyclopedia[46] and its principles felt a new
emotion at the birth of the United States of America, created by
Freemasonry,[47] so in the twentieth century the first country to
apply a nationalist and social doctrine was Italy.[48] Then came
Oliveira Salazar's Portugal.[49] Founded on Christian principles,
it provided the model of the corporative system, inspired by
La Tour du Pin[50] and applied in Italy within a more rigid
state administration. When in her turn Germany accomplished
her revolution,[51] she contributed her own personality. The cult
of the Fatherland was transposed into daily and nightly rites—
Walpurgis Nights[52] illuminated by projectors and torches,
heroic tunes, songs of war and peace sung by millions of men.
Finally, in the years which followed, the various national movements, both conquerors and candidates for power, whatever
their divergences, made an individual contribution and strengthened the notion of a universal revolution similar to the one
which raged through Europe in 1848.

We took an interest in Mustapha Kemal's[53] efforts to create
a national Turkish feeling. We saw the fire alight everywhere.
We saw it burn with a feeble or powerful flame and gradually
menace the old world. On the plains and canals of Holland, in
the meadows, tulip fields, and armies of cyclists, it was Mussert's
National-socialistische Bewegung; in the London suburbs, in
the English pastures and mines, it was Oswald Mosley's British
Union of Fascists (however much fun was made of Mosley);
it was the nationalists in Switzerland. From the Balkans to the

dry landscape of Greece and the icy fjords, from the red plains of Castile to the green and white mountains where a lost bell tolls, a long, turbulent, and sleepless night began in which every country heard a shout: "Nation, awake!" In Rumania, Corneliu Codreanu addressed his legionaries in a rough and gaudy lyric style; he appealed to the spirit of sacrifice, honor, and discipline; he demanded that "state of collective illumination which has hitherto been found only in religious experience" and which he called "national universality"; he founded the original, monastic, and military order of the Iron Guard. In Belgium, the land of traditional liberalism, rexism, with its thirty-year-old leader, stressed the most spectacular and attractive element of the new world: youth. The universe was ablaze; the universe sang, united, and set to work. Germany, attentive to these new times, awaited her hour and ceaselessly prepared for the future.

Finally, while all the different doctrines were awaiting power or had attained it without too long a war—even German National Socialism—a terrible struggle broke out on one of the noblest grounds of Europe and opposed in bloody battles *fascism* to *antifascism*. Thus Spain ended by transforming into spiritual and material combat, into a true crusade, the long opposition which lurked in the modern world. Her international brigades, on both sides, sealed alliances in blood. Over the whole planet men felt the sieges of Toledo and Oviedo, the battles of Teruel, Guadalajara, Madrid, and Valencia,[54] as their own war, their own victories and defeats. The Chinese coolie, the laborer of Belleville,[55] the stray urchin in the mists of London, the poor, disappointed gold seeker, the master of the Hungarian or Argentinian pastures, could quake with fear or pleasure before some ill-spelled name in some unknown newspaper. In the gray smoke of the shells, under the fiery sky infested with fighter planes, Russians fighting Italians,[56] the ideological contradictions were being resolved in an ancient land of acts of faith and conquerors by suffering, blood, and death. Spain gave her blessing and nobility to the war of ideas.

So are myths created. "Myths are not astrological almanacs," said Sorel,[57] "and to know what details they contain which will appear like dry stones on the surface of future history is unimportant . . . One must judge myths as a means of acting on the present . . ." The flames of the Spanish war have finally given these images their power of expansion, their religious hue. We cannot have ignored them.

ALASTAIR HAMILTON

NOTES

1. *Tardieu*: André Tardieu (1876–1945), conservative republican; Prime Minister of France in 1929.

2. *1931*: in that year, the government of Alfonso XIII of Spain was overthrown in favor of a republic.

3. *Pierre Gaxotte*: (1895–   ), member of the French Academy and well-known right-wing historian.

4. *Je suis partout*: one of the leading right-wing and later collaborationist newspapers founded in 1930 by Arthème Fayard, edited by Pierre Gaxotte, who dealt with foreign policy. After Brasillach became its editor in 1937, the paper was concerned more with domestic issues, taking a traditionalist and antiparliamentarian viewpoint.

5. *Herr Bruning*: Heinrich Bruning (1885–   ), German politician; Chancellor of the Reich in 1930–1932.

6. *Monsieur Frédéric Sieburg*: (1893–   ), author of *Dieu est-il français?* which rather wittily criticizes French cultural complacency and patronizing attitudes toward other nations.

7. *Stahlhelm (Casque d'Acier)*: German nationalist association founded in 1918 and again in 1952.

8. *Herr Treviranus*: German statesman, a conservative belonging to the German Nationalist Party.

9. *All Quiet on the Western Front, Class 22*: there were at the time a series of such war documentaries drawn from novels with a *"nicht mehr Krieg"* message.

10. *evacuation of Mainz*: according to the terms of the Treaty of Versailles (1919), Mainz was to be occupied for fifteen years by French troops in the name of the Allies. The evacuation of these troops was anticipated in 1930 when the Germans accepted the Young Plan (presented at the Hague Conference of 1929–1930).

11. *Monsieur Briand*: Aristide Briand (1862–1932), ten times Prime Minister; as a Socialist, Minister of Foreign Affairs in 1925–1932, he worked toward a policy of reconciliation with Germany; one of the creators of the League of Nations.

12. *Paul Doumer*: Governor of Indochina 1896–1902; president of the French Senate in 1927; President of the Republic in 1931; assassinated in Paris in 1932.

13. *L'Action française*: French daily newspaper of the right (1908–1944), founded by Charles Maurras, propounding the political doctrine of "integral nationalism": hereditary monarchy, and an antiparliamentarian, decentralized government.

14. *François Coty*: wealthy French businessman (1874–1934), who intended to make his new way in politics by purchasing and editing newspapers; founder of the low-priced *Ami du peuple* (1928).

15. *Maginot*: André Maginot (1877–1932), French War Minister after whom the French fortifications built along the Franco-German frontier between 1937 and 1939 were named.

16. *Oustric case*: financial scandal (1926–1933) concerning the French Stock Exchange which implicated the French Ministry of Finance.

17. *Alain Laubreaux*: one of the French fascist intellectuals, journalist of *Je suis partout*, who became a fervent collaborationist.

18. *Colonel de La Rocque*: head of the semifascist Croix de Feu, originally an exclusive ex-servicemen's organization which expanded as it took part in demonstrations against the "Red Menace." He organized the Volontaires Nationaux in 1934 and the Parti Social Français. An avid supporter of Pétain, he was later deported to Germany as a possible American spy. He returned after the Liberation in 1945 and died soon afterward.

19. *Monsieur Blum*: Léon Blum (1872–1950), head of the Socialist Party, the SFIO. He set up a Popular Front government in 1936. Deported to Germany in 1943, he was again head of a Socialist government in 1946.

20. *Popular Front*: here, a coalition of left-wing Spanish groups. In 1936, under the leadership of General Franco, the anti-Republican forces in Spain started a civil war which ended two and one-half years later with the establishment of the Franco dictatorship.

21. *Maison de la Culture*: founded in 1933 by Louis Aragon under the initiative of the Communist Party throughout France.

22. *Langevin, Perrin, and Joliot-Curie*: three of France's most eminent scientists: left-wing socialists in politics.

23. *Vendredi*: liberal, pacifist weekly.

24. *Exhibition of 1937*: an artistic and technical exhibition in Paris, for which the Palais de Chaillot was built.

25. *two hundred families*: the Communists drew up a list of two hundred French families who supposedly controlled France financially.

26. *PSF*: Parti Social Français, a right-wing paramilitary organization, headed by Colonel de La Rocque.

27. *Louis-Philippe*: Restoration monarch (1830–1848) of Bourbon lineage.

28. *Henri Barbusse*: French writer (1873–1935), director of *Clarté*, one of the first Marxist socialist reviews.

29. *Maurice Thorez*: (1900–1964) leader of the French Com-

munist Party who disappeared in October 1939 from his army unit and eventually turned up in Russia. He returned to France after the Liberation.

30. *Lucien Rebatet*: French fascist and future collaborationist, writer, and journalist of *Je suis partout*.

31. *Father Ubu*: reference to Alfred Jarry's play *Ubu Roi* (1896), a burlesque comedy about a peasant king of Poland.

32. *Monsieur Blum . . . Monsieur Moch*: French Jewish politicians.

33. *But when we left*: that is, the Exhibition.

34. *Marty*: French Communist leader.

35. *Dreyfus Affair*: Alfred Dreyfus, a French Jewish officer, was tried by court-martial on charges of espionage and condemned. After twelve years of legal battles (1894–1906), he was vindicated of treason. The Affair signaled the moral crisis of a nation. France was divided between those who felt that individual rights were involved and that the case should be reopened, and those who were against such action as endangering the interests of the state and national security. The Affair pitted the military and the conservatives against the liberals in a contest between the military and civil powers of the Republic, and it touched off a wave of anti-Semitism followed later by anticlerical legislation. In a literary and intellectual sense the Affair was the experience of a generation.

36. *Gringoire*: a leading collaborationist political and literary weekly (founded in 1928) published in the southern zone until May 1944.

37. *criminal sanctions policy*: in the thirties the Popular Front government of France agreed to the economic sanctions imposed by the League of Nations on Fascist Italy at the time of its invasion of Ethiopia.

38. *Geneva in 1925*: a general reference to the activities of the League of Nations, and more precisely to the Protocols of Geneva, signed in September 1924, forbidding wars of aggression, setting up machinery for arbitration of international disputes, and guaranteeing certain measures of security, with disarmament as the goal. Britain, preferring regional agreements, would not assent to this international pact. In December 1925 the Locarno Peace Pact was signed whereby Germany renounced the use of force to change its frontiers, became a permanent member of the League, and agreed to arbitration concerning its eastern frontiers. For a time the way to disarmament seemed clear.

39. *nationalist youth*: in the twenties fascist groups sprang up in virtually every country of Western Europe, creating large youth groups.

40. *Cartesian hero*: the "generous man" of Descartes (1596–1650), free from pride and baseness, beneficent, affable.

41. *sensitive Encyclopedist intellectual*: the concept of man proposed by the philosophers of eighteenth-century France—toler-

ant, deist, politically involved, possessing a broad, all-encompassing education, classical in aesthetic taste, capable of enjoying nature.

42. *Jacobin "patriot"*: the revolutionary hero.

43. *Homo faber*: "man the maker."

44. *Homo sapiens*: "man the knowing (animal)."

45. *Homo fascista*: "man bound together" (Italian *fascismo*, from Latin *fascis*, meaning a group, club, literally a bundle).

46. *Encyclopedia*: the Encyclopedia of the liberal eighteenth-century philosophers, especially Diderot, D'Alembert, Voltaire, Rousseau, Marmontel, Condillac, Turgot, D'Holbach and Helvétius, published in 35 volumes (1751-1780).

47. *Freemasonry*: secret society, liberal, anticlerical, especially influential throughout the Western World during the eighteenth and nineteenth centuries as a revolutionary force, and seen by the fascists as a conspiratorial, antinationalist organization.

48. *Italy*: the Italian Fascist party was founded in 1919 and came to power under Mussolini in 1922, twelve years before Hitler took control of the German government.

49. *Oliveira Salazar's Portugal*: Antonio de Oliveira Salazar (1889-1969) became premier of Portugal in 1932. The Portuguese monarchy had been overthrown in 1910 and a republic established. After several short-lived ministries, the military took power in 1926. Salazar, a former professor of economics, became Finance Minister in 1928 and rescued the country's economy. As premier, he established a new constitution in 1933, which provided for a purely consultative corporate assembly to be elected in addition to a national assembly. The speeches Salazar delivered between 1928 and 1936 were published in France under the title *Une Révolution dans la paix* (1937).

50. *La Tour du Pin*: René, Marquis de (1834-1924), a proponent of "social Christianity."

51. *revolution*: Hitler took power in 1934, after being Chancellor in 1933.

52. *Walpurgis Nights*: reference to the dramatic youth rallies held at night throughout Germany at which speeches were made by various Nazi leaders, including Hitler. Brasillach later describes one such rally at Nuremburg in extremely graphic terms.

53. *Mustapha Kemal*: Mustapha Kemal Atatürk (1881-1938), head of the Turkish Nationalist party, elected President of the Turkish Republic in 1923; the "Father of Modern Turkey."

54. *Toledo . . . Valencia*: the Spanish Civil War began in 1936 and ended with the triumph of Franco's fascist party, the Falange. The battles mentioned from Toledo to Valencia are the great battles of the war.

55. *Belleville*: working-class district of Paris.

56. *Russians fighting Italians*: foreign intervention, with the Germans and the Italians on the fascist side and the Russians

supporting the government forces, made of the Spanish Civil War
a prelude to World War II.

57. *Sorel*: Georges Sorel (1847–1922) French sociologist, author
of *Reflections on Violence* (1908). He developed the thesis that
irrational elements directed men's actions and that myths—such as
the myth of a general strike—must be developed to motivate revolutionary action.

JEAN GUÉHENNO

1940

JULY 1940

We shall not let it be said that the France of the last fifty
years was so base and ugly. Everyone who envied her would
deny it. If she was happy, what is wrong with happiness? What
hypocrites despise it? We have, admittedly, made a great effort
to be happy. But all men are French in this, and the German
critic[1] who accused God of wanting to nationalize himself
French was merely envious.

If God, that eternal spectator, exists, if he is neither absurd
nor cruel, if he does not believe that men must work for the
sake of working but rather to embellish the earth, and if he ever
wants men to raise their eyes and look to heaven, he must have
glanced at France from between two clouds at a moment when
he was not too displeased with us.

The domain of the French, what God gave them on earth,
was adequately cultivated. Here and there the mountain peaks
lay fallow—but the French had found a way of fertilizing the
plain. They had more bread than they could eat, more wine
than they could drink. They gave their corn to their chickens
and burned their wine. The villages, however dirty, had never

SOURCE NOTE: Jean Guéhenno (pseud. Cévennes), *Dans la prison* (Paris,
Éditions de Minuit, 1944), pp. 18–21.

been so clean. The new roofs of slate or tiles sparkled. Between the church and the town hall God could see a fine building where little children learned to read, to write, to count, and to think. To think—what an ambition! Everybody wanted to be somebody. What aristocrats these French democrats were! Across the corn, the vineyards, the woods, the meadows, from borough to borough, from village to village, shone the roads between the plane trees, a canvas stretched over the whole country, a network of companionship. The cars, blue Peugeots, black Renaults, ran toward each other like kindred thoughts. The towns swelled, the suburbs stretched out as though they were hauling in the countryside. And there was quite a fuss about these new outskirts. The town planners protested. What a mess! What anarchy! These French would never improve. A race of peasants who want the whole horizon to themselves, they built their town houses like farms. They did all they could to turn their backs on their neighbors and to be the only ones "at home." They would rather have given up the sun than stand in a row.

From these strange gatherings which they formed in the towns where they lived, together and yet on their own, arguments arose like clouds of dust which blurred the landscape. Prophets startled them for a moment, but once the dust had settled these impenitent individualists returned home, dreaming of bread and a way to earn it—of bread and liberty. That was their goal; they never separated the two: bread and liberty. They dreamed of these, not only for themselves, no, but for everybody. It was a fad of theirs never to dream or to think for themselves. They were sometimes petty in small things, but only they were generous in big ones. They served the mind, and they served humanity.

ALASTAIR HAMILTON

NOTE
1. *the German critic*: Frédéric Sieburg (see above, page 56, note 6).

FRANÇOIS MAURIAC

From *THE BLACK NOTEBOOK*

How long it is since I have been alone! All the buzzing around my person, in which the very attacks reinforced the praise, has stopped at last! Today the worst outrages are annihilated in the great silence after the storm. Those who insult me are the very men who are bursting with joy because the Republic is dead (because they believe it is dead). Look at them: each one identifies himself with the calamity. The prophets of disaster mount to the Capitol[1] side by side with the conqueror whose coming they have announced and prepared for. They indulge the hallucination of having, to all appearances, been right, right for a little while . . .

But come! Weapons decide nothing in a conflict of ideas. Our victory of 1918 did not prove that the democracies were right, any more than our defeat in 1940 has proved them to be guilty. The methods which have defeated them are a guarantee that one day they shall triumph.

And we too, in the depths of the abyss, we declare that the result justifies us. It is the separation between politics and morality, which we used to denounce with all our feeble strength, that has brought about this blood-bath for the world. Machiavelli[2] is the father of collective crime; he prepares and organizes it; he makes it lawful, justifiable, and glorious. True enough, this eternal assassin is not always to be found in the same camp; we are not so pharisaical as to claim that! But we know on which side he has ranged for the last twelve years in Europe, and with what furious virulence.

SOURCE NOTE: François Mauriac (pseud. Forez), *Le Cahier noir* (Paris, Éditions de Minuit, 1943), pp. 10–49. The manuscript was received by the editors in June of 1943 and published in August of the same year.

We are not ashamed of having wanted the moral law which governs individual relationships to operate also among the nations. We were not quite so simple as to suppose that Machiavelli could be completely overcome both within us and around us. We never forgot the meditation on the Pharsalian plains[3] in Part II of *Faust*. "How many times has this struggle recurred," ponders Goethe; "and it will recur always and for all eternity. No one wants to surrender sovereignty to another." We admitted this view. But it was enough for us that Europe was advancing, however gropingly, toward a world in which Machiavelli could have been at least partially subdued—by the organization of force in the service of justice. It only requires the patience of a few determined men, who swim against the tide, to keep Machiavelli at bay . . .

But our misfortune was to embark on public life directly after the last war when Europe seemed to have acquired a distaste for liberty. How out of date this old country suddenly appeared in 1919, bled white for a cause in which the peoples no longer believed! At that time I remember I made some boys laugh when I quoted the proud phrase with which Saint-Just[4] concluded his plan for a constitution: "The French nation votes the liberty of the world!"

It took us some time to realize that this faith in liberty had been extinguished in the hearts of the nations. One of our friends, however, perceived it and proclaimed it before the names of Hitler and Mussolini had resounded in Europe. On September 1, 1919, Jacques Rivière,[5] coming out from a long imprisonment, wrote in the *Nouvelle Revue Française*: "It is by no means certain that the world needs this liberty which we have bought for it at the cost of such enormous sacrifices. It is by no means certain that liberty is its dearest desire just now, the food for which it hungers most. It is very doubtful. We have reason to fear that its appetites are altogether different. It seems that the demand for the commodity of liberty—taking mankind as a whole—is much lower than the supply which we have of it. The market is perhaps not at all what we imagined.

We are running a grave risk of being left with our stock on our hands."

Jacques Rivière died too soon to see what an astonishing prophet he was. Before the love of liberty was rekindled in the hearts of the nations there had to be the ordeal by gag and pillory; there had to be the massacre of whole races, the deportation of the working class of Europe,[6] the torture of children— horrors unknown since the Assyrians. Once again France has *her word* to say. Her word: Liberty.

Another misfortune: it is a fact that the individual never seemed more mediocre than at the moment of our history which fell between the two wars. If we are to believe Nietzsche, the individual becomes strong in circumstances precisely opposed to those in which our liberal civilization flourished. What is our answer? Dare we claim that Western democracy has safeguarded the dignity of man of which she makes herself the champion today? Look at the proletariat: millions of slaves whose eyes have been blinded by Freemasonry, Big Business, and each one of us bourgeois, while they turn the grindstone for us in their darkening towns. But Samson, under the whip of the Philistines, lifted his blind eyes toward the sky. Pernod, the *Vel d'hiv*,[7] the brothel, what reasons are these for living! There again we had to touch the rock bottom of the abyss before we could hope again. The martyrs bear witness to the people. Only the working class, *in its entirety*, has been faithful to desecrated France.

At the moment of writing (November 1941) so many other Frenchmen are moved by an elementary passion: fear! They don't admit it. They idolize the Marshal[8] and invoke Joan of Arc, but in their heart of hearts everything leads back to what seems to them the only necessity: saving their privileges and avoiding settling their accounts—"as long as the Germans are here . . ." A reassuring little phrase which Renan and Taine[9] had already murmured in front of the burning Tuileries: that same Renan who, on September 6, 1870,[10] leaned out of the window of Brébant's[11] and, looking at the carefree crowd strolling beneath him, said to Goncourt:[12] "That is what will save us—the flabbiness of our population."

No, never. We believe in man. We believe with all our moralists that man can be convinced and persuaded; even those bourgeois who hide their cash boxes in their begonia beds; yes, even the middlemen who regulate the sale of every consumable good; we believe they shut their eyes and perhaps clench their fists on the Place de la Concorde when they behold the flags (which I have never seen except through a mist of tears)— the flags on which the swastika looks like a bloated spider bursting with blood.

We must overcome our temptation to despise man. Our adversary will gain the advantage over us just so long as we give way to this contempt—for it is the basis of his doctrine. In his preface to Machiavelli's *Prince*, Mussolini corroborates, and even exceeds, the pessimism of his master about human nature. "If I were asked to say what I think about my fellow men and contemporaries," affirms the Duce, "I could not in any way modify the judgment of Machiavelli. Perhaps I should even have to add to it . . ." The fact is that contempt of man is necessary to those who want to use or to abuse man. But a creature who is immortal and half divine cannot be used as an instrument to serve all ends. That is why whosoever wants to use man thus has to debase his victim in advance.

We must not play their game. We must not allow our wretchedness to blind us to our grandeur. We must not let the shameful things we see around us and in our own hearts discourage us from giving man his due. Because on that depends our reason for living—and for survival.

* * * * *

"Happiness is a new idea in Europe . . ." proclaimed the young Saint-Just. And now, a century and a half after this was said, we know that happiness in Europe is a lost illusion. In order that the designs of Machiavelli may be fulfilled, whole populations are reshuffled and deported and whole races are condemned to perish. At what other moment in history have prison bars shut down on so many innocent people? At what other time have children been wrenched from their mothers, and herded into cattle trucks, as I saw them one somber morning in the Austerlitz[13] station? Happiness in Europe has become an impossible dream, except for the mean in spirit. No, there is no longer any question of happiness. All we can do is to form a united front against Machiavelli, whose crimes, even after the collapse of Germany, will not be suppressed by any number of executions; because he is stirring furtively in a million consciences, even in France. *Action française, Gringoire, Je suis partout*,[14] find numerous readers; and these are the strongest, the richest, the most cunning.

The offspring of Machiavelli—and this is what makes their strength—believe that they are in tune with the eternal laws of the human species. In their eyes we seem to be visionaries and hypocrites. Reality is their monopoly. It is significant that the *Anthology of New Europe*, in which Alfred Fabre-Luce[15] has assembled all the essential texts concerning basic totalitarian ideology, makes such display of the famous maxims of René Quinton:[16] "Nature loves struggle and death. War provides man with his natural outlet. War is the natural state of the male. The primary mission of the male is not to reproduce but to kill. Nature creates a species, she does not create beings. It is the individual's nature to deceive himself as to his destiny and to believe that he is born for himself alone . . ."

It is useless to deny that now and again our hopes have been baffled by this ferocious outlook. It is not the silence of the infinite spaces that frightens me; it is the implacability of this limitless destruction.

But we have made our choice. We are laying a wager against Machiavelli. We are among those who believe that man can escape from the internecine law; and not only that he can escape from it, but that his whole dignity hangs on the resistance that he offers it with his entire heart and his entire mind. No, the human mind is not deceived as to its destiny. And it makes no mistake when it protests that the condition of ants and termites throws no light upon its own. If there had only been, in the course of the centuries, in one brief interval of time and space, a single impulse of charity, the endless procession of beast and victim would have been forever broken by it.

Here I shall stop quoting from my Black Notebook, which is becoming a little too rosy for my taste. It seems to me that in this murderous world the enemy of Machiavelli will always be among the hunted. There is a vocation to be a victim. As if I could forget the victor, the giant who oppresses us with his shadow and crushes little France between his two palms . . . In order to oppose him, does he not condemn us to become like himself? Will he not oblige us, even when we have defeated him, to die to ourselves so that he can re-create us in his own horrible image? Force in the service of Justice, Liberty protected by Force, imposed by Force . . . We know how our forefathers escaped this contradiction in 1793. I shrink from offering to my readers a refinement which has no place for mercy. Our young scouts are beginning to suspect that the dark world of the Fall is a jungle where they pay dearly for the pleasures of playing Robinson Crusoe, and dancing innocently round the bonfires on the Eve of Saint John.[17] But first and foremost we must wrench ourselves from the grip of the giant, tear his hands from our throat and his knee from our breast . . . There will be time then to learn how a free people can become a strong people—and a strong people remain a just people.

ALASTAIR HAMILTON

NOTES

1. *the Capitol*: allusion to the fall of Rome and the capture of the Capitol by the barbarians.
2. *Machiavelli*: Italian statesman and historian (1469–1527) whose political theories exclude moral considerations from politics, so that the end justifies the means (*Il Principe*).

3. *Pharsalian plains*: plains in Thessaly where Caesar was victorious over Pompey in 48 B.C.

4. *Saint-Just*: Louis-Antoine de (1767–1794), a soldier and member of the Committee of Public Safety, which ruled during the Reign of Terror (1793–1794); executed with Robespierre. He proposed a Spartan republic devoted to the cult of virtue and happiness (then considered a new idea in the West).

5. *Jacques Rivière*: French author and critic (1886–1925), director of the *Nouvelle Revue Française* from 1919 until his death; a prisoner of war in Germany during World War I.

6. *deportation of the working class of Europe*: reference to the policy of forcing the proletariat of conquered nations to work in German war industries.

7. *Pernod*: an alcoholic drink, comparable to absinthe; *Vel d'hiv* (*Vélodrome d'hiver*): winter bicycle race.

8. *The Marshal*: Marshal Pétain.

9. *Renan*: Ernest Renan (1823–1892), French philologist and historian of comparative religions, rationalist and anti-Catholic; *Taine*: Hippolyte Taine (1828–1893), French philosopher, art critic, historian, and critic of the French Revolution.

10. *September 6, 1870*: allusion to the subsequent "Commune," the 1871 insurrection of the Paris proletariat, who were bitterly opposed to the peace treaty with the Germans signed at Versailles and to the conservative bourgeois government which signed it and which, strengthened by the presence of German forces, pitilessly repressed the insurrection. The Tuileries palace, not far from the Louvre, was partially burned down by the insurrectionists.

11. *Brébant's*: a Paris restaurant.

12. *Goncourt*: Edmond de Goncourt (1822–1896) and his brother Jules (1830–1870) were men of letters and of their times (social and literary) who wrote novels concerning the working class in a curiously mannered style.

13. *Austerlitz*: Paris train station and point of departure during the Occupation for trains of deportees going to Germany.

14. *Action française, Gringoire, Je suis partout*: leading collaborationist newspapers; see above, pages 56–58, notes 4, 13, 36, respectively.

15. *Monsieur Alfred Fabre-Luce*: right-wing journalist and writer who, in 1936, joined Jacques Doriot's Parti Populaire Français; an articulate collaborationist whose works were barred by the Comité National des Écrivains in 1945.

16. *René Quinton*: see above, page 16, note 1.

17. *Eve of Saint John*: August 29, the feast of Saint John the Baptist, is celebrated in southern France by building wood fires through which one jumps, a pagan rite.

THE NATIONAL CONSCIENCE:
POINTS OF VIEW

THAT FRANCE WENT TO WAR RELUCTANTLY is a generally recognized fact, discussed and quite diversely interpreted in the three passages given below. In 1940, Charles Maurras was over seventy. He had been at war with French democracy for some forty years as the leader and political theorist of the activist Action française, a revolutionary Royalist group whose tactics included demonstrations, denunciation, and slander. Maurras was opposed to the republican mystique, in the name of a realistic diplomacy based on national interests. France, a Mediterranean country in his eyes, with a culture rooted in a Greco-Roman past vivified by Christianity, had found in the institutions of seventeenth-century monarchy the principles of order and national unity best suited to its potentialities. Rousseau (a foreigner), the French Revolution, republicanism, and romanticism had, he believed, adulterated and weakened France's sense of its intellectual and spiritual identity. Starting from these premises Maurras, a theoretician primarily, was concerned more with establishing an elaborately reasoned frame of discourse that would account for all political facts than with testing his theories against those facts or attempting to formulate definite reforms. Maurras's analysis of the frame of mind of the French people with regard to the war and its interpretation is based on his distinction between "le pays réel," the real French nation, and "Le pays légal," the French Parliament. He impugns the Parliament on the grounds of willful conspiracy in the betrayal of the national will and interest, through its cowardly sacrifices to humanitarian ideals and its evasion of its responsibilities. France, betrayed, required that the traitors be indicted. It was in September 1940 that the ministers of the Third Republic, Paul Reynaud, Edouard Daladier, Léon Blum, and Georges Mandel, were arrested, a prelude to their trial at Riom.

Three years later, in the clandestine press the thirty-year-old Albert Camus, from the ranks of the Resistance, recalled his own prewar pacifism in a "letter to a German friend," in which he fiercely defended the positions he and his countrymen, with whom he identified completely, had taken in 1939 when they opposed in France the nationalistic form of patriotism that his Nazi friend was supporting in Germany. The question the two young men had argued was the question of patriotism, of the primacy of national interest over any other consideration. What Camus attacks is the misuse of power and the subversion of patriotism when a nation identifies national power with virtue. In the contrast between Nazi ruthlessness uncritically condoned and French scrupulousness and resistance to "patriotic" slogans—idealized by his despair and revulsion against Nazi brutality—Camus sees the qualitative difference that, other forces being equal, will bring about the defeat of Germany and for France hardly a victory, but at least a future without indignity. His letter is an almost desperate assertion of faith that a liberal, humane, open-ended society must in the end prevail whatever the price.

Unlike Mauriac and Camus, Guéhenno interprets French irresolution in 1939 as a sign of the weakening of the national conscience and revolutionary faith. On the anniversary of the battle of Valmy, fought in 1792 when the Revolutionary army won a much-needed victory over the joint forces of the Royalist *émigrés* and the Prussian invaders, he rediscovers in the rhetoric of the Revolutionary leaders the language of absolute commitment. They understood freedom as a difficult conquest rather than as a concept for abstract definition and argument. Like Maurras, Guéhenno refers to the collective conscience. But he predicts it is awakening and apparent in the commitment to freedom reborn in the hearts of thousands of individual Frenchmen, ready to defend that freedom as best they can wherever they may be.

CHARLES MAURRAS

August/September 1940

TO LA NACIÓN OF BUENOS AIRES

Any foreigner at all acquainted with France must have been less astonished by her military defeat than by the war itself—her war.

An offensive war led by the party of people like Rouvier and Briand,[1] and their immediate successors.

THE SILENCE OF OPINION

Who wanted such a war in France? Who could have wanted it?

What section of the population could cry: "Come on, let us fight for Poland, Danzig, the Corridor, or (last year) for the Czechs or the Austrians"? Absolutely none.

During the domination of the Popular Front,[2] in the years 1936, 1937, and even 1938 there were warlike demonstrations in which Socialists or Communists demanded *cannons and planes for Red Spain*. These processions, organized in agreement with the Russian police in Paris and Blum's cabinet, had nothing very nationalistic about them. They were too mechanical. But nevertheless they *had taken place*, they *did exist*. There was *nothing similar* in favor of the 1939 war.

The opposite happened in September 1938.

AFTER MUNICH

When Monsieur Edouard Daladier[3] descended from the sky on his return from Munich, whence he had brought peace, an enormous crowd covered the plain at Le Bourget.

SOURCE NOTE: Charles Maurras, "A *La Nacion* de Buenos Aires," *La Seule France, chronique des jours d'épreuve* (Lyons, Lardanchet, 1941), pp. 317–28. Reprint of an article sent to *La Nacion* in August or September 1940.

"Well! Well!" said Monsieur Daladier, anxious as usual, "the Communists have come to run me in . . ."

Not at all. The real country had come to congratulate the Prime Minister on having exorcised the specter of a war which corresponded neither to our desires nor to our interests.

This crowd accompanied Monsieur Daladier all the way back to his hotel in the Rue Saint-Dominique with triumphant cheers.

The sequel? It was like the beginning. The "deep masses" of the French nation continued to live in the same desire for peace, and nothing changed their attitude.

OFFICIAL MANEUVERS

In fact the government wanted and even tried to change their attitude, and did what it could to succeed.

From 1938 to 1939 three measures were taken for this purpose.

First the government struck at the independent press, which had favored pacifism in September 1938. The government tried to curb it by promises, polemics, insults, defiances. How far did it get? Nowhere. It despaired of getting anywhere as far as L'Action française[4] and a few other papers were concerned, because, six days before war was declared, a law was passed which delivered all our papers to the government's mercy. The Ministry accorded itself the power of suppressing them—an event unprecedented on French soil since the Second Empire. In 1914 an arbitrary control was established only after mobilization; until then the press was free to say what it liked about war and peace. This measure before the outbreak of hostilities in 1939 showed how much our firebrands feared that certain papers would prevent THEIR war.

They were rightly worried. If the press had remained free a few of us would have been absolutely determined to try everything to avoid this stupidity and folly.

Having already spent two hundred and fifty days in prison for threatening some overwarlike politicians, I would willingly

have served two thousand more to oppose these parliamentary
warmongers. With the new law I lost the only means of action
—the newspaper—and I was unable to prevent the crime. I
had to devour my rage and pain.

A second measure had been taken to reduce the opposition
to war. For about a dozen months men had been spasmodically
called up. This annoyed the recruits and their families, whose
work and means of support were interrupted. Once in existence
this discontent was increased and stimulated into a state of
exasperation. "If that's how it is, let's get it over with! And
say no more about it! Better a definite alarm than these interminable annoyances." As we have seen, Messieurs Daladier,
Mandel,[5] and their colleagues had successfully manipulated the
nerves of the country. Nevertheless there was no mass demonstration in favor of war. No. Not the slightest. France groaned
at their words; she did not march.

There was a third official maneuver. These gentlemen said,
and made people say: "There will be really nothing but words.
We won't have war because Hitler doesn't want it. His politics
are only prestige. If one brags along with him, he'll recoil.
That's for sure! Last year threatening ultimatums would have
saved Austria and Bohemia. We were wrong not to make
them." (Monsieur Daladier ended by believing this, thus
destroying what he had so fortunately achieved in Munich.)
"Categorical ultimatums will save Poland. It's enough to show
that we are ready to help her at her first call." That's what a
part of the government press claimed. Did it convince the
French? Did it affect them? This is another fact, I repeat it.
These articles caused no reaction, either in the street, at official
assemblies, or in public meetings. None! Literally none.

AGAINST WAR

The youth of the Action française, which was the most warlike in France, was as hostile to this war as we were.

Next to us, the nationalist group least favorable to Germany, led by Jacques Bainville,[6] thought it was enough to be on our guard, to arm, to rearm, to overarm. The French nationalists never said we should resort to force.

SHOCKING CONTRASTS

And since then the same nationalists considered this policy of warlike democracy unreasonable and dangerous. Since July and September 1935, just three months after the evacuation of the Saar,[7] this warlike feeling had been expressed in England by Lord Robert Cecil—in Geneva, by Messieurs Eden, Winston Churchill, Litvinov, and their left-wing French parliamentary allies.

All these gentlemen were very pacific when France was strong. Now that France had purposely weakened herself, they wanted war. Absurd? Yes, but very odd. As for me, I had sworn to point out this shocking state of affairs every time I stood up before a meeting of Frenchmen. Since my release from prison[8] in July 1937 I have denounced it, at more than two hundred and fifty public meetings, and my listeners shared my amazement and indignation.

DISCREET FIREBRANDS

The last of these meetings was held on August 12, 1939, at the Castle of Barbazan, near Tarbes. Ten orators had aroused passionate applause by expressing the same ideas.

"We are disciplined Frenchmen and we will answer the call of general mobilization because we do not want to cause any internal trouble if a war breaks out. But it must not break out. Whoever declares it is betraying national interests."

These were the opponents of war. They met, talked, discussed, affirmed or denied.

No one stood up to them.

There were no meetings, discussions, speeches, popular cries *in favor of war*. In the bourgeois circles of the official world there was no determination. We were alone in saying no. And nobody answered us by saying yes.

Nobody answered those who asked: "What can you do for Poland?" nor those who replied, like us: "You can't do anything."

And they remained speechless as soon as a writer, an orator, a mere drawing-room speaker said it was stupid to take Hitler's game for politics of "prestige" or "bluff."

"Hitler's 'game'? In the last two years he has raised the population of his country from sixty-three to seventy-five million. He has united the territories of Austria, Bohemia, and Slovakia . . . What could be more realistic?"

No reply.

Silence! War's only advocates were the two or three public papers which remained discreet and reticent about the main points.

The Ministry itself was split until the end. The Chamber did vote for military credit; war was not declared by regular election. So Parliament and government were presented with the accomplished fact. A feeble government had been manipulated by international intrigue; nothing was expressed by national will, and still less by a national feeling.

AN OFFENSIVE WAR WITH NO NATIONAL OBJECTIVE

This is a very strange thing: after war was declared those who had wanted it and who directed it made sure it was given no national objective.

According to what was whispered to the papers, we were fighting to wound and threaten the form of the German government.

We were fighting a war of Democracy; in the name of the Rights of Man[9] we were going to free the oppressed and the enslaved; in short, the government wanted to mobilize all citizens to wage a terrible war without giving them a common aim.

The soldier could say that he was fighting because the Minister had decided he should.

WAR AND INDUSTRY

The same infantile ideology applied, to a worse degree, to the industrial conduct of the war. For the democratic cause to win we needed cannons and ammunition. But so that the Creed of Demos[10] should not be transgressed, the manufacturers of victory's tools were not to make a profit at which Holy Equality could take offense. That is why the government, unprepared and unarmed by three years of the Popular Front, had the quaint idea of limiting the profits of war industries, without realizing that it was also limiting the productivity of the industries, the quantity of its own armament, and the chances of victory. Few people wanted to produce goods at such a low profit. The brilliant and fruitful improvisations of 1914-1918 were not repeated. We did not open factories for the disinterested love of pure victory; once more stoicism engendered such sterility* that, in a considerable number of fields, we had no material.

Oh, of course, here and there we fought with all the valor of our race, sometimes with the heroism of despair. But eight months inactivity had been imposed on the factories and the fortified area,[11] and not only did the Crusaders of Democracy hardly believe in their Goddess, but their civilian leaders had failed to provide them with the necessary material.

THE FEAR OF VICTORY?

When a good reason to fight appeared in May–June 1940 and we had to defend occupied territory, it was too late! Over thirty weeks had been wasted in idleness, immobility, and vain defense. After five more weeks Monsieur Paul Reynaud's[12] terrifying message to America proved such an admission of defeat and disorganization that it broke what resistance the

* See La Fontaine's *Scythian Philosopher*

most energetic troops had left, and disaster crowned, if one can say so, a war to which soldiers had marched with decency but without national enthusiasm.

There had been no deep public support. There had also been no preparatory alliances, an insufficient amount of trained troops, and inadequate enthusiasm and discipline; the favorable positions had long been abandoned, and the real experts, Pétain and Weygand,[13] had only been appointed to the High Command at the last minute. It was as though those who had declared the war were afraid of winning it!

THE TRUTH

The French do not like to talk of treachery or pitfalls. But one day the *positive* truth will appear. In the meantime a *negative* truth is certain, uncontested, and incontestable, as our impartial analysis has just shown.

Never has a potentate of divine right, never has an absolute despot sent anonymous masses of his subject-slaves to battle as freely, crazily, arbitrarily, as a very small group of democratic leaders have just sent their king-citizens to the slaughter.

Never have national realities been so alien to an initiative, concept, or wish as to the declaration of this war, this *phony war* of which we are now paying the terrible price.

I mean that before moping about this iniquitous disparity of fate, people want their curiosity satisfied, they will insist, they will ask:

"But then? How could such an evil befall France, such an immeasurable evil which surpasses the strength, the mind, the stature of its miserable agents to such an extent?"

We must reply: "That is just what France is finding out. Her Judges[14] are at work, her Historians are starting to work. We shall soon find something."

ALASTAIR HAMILTON

NOTES

1. *Rouvier*: Pierre Maurice Rouvier (1842–1911), French states-man, twice Prime Minister and Minister of Finance several times, a convinced supporter of the Republic, *Briand*: Aristide Briand (see above, page 56, note 11).

2. *Popular Front*: coalition of left-wing radicals, Radical Social-ists, the SFIO party of Léon Blum, and the Communists which was organized under the leadership of Léon Blum's government in 1936.

3. *Edouard Daladier*: (1884–   ), a liberal, Prime Minister from 1938 to 1940. Under pressure from Britain in 1938, he reluctantly signed the Munich Agreement which ceded part of Czechoslovakia to the Third Reich as a measure of appeasement. He was greeted, to his astonishment, at Le Bourget airport in Paris by an enthusiastic crowd, relieved that war had apparently been avoided.

4. *L'Action française*: a right-wing newspaper under Maurras's direction, it was to become collaborationist; the exceptional meas-ures alluded to applied equally to the extremists on the right or on the left. See also above, page 57, note 13.

5. *Mandel*: Georges Mandel (1885–1944), associated with Clémenceau; Prime Minister in 1916; several times held a minis-terial position; Minister of the Interior in 1940. Deported to Germany, he was returned, particularly vulnerable because he was Jewish. Executed by the Milice in 1944.

6. *Jacques Bainville*: (1879–1936) French historian, one of the founders, with Maurras, of the Royalist movement in France and of the Action française.

7. *evacuation of the Saar*: according to the Treaty of Versailles (1919) Germany was to be deprived of this western region, rich in minerals, which was to be ruled over by the League of Nations. In 1935 a plebiscite was held which determined that it was to be returned to German rule.

8. *my release from prison*: angry over the sanctions imposed on Fascist Italy, Maurras wrote a letter to Parliament threatening the lives of the members. For this he was imprisoned from 1936 to 1937.

9. *Rights of Man*: Declaration of Constituent Assembly of 1789 establishing freedom of press, religion, and speech, social and political equality, the inviolability of the right to property.

10. *Creed of Demos*: faith in the people.

11. *the fortified area*: the Maginot Line reference to the "phony war" beginning in September 1939; see chronology at end of volume.

12. *Paul Reynaud*: French politician (1878–   ), succeeded Daladier as Prime Minister on March 21, 1940. On June 13, he

appealed to the Americans for assistance but received a negative
reply from Roosevelt. He then resigned; Pétain succeeded him on
June 17 and immediately requested an armistice with Germany.
    13. *Pétain*: Henri-Philippe Pétain (1856–1951), renowned
French general of the First World War; entered Reynaud's government May 18, 1940, and succeeded him on June 17 to conclude
an armistice with Germany and set up a French government at
Vichy. *Weygand*: Maxime Weygand (1867–1965), supreme commander of the French forces in May 1940.
    14. *Her Judges*: general reference to evaluation of the causes of
the war and more particularly to the "Procès de Riom"; General
Gamelin, Commander in Chief of the French forces, and the
Parliamentarians Reynaud, Blum, Daladier, and Mandel were
arrested in September 1940, tried, and imprisoned for their declaration of war against the Germans.

ALBERT CAMUS

July 1943

FIRST LETTER

    You said to me: "The greatness of my country is beyond
price. Anything is good that contributes to its greatness. And
in a world where everything has lost its meaning, those who,
like us young Germans, are lucky enough to find a meaning in
the destiny of our nation must sacrifice everything else." I
loved you then, but at that point we diverged. "No," I told
you, "I cannot believe that everything must be subordinated
to a single end. There are means that cannot be excused. And
I should like to be able to love my country and still love justice.
I don't want just any greatness for it, particularly a greatness
born of blood and falsehood. I want to keep it alive by keeping

SOURCE NOTE: Albert Camus, "Lettre I," *Lettres à un ami allemand*
(Paris, Gallimard, 1948), pp. 19–23. Reprint from *Revue libre*, No. 2,
1943.

justice alive." You retorted: "Well, you don't love your country."

That was five years ago; we have been separated since then and I can say that not a single day has passed during those long years (so brief, so dazzlingly swift for you!) without my remembering your remark. "You don't love your country!" When I think of your words today, I feel a choking sensation. No, I didn't love my country, if pointing out what is not just in what we love amounts to not loving, if insisting that what we love should measure up to the finest image we have of her amounts to not loving. That was five years ago, and many men in France thought as I did. Some of them, however, have already been stood up against the wall facing the twelve little black eyes of German destiny. And those men, who in your opinion did not love their country, did more for it than you will ever do for yours, even if it were possible for you to give your life a hundred times. For their heroism was that they had to conquer themselves first. But I am speaking here of two kinds of greatness and of a contradiction about which I must enlighten you.

We shall meet soon again—if possible. But our friendship will be over. You will be full of your defeat. You will not be ashamed of your former victory. Rather, you will longingly remember it with all your crushed might. Today I am still close to you in spirit—your enemy, to be sure, but still a little your friend because I am withholding nothing from you here. Tomorrow all will be over. What your victory could not penetrate, your defeat will bring to an end. But at least, before we become indifferent to each other, I want to leave you a clear idea of what neither peace nor war has taught you to see in the destiny of my country.

I want to tell you at once what sort of greatness keeps us going. But this amounts to telling you what kind of courage we applaud, which is not your kind. For it is not much to be able to do violence when you have been simply preparing for it for years and when violence is more natural to you than thinking. It is a great deal, on the other hand, to face torture and death when you know for a fact that hatred and violence are empty things in themselves. It is a great deal to fight while despising war, to accept losing everything while still preferring happiness, to face destruction while cherishing the idea of a higher civilization. That is how we do more than you because we have to draw on ourselves. You had nothing to conquer in your heart or in your intelligence. We had two enemies and a military victory was not enough for us, as it was for you who had nothing to overcome.

We had much to overcome—and, first of all, the constant temptation to emulate you. For there is always something in us that yields to instinct, to contempt for intelligence, to the cult of efficiency. Our great virtues eventually become tiresome to us. We become ashamed of our intelligence, and sometimes we imagine some barbarous state where truth would be effortless. But the cure for this is easy; you are there to show us what the imagining would lead to, and we mend our ways. If I believed in some fatalism in history, I should suppose that you are placed beside us, helots of the intelligence, as our living reproof. Then we reawaken to the mind and we are more at ease.

But we also had to overcome the suspicion we had of heroism. I know you think that heroism is alien to us. You are wrong. It is just that we profess heroism and we distrust it at the same time. We profess it because ten centuries of history have given us knowledge of all that is noble. We distrust it because ten centuries of intelligence have taught us the art and blessings of being natural. In order to face up to you, we had first to be at death's door. And this is why we fell behind all of Europe, which wallowed in falsehood the moment it was necessary, while we were concerned with seeking truth. This is why we were defeated in the beginning: because we were so concerned, while you were falling upon us, to determine in our hearts whether right was on our side.

We had to overcome our weakness for mankind, the image we had formed of a peaceful destiny, that deep-rooted conviction of ours that no victory ever pays, whereas any mutilation of mankind is irrevocable. We have to give up all at once our knowledge and our hope, the reasons we had for loving and the loathing we had for all war. To put it in a word that I suppose you will understand, when it comes from me whom you counted as a friend, we had to stifle our passion for friendship.

Now we have done that. We had to make a long detour, and we are far behind. It is a detour that regard for truth imposes on intelligence, that regard for friendship imposes on the heart. It is a detour that safeguarded justice and put truth on the side of those who questioned themselves. And without a doubt, we paid very dearly for it. We paid for it with humiliations and silences, with bitter experiences, with prison sentences, with executions at dawn, with desertions and separations, with daily pangs of hunger, with emaciated children, and above all with humiliation of our human dignity. But that was natural. It took us all that time to find out if we had the right to kill men, if we were allowed to add to the frightful misery of this world. And because of that time lost and recaptured, our defeat accepted and surmounted, those scruples paid for with blood, we French have the right to think today that we entered this war with hands clean—clean as victims and the condemned are— and that we are going to come out of it with hands clean— but clean this time with a great victory won against injustice and against ourselves.

For we shall be victorious, you may be sure. But we shall be victorious thanks to that very defeat, to that long, slow progress during which we found our justification, to that suffering which, in all its injustice, taught us a lesson. It taught us the secret of any victory, and if we do not lose the secret some day, we shall know final victory. It taught us that, contrary to what we sometimes used to think, the spirit is of no avail against the sword, but that the spirit together with the sword will always win the day over the sword alone. That is why we have now accepted the sword, after having made sure that the spirit was on our side. We had first to see people die and to run the risk of dying

ourselves. We had to see a French workman walking towards
the guillotine at dawn down the prison corridors and exhorting
his comrades from cell to cell to show their courage. Finally,
to possess ourselves of the spirit, we had to endure torture of
our flesh. One really possesses only what one has paid for. We
have paid dearly, and we have not finished paying. But we have
our certainties, our justifications, our justice; your defeat is
inevitable.

I have never believed in the power of truth in itself. But it
is at least worth knowing that when expressed energetically
truth prevails over falsehood. This is the difficult equilibrium
we have reached. This is the distinction which gives us strength
as we fight today. And I am tempted to tell you that it so
happens that we are fighting for fine distinctions, but the kind
of distinctions that are as important as man himself. We are
fighting for the distinction between sacrifice and mysticism,
between energy and violence, between strength and cruelty,
for that even finer distinction between the true and the false, between the man we hope for and the cowardly gods you revere.

This is what I wanted to tell you, not above the fray but in
the thick of the fray. This is what I wanted to answer to your
remark, "You don't love your country," which is still haunting
me. But I want to be clear with you. I believe that France lost
her power and her sway for a long time to come and that for
a long time she will need a desperate patience, a vigilant revolt
to recover the element of prestige necessary for any culture.
But I believe she has lost all that for reasons which are pure.
And this is why I have not lost hope. This is the whole meaning
of my letter. The man whom you pitied five years ago for being
so reticent about his country is the same man who wants to say
to you today, and to all those of our age in Europe and throughout the world: "I belong to an admirable and persevering nation
which, admitting her errors and weaknesses, has not lost the
idea that constitutes her whole greatness. Her people are always
trying and her leaders are sometimes trying to express that idea
even more clearly. I belong to a nation which for the past four

years has begun to relive the course of her entire history and which is calmly and surely preparing out of the ruins to make another history and to take her chance in a game where she holds no trumps. This country is worthy of the difficult and demanding love that is mine. And I believe she is decidedly worth fighting for since she is worthy of a higher love. And I say that your nation on the other hand has received from its sons only the love it deserved, which was blind. A nation is not justified by such love. That will be your undoing. And you who were already conquered in your greatest victories, what will you be in the approaching defeat?"

JUSTIN O'BRIEN

JEAN GUÉHENNO

September 20, 1940

FOR THE ANNIVERSARY OF VALMY

If France were to die it would not be for her principles but for having failed them, for not having applied them boldly and loyally enough. We were weak because we were not sufficiently pure. We were not consistent enough.

I could feel disaster coming. Maybe we no longer knew the value of liberty. We talked about it too much. We believed we were enjoying its fruits. But for too many of us it had become a mere word. People unconsciously gave in to constraint. They became the prisoners of diverse forms of "propaganda," swearing, at the same time, that they were free citizens. The impetus had lost its force after a hundred and fifty years of compromise. In 1850 Renan[1] advised the liberals to talk as

SOURCE NOTE: Jean Guéhenno (pseud. Cévennes), "Pour l'anniversaire de Valmy," *Dans la prison* (Paris, Éditions de Minuit, 1944), pp. 24–35.

little as possible about liberty and to concentrate on thinking freely: that was liberty's best hope of survival.

In 1939 there were some free men left—a few artists intent on continually killing habit within themselves and renewing their interests. Most of the time this liberty was a luxury—the product of happiness, the liberty of rich men hounded by boredom, the fantasy of traveling dreamers, searching outside themselves for the enthusiasm which they no longer found within. But where was the true liberty of a mind that fights, that liberty which is hard to attain?

The men of 1789 knew what liberty was: they emerged from servitude. We shall soon know what it is if we become slaves again.

In June 1939, to escape from the lies and cowardly confusion of the time, in order to return to the true path, I studied the French Revolution. Its hundred and fiftieth anniversary had drawn on. The French government was in a difficult position: as the very principle of its establishment it had to exalt an act, a principle which inevitably threatens to ruin both the government and itself. Festivities were decreed, but not without scruples. The Revolution was going to have its due, a funeral service and a splendid burial.

The finest festivity was going to take place on September 20, 1939! That day a magnificent "military ceremony" was to be performed on the battlefield of Valmy,[2] "planned in advance." What surveyors, guided by what historian-topographers, were to occupy the site? Was the battle to be repeated? Was it going to be performed like a play? What recruits of 1939 were to wear the livery of Brunswick,[3] who the white and blue uniform of the French Guards, who the blue and red of the National Guard? Who was to play Kellermann and who Dumouriez?[4] Were the gun-pits and the hail of bullets to be repeated? The trenches where the recruits would pretend to die? And what machine would spread that light morning mist over the hills which always envelops a victorious French army? "On the battlefield of Valmy planned in advance . . ." Was that all history could do? Make the children tread in their fathers' footsteps, show them just how far they can go, and mark the hill, the trench where their charge must stop?

Drunken forces reeled over Europe, and we seemed ashamed of our clearheadedness amongst those drunkards. France's tragedy was not what threatened her from outside. The main danger was neither Chancellor Hitler nor Signor Mussolini. The disease was in herself; it was this crisis of confidence she was experiencing, this fear of being herself. Taken individually the young French boys were as active and intelligent as ever. But they lacked that unanimity in hope and aspiration which is the health of nations. The fact that the commemoration of the hundred and fiftieth anniversary of the Revolution should have been nothing but a funeral service revealed this weakness and sluggishness.

It was clear that the only good way of celebrating the Revolution would have been to continue it. France is an eager country. If we had believed firmly enough in liberty and justice we could have proposed them to Europe as a means of peace. But we lacked faith. We had been dragging our feet along the road for twenty years.

On September 20, 1939, the anniversary of Valmy, the French Army began to sink into the mud of the Maginot Line.

When the battle started, all those books from which I thought I had learned the conditions of liberty sounded different. I found the word "death" on every page. "Liberty or death." "Equality or death." "The welfare of the nation or death." "The whole republic or death." This bell toll accompanied every word of the French Revolution. Nobody screamed out "Vive la liberté!" But this low and lasting note, behind all mental concepts, implied a commitment of the whole being, sustained by the whole being. The Revolutionaries never just wrote, said, or thought "to live free," like avid pleasure seekers; they always added "or die." They knew that otherwise they were uttering empty words. They knew it was not so easy to "live free," and that it was not enough to wish it and say it.

They knew that liberty is always threatened by death, and that to face death you must be ready to die at any moment. Because only death balances death, only readiness to die puts death to flight. They knew that liberty exists inside oneself; that it can form an explosive pressure, beyond human control; that it wants to be brought out, needs to be wanted; that it is not something natural, and that just as our nonliberty is God's share in our life, liberty is our share, our will, our creation.

They had written in the Declaration of the Rights of Man:[5] "Men are born free and equal in rights." But they were not dupes. They proclaimed it against fate, against nature, against every tyranny. They knew about our weaknesses. They knew that nature does not care for this justice which only exists deep within ourselves. But if nature constantly undoes what we do —liberty, equality, fraternity—that is a further reason to re-create it by our will, our laws, and oppose human order to natural disorder. Of course, we must be ready to pay the full price of these claims. The condition of this great existence which the Revolutionaries dreamed of for themselves and for all men was to be ready for life, but also to be ready for death —and this is the most difficult part.

Whoever they were—Feuillants, Girondins, or Montagnards[6] —they all agreed on this point. Their idea of "valor" consti- tuted their honor and their life. If "valor" were to die, they might as well die too.

"Liberty or death." Slanderers maintained that this was a threat for others. But the death which the Revolutionaries named and invoked was their own. "The day," said Saint-Just, "when I know that it is impossible to give the French gentle, vigorous, tangible moral values impermeable to tyranny and injustice, I shall stab myself . . . One quits little when one quits a wretched life in which one is condemned to vegetate, the complice or the powerless spectator of a crime. I despise the dust of which I am made—the dust which is talking to you: you can persecute and kill it. But I defy you to wrench from me this independent life which I have given myself . . .

for all eternity." He could only live in a condition of liberty, and he thought himself responsible for it in the present, and above all in the future. He had announced it and promised it. If it perished he had to perish too. At least his sacrifice would be remembered through the ages, and liberty would spring from its memory.

It does not matter that the heroism of the founders of liberty could never be sustained by a whole nation. Nor does it matter that the history of our liberty over the last hundred and fifty years has all too often been nothing but the history of our bewilderment. The sole culprits are those who bewildered us. It is interesting to note that only the candidates for tyranny take such pleasure in proving that liberty is an illusion. Too much charity should put us on our guard. Besides, these dialecticians who are so good at proving us the victims of deception never doubt their own liberty, which is a desire for power and subjection. They would not intrigue against the illusion of liberty if they did not fear that illusion ends by creating liberty itself. Belief in liberty is the beginning of freedom. A "free country" may well be nothing but a country where we think we are free. But it is surely different from the country where we know we are not free. This difference suffices.

We sense a free world better than we know it. Light does not shine only on men who can define it. In a free society light, or even a reflection of light, reaches the humblest and heralds the dawn in the darkest night. France may only have been waiting. But that formed its climate.

"If liberty dies, France dies too."

I am thinking of those millions of Frenchmen who earn their daily bread by working under foreign rule. They serve, but they know that they serve. They are serving temporarily and with such disgust that they have almost lost their desire for bread. But one thing saves them: they have not lost the desire for liberty. If you tell them that they are "collaborating" they laugh; within themselves they know what they are doing. Their heart is not in their work. They are doing forced labor. Bread is sometimes hard to earn, but they are full of contempt and that is their liberty. They complain about their work: they wait and hope.

Leave us to our misery. The knowledge of our servitude is all that remains of our honor.

ALASTAIR HAMILTON

NOTES

1. *Renan*: see above, page 68, note 10.
2. *Valmy*: first victory of Revolutionary France against a European coalition. Prussians, Austrians, and French aristocratic *émigrés* were defeated at Valmy on September 20, 1792.
3. *Brunswick*: Karl Wilhelm Ferdinand, Duke of (1735–1806), leader of the Prussian and Austrian armies at Valmy.
4. *Kellermann and Dumouriez*: François-Christophe Kellermann (1735–1820) and Charles-François Dumouriez (1739–1823), leaders of the French Revolutionary forces at Valmy.
5. *Declaration of the Rights of Man*: the Constituent Assembly of 1789 defined in the Rights the basic principles of democratic ideology. See above, page 79, note 9.
6. *Feuillants, Girondins, Montagnards*: political parties of the Revolutionary period.

THE ARMISTICE

ON JUNE 22, 1940, the Armistice between France
and Germany was signed. On July 10 the French National Assembly voted full powers to Marshal Pétain.
On October 24, 1940, the first act in the drama of collaboration took place with the meeting of Pétain and
Hitler at Montoire. Although it is not absolutely clear
what agreements, if any, were made, the meeting was
followed by Pétain's appeal to the French nation on
October 30. Pétain informed the nation that he was
adopting a policy of reconciliation with Germany based
on the principle of collaboration and called upon all
Frenchmen, in the name of unity and the future, loyally
to participate side by side with Germany in the building
of a new European order. France would defend its soil
against all outside aggression and by every means attenuate
the rigors of the Armistice: the division in zones, the fees
of occupation, the detention in Germany of some two
million prisoners of war. "Collaboration" became a major
issue, with its appeal to the future and its slogan, "Neither
victors nor vanquished," projecting the image of a dignified
"new deal" in contrast to the humiliation of defeat. Almost all the passages collected below take the form of
dialogues; the issue seems to have been debated in every
French mind, from every angle.

For Charles Maurras, it is clear that Pétain has chosen the only way toward the preservation of France's national integrity. What he most fears and inveighs against is the spirit of dissent, the climate of free, irresponsible discussion to which he attributes France's lack of direction under a liberal democratic regime. To this heresy he opposes the principle of authoritarianism and national discipline in the interests of national welfare realistically assessed. And to this attitude many of France's outstanding officers, among others, adhered, bound by their profession itself to the service of France.

Younger men, such as Pierre Drieu La Rochelle, saw collaboration from a less narrowly national viewpoint. Looking back over the past in November 1944, with the defeat of Germany now inevitable, Drieu in his *Journal* confronted the futility of a dream he had pursued, more mystical, less sentimental, but not unlike Brasillach's. A talented novelist, he had been twenty-one in 1914 and had deeply felt the shock of war, seeking some positive credo or mode of existence and action successively in surrealism, communism, and finally fascism. An idealist, concerned with the future, Drieu, unlike Montherlant, had engaged in what he calls the "shit" of practical politics, joining the ranks of the French fascists, persuaded that only fascism could lead to European unity and assure French independence from the hegemony of either Russia or America. For Drieu, a post-Nietzschean, what France had to discover was some deep source of faith to replace a lost Christianity and offset the "religion" of communism. Combining European internationalism, socialism, and a new mystique, fascism, Drieu believed, could inaugurate a new political, social, and metaphysical era. Collaboration was merely one phase in a practical struggle for independent survival against long-term opponents. His dispassionate view in 1944 of the French Resistance and of the consequences of World War II are a measure of the man's lucidity.

Guéhenno's bitter anti-Pétainism is colored by the prewar rift in France between right and left and his hatred of the "national revolution" carried forward by the Vichy regime under mandate from the National Assembly. For Guéhenno, France was engaged in a class war, a civil war against a bourgeoisie intent on holding down the working class and the French "people." The collaborationist is, first, a class enemy.

When Camus wrote his play *Caligula*, he had not, he tells us, had in mind the Nazi adventure. But the situation in *Caligula* raises the question of revolt and political murder. Caligula, the all-powerful emperor, deeply shaken by the futility of all human activity in the face of impending death, undertakes to drive to its ultimate limits the nihilism implicit in his discovery. His aim is to test the limits of a man's freedom to act with the arbitrary inhumanity of brute force. In the scene below, his grim experiment is bearing fruit: violent revolt is simmering among the patricians. The confrontation between Cherea and the patricians defines two quite different sources of revolt: personal vengeance for pride humiliated and privileges destroyed is the patrician's motivation; for Cherea it is the defense of what Cherea calls "the meaning of life," the freedom to exist as a human being which Caligula denies. Éluard's short poem transmits the sullen, tense mood of Paris as the city sinks into night and the underground life of the Resistance begins: crime, made legitimate by crime.

Dispassionately and lucidly the seventy-year-old Gide, shortly after Montoire, examines the fallacy behind the collaborationist arguments and slogans. He makes a realistic appraisal of the value, in 1940, of a policy of non-collaboration. Only the sense of what defeat and Nazi rule really entail could, he feels, and would in time give birth to the renewal of a conscious patriotic drive. Retrospectively speaking, he was right.

The issue of collaboration, as posited, was ambiguous. For the problem could be and was seen from different angles, sometimes by the same men. Was it better for the French in 1940, facing the chaos of defeat, to maintain French rule, albeit relative, thereby attenuating German control? Would a general respect for the terms of the Armistice have enabled the French to avoid some of the more stringent measures of defeat? Could the disorders attendant upon what was in fact a civil war have been avoided? For Maurras, Drieu, and Guéhenno, the terms of the debate are political and rest on prewar ideological positions. For Camus, they are psychological: violence necessarily breeds revolt, uniting those against which it is directed. But crucial and qualifying all positions was a single fact: the decisive qualifying factor was to be the course taken by the war—the future, not the past.

CHARLES MAURRAS

November 1, 1940

AFTER THE MONTOIRE MEETING

The Head of State's announcement[1] about his meeting[2] with Chancellor Hitler almost made us forget his previous messages. In a way it summed them up . . . Very brief, very condensed, of great significance, it may well be the Marshal's masterpiece. Let us reread it.

The grounds and reasons for this Act—because it is above all an act—are undoubtedly more interesting than its application: they allow capital distinctions of considerable importance for a country which has spent seventy years on the slopes of a regime of Discussion.[3] Owing to this bad habit, speech has been corrupted; hardly had a fact been established when it was generalized into an agreeable or disagreeable theory, something to laugh or cry about, to celebrate or to mourn for . . . And this only goes for the political rabble and those who benefit from it.

This was not politics.

The great act accomplished by the Marshal is at the antipodes of certain pretentious intrigues[4] denounced and branded by ourselves and others from July to December.

Read this speech which was so personal. What does it announce? That an event we esteemed favorable or fortunate has become *possible*. How was this managed? Was it by hurling ourselves at the conqueror's feet? By offering him what he didn't ask for? By defying all decency and honor? That was what certain wretches wanted . . . they hated one word and made no secret of it: that word was DIGNITY, and it was the first word in the Marshal's speech:

SOURCE NOTE: Charles Maurras, "Après l'entrevue de Montoire," *La Seule France* (Lyons, Lardanchet, 1941), pp. 283–90. Reprinted from *L'Action française*, November 1, 1940.

"Thanks to the DIGNITY of the French during this ordeal . . ."

Indeed, neither the revival of which the Marshal speaks nor this "recovery" would have been possible without the dignity and reserve of the French during their worst *ordeal*.

Whatever policy we were to adopt, we first needed that moral element which is a powerful ingredient of every human reality.

And the effort of all political spirits caught in the movement of regeneration inspired by the Marshal, the defense of the Empire by our sailors, airmen, and colonial leaders, native loyalty—all this will have helped to establish this *act* of national existence which surmounts everything. Neither its spirit, nor its conscience, nor its passion can be contested, for all that proceeds from it is the sublime resolution of devotion until death. The event of which the Marshal is so proud would have been delayed to the extent that national pride had been diminished or national feeling blunted.

To those who look to their right and their left, to those who nurture sterile hopes and indulge in decadent speculations, the Marshal says "No!" It is not to others that we must turn, it is to ourselves: *our welfare is in our hands.*

Obstacles, scruples, aversion, instinctive alienation can have just or even, as the Marshal says, "noble" causes. That is not the point. It isn't a matter of mere heart-throbs or states of sensibility. The Marshal puts his *country's* INTERESTS first. This is what the most honest man in the world owes to himself and his people. This sacred idea springs from two sources: *honor* and the necessity of maintaining French unity, a unity ten centuries old in a new, mobile framework which the somber light of our days can bring, propose, and impose.

Once this distant goal has been distinguished, others arise and can be progressively attained: the return of prisoners, the fees of occupation, the demarcation line, territorial administration, food. These may be secondary issues, but they are relevant.

What is the main issue? The *sovereignty* of France, her greatest right and highest duty which can now be satisfied, and which has been satisfied. That is the source of our salvation.

The French have not forgotten how, last summer, a clown from show business called Sordet publicly defied what remained of national sovereignty. The Marshal's words do justice to such deliberate and biased stupidity and folly. Yesterday's speech restored the pure face of our country: it contained the leading idea and showed up its ideal and moral sense.

Let us proceed to the application.

"Are you in favor of what the Marshal calls 'collaboration'?"

"It is not for me to be in favor of it."

"Are you against it?"

"No."

"Neutral?"

"No."

"So you allow it?"

"It is not for me to allow it, still less to discuss it."

At last we are out of that regime of Discussion in which everything went to wrack and ruin because nothing could receive consistent direction. Nothing was respected, neither loyalty nor responsibility. Since we have changed all that, the country must benefit from it.

In other times people didn't hesitate to assume universal and tragic responsibilities in the absence of a government or state. Where the state exists, where it works, our duty is twofold: to let it perform its task and to facilitate the performance of its task.

To let it perform its task we must know how not to meddle in the essence of its activity, which is the free choice of policy from various systems which may or may not be acceptable. So as to facilitate the government's work we must do our best to assemble the greatest number of good citizens, create an atmosphere of complete *confidence,* and provide the immense strength produced by the positive adherence of a well-organized, firmly directed crowd.

But it is not for us to discuss the basis of the government's policy: that would be pure anarchy.

France's greatest misfortune would be if people were to take

sides over "collaboration" and form opposing factions. This
dispersion and diversion would be fatal. Everything should lead
to inclusion and concentration.

The Marshal is responsible. He expressed it admirably. Let
us understand . . .

"But if . . ."

"There is no if. First concentration. We must think of
France, France alone . . .[5] It is for her we must work."

So our mission is to fortify the pivot on which everything
rolls and turns, without questioning the political tendency.

We must try to facilitate the maneuvers of the state, whatever they may be, and make them as strong, supple, and
productive as possible. If the direction chosen by the Head of
State is perfect, its good results will be accelerated and increased
by the country's cooperation. If some error has slipped in at
the start, the suppleness and solidity of the machine of the
state could attenuate it and compensate for it with the same
cooperation.

Everything can have liabilities, even serious defects. Some
things more, others less. And time blows them on. We could
hesitate and stagnate, or pull ourselves together after Mers-el-
Kebir.[6] There the bleeding dice were thrown as insolently as
a gauntlet by the British government, and the blows of a wild
campaign aimed straight at the head and heart of France—at
the government—showed that the British wanted to saddle us
with a new revolution. The only course left was to march
against London, against her radio and her evil, perfidious stupidity. So one alternative was eliminated. On the other hand
other currents and other reactions were produced which we
had to keep in mind.

"But what do you think of the side that has been taken?"

"Nothing at all. I have no opinion. None. 'The heretic,'
said Bossuet,[7] 'is he who has an opinion.' "

I was not present at the debates; I did not see the dossier.
I don't think anything. And that doesn't worry me. In the
first place I have other things to think about. In the second

place it would be horrible to be wrong without the necessary elements for being right. And in the third place it is our duty to apply ourselves entirely to more immediate, necessary, and urgent matters, like rendering a service to the government and assisting it in its lofty duty. The whole of France must stand by the government. At present unity remains our only chance of survival.

The main thing: *the Marshal should carry out his policy*, in the best conditions constituted by the attitude and opinion of the country. Let us support and acclaim him. There is no other way of helping him to steer the French vessel between the area of her greatest good, which is still accessible, and that of the least evil, where she can always seek refuge.

That is why, speaking yesterday as a father, the Marshal decided to speak as a *leader*—a leader and a doctor—whose supreme lesson was *faith in eternal France*.

ALASTAIR HAMILTON

NOTES

1. *announcement*: this address was given by Pétain over the French radio on October 30, 1940, after his first interview with Hitler.

2. *meeting*: Hitler and Laval met at Montoire on October 22 and Hitler and Pétain on October 24, 1940, to discuss collaboration between their two governments. Pétain refused outright the possibility of military collaboration. As for political collaboration, little was agreed upon except that Pétain would make a speech on the French radio inviting the French people to collaborate. In return for political collaboration, Pétain demanded certain concessions: the return of war prisoners, a lowering of war indemnities, and a relaxation of control at the line of demarcation.

3. *regime of Discussion*: reference to the Third Republic, which debated a great deal and produced, in Maurras's eyes, very little other than new cabinets.

4. *pretentious intrigues*: allusion to General de Gaulle's appeals to the French nation.

5. *France, France alone (La Seule France)*: name of Maurras's book; a sort of motto for the Action française and its political ideal of "integral nationalism."

6. *Mers-el-Kebir*: On July 3, 1940, the British attacked the

French fleet near Oran, presumably to prevent German control of the fleet. This incident was to serve the collaborationists in their propaganda efforts against the English, and is now considered to have been an error in judgment.

7. *Bossuet*: Jacques Bénigne Bossuet (1627–1704), French bishop and eloquent orator.

PIERRE DRIEU LA ROCHELLE

1944

From *JOURNAL (1944-45)*

November 3, 1944

I have always looked beyond France's frontiers: that is why my situation is so dramatic. In my taste and manners I shocked many of my compatriots by my acquaintance with other countries. Then I judged France far too outspokenly, with an objectivity which seemed almost sacrilegious. Finally, my nationalism was always level with my internationalism: first the League of Nations, then non-Russian, non-Anglo-Saxon Europe.

I always wanted to assemble and combine opposites: the nation and Europe, socialism and aristocracy, freedom of thought and authority, mysticism and anticlericalism.

But maybe I should have remained in a "superior sphere" and not occasionally committed myself to individual comparisons? Well no, I wanted to be human till the end and share in the shit of opinions, ephemeral furies, local hatred. Yes, I wanted shit on my heels. But no higher.

November 7

The suppression of the absolute on a divine level forces us

SOURCE NOTE: Pierre Drieu La Rochelle, *Récit secret, suivi de Journal (1944-1945) et d'Exorde* (Paris, Gallimard, 1961), pp. 58–59.

to reduce the absolute to a human level. Our age is an age of atheism and "totalitarianism." The state is god and the politicians are its priests. Only a "religion" will be able to stand up against triumphant communism in the long run, but communism knows it.

I follow the political situation in the papers. I have nothing to say. I had analyzed its inevitable development accurately in my articles and books.

The Resistance is fascism which doesn't call itself fascism and will never dare develop the germ of fascism. So the Resistance is stillborn. It will be crushed between resurgent democracy and communism. Its elements, which have always been secretly divided, will be rejected to right and left. Then democracy (capitalism) will stand naked before communism. It will not dare become fascism either, or it will try when it is too late—and communism will devour it. That's all. That's all too obvious to be interesting. I prefer to walk in the woods, crush the last leaves, write *Dirke-Raspe*,[1] read the poets and philosophers.

ALASTAIR HAMILTON

NOTE

1. *Dirke-Raspe*: a work Drieu was planning to write.

JEAN GUÉHENNO

July 1940

JULY 1940

The only right we have left is to comment upon the messages and extol the wisdom of a marshal of the last war who can hardly even count his decorations, an old army pensioner who repeats the words of his prompters. We thought this veteran had been dismissed long ago. But since we failed to accuse ourselves in time, the exploiters of our defeat thrust him forward and made him read the act of contrition and submission which they had drawn up for us.

Stupidity and hypocrisy, the moral order of the rich, have triumphed. The housewives gloat. They no longer have to haggle over a hen with peasants at the market. They can at least eat according to their rank.

The French defeat is nothing but an episode in the European civil war. The conflict of nations covers a still deeper social conflict. Each nation is so deeply divided that one of its parties can hope to win when their country loses: the misfortune of France is an unexpected victory for a certain group of Frenchmen.* The Republic has lost, but they have won.

This is a revealing moment. Looking back on our history over the last fifty years, on the amazing effort which so many Frenchmen have made to attain a certain comfort and dignity, we realize to what an intolerable extent the former "notables" must have suffered. What pleasure is there in possessing what everyone else possesses? People are made in such a way as to feel less happy and less free when anybody else is as happy and free as they are. The happiness of others seems to diminish their own happiness.

The liberty of others seems licentious, anarchic—even threatening. They grow to hate these upstarts and thieves. That's how far we've got. The moment of vengeance has arrived after fifty years of hatred. Our miseries upset those notables, no doubt: but there are compensations. Once again they think they are happy and free. Fools! They talk of their wretched country as a master talks of his sick valet: they call it idle.

The masses, always so credulous, are dazed by their mis-

* A "divine surprise" said Monsieur Maurras.

SOURCE NOTE: Jean Guéhenno (pseud. Cévennes), *Dans la prison* (Paris, Éditions de Minuit, 1944), pp. 14–16.

fortunes, and wonder, rubbing their eyes, whether they are guilty rather than miserable.

ALASTAIR HAMILTON

ALBERT CAMUS

1938

From CALIGULA

(The patricians, angered by Caligula's arbitrary and cruel acts, have gathered in Cherea's house to plot a revolt. Cherea joins them.)

CHEREA Where are you running?

THIRD PATRICIAN To the palace.

CHEREA I know that. But do you think they'll let you in?

FIRST PATRICIAN We're not going to ask permission.

CHEREA You're so energetic all of a sudden! May I at least sit down in my own house?

The door is closed. CHEREA *walks up to the overturned table and sits on one of the corners. All turn toward him.*

CHEREA It's not as easy as you think, my friends. Your fear can't replace courage and cold blood. All this is premature.

THIRD PATRICIAN If you're not with us, go away. But hold your tongue.

CHEREA I think I am with you. But it's not for the same reasons.

THIRD PATRICIAN That's enough talk!

SOURCE NOTE: Albert Camus, *Caligula*, in *Malentendu suivi de Caligula* (Paris, Gallimard, 1958), pp. 132–36. First performed at the Théâtre Hébertot in Paris, September 25, 1945.

CHEREA *(getting up)* Yes, that's enough talk. I want things to be clear. Because if I'm with you, I'm not for you. That's why your methods don't seem any good to me. You haven't distinguished your real enemy, and you attribute petty motives to him. He has only great motives, and you're running to your doom. To start with, get to know him: you'll be able to fight him better.

THIRD PATRICIAN We see him as he is, the maddest of tyrants!

CHEREA Not necessarily. We know about mad emperors. But this one isn't mad enough. And what I hate about him is that he knows what he wants.

FIRST PATRICIAN He wants our death.

CHEREA No, that's a secondary issue. He puts his power at the service of a higher and more mortal passion; he threatens us in what is deepest within us. No doubt it isn't the first time that a man has had unlimited power in our country, but it's the first time he has used it without limits and denied both humanity and the world. That's what frightens me about him and that's what I want to fight. To lose one's life is not so important: I would have the courage for that if necessary. But to see the sense of life evaporate, the reason for our existence disappear—that's unbearable. One can't live without a reason.

FIRST PATRICIAN Vengeance is a reason.

CHEREA Yes, and I'm going to share it with you. But understand that it isn't to side with your petty humiliations. It's to struggle against a great idea whose victory would mean the end of the world. I can allow your being turned to ridicule, but I can't allow Caligula to do what he dreams of doing and all he dreams of doing. He is transferring his philosophy into corpses, and unfortunately for us, it is a faultless philosophy. One must strike when refutation is impossible.

THIRD PATRICIAN Then we must act.

CHEREA We must act. But you won't destroy such unjust power by facing it head on, when it is in full force. You can fight tyranny, but you must intrigue against disinterested wickedness. You must push it along, and wait for logic to become insanity. But I've only spoken out of honesty. Remember that I'm with you part of the way: after that I won't serve any of your interests. I only want peace in a coherent world. I don't act out of ambition but reasonable fear, the fear of this inhuman lyricism in terms of which my life is worth nothing.

FIRST PATRICIAN *(advancing)* I think I see, or almost. But the main thing is that you should agree with us that the bases of our society have been shaken. For us, of course, the question is primarily a moral one. Families tremble; there is no more respect for work; the whole country is delivered up to blasphemy. Virtue calls us to its aid. Can we refuse to hear it? Conspirators, do you accept that every evening the patricians be made to run around Caesar's litter?

OLD PATRICIAN Will you let him call them "my darling"?

THIRD PATRICIAN Abduct their wives.

SECOND PATRICIAN And their children.

MUCIUS And their money?

FIFTH PATRICIAN No!

FIRST PATRICIAN Cherea, you have spoken well. You have also done well to call on us. It is too soon to act: today the people are still against us. Will you wait with us for the right moment?

CHEREA Yes, let Caligula continue. Let us encourage him. Let us organize his folly. The day will come when he will be alone before an empire full of corpses, and the relatives of corpses.

A noise is heard. Trumpets sound outside. Silence. Then a name is muttered from mouth to mouth: Caligula.

ALASTAIR HAMILTON

PAUL ÉLUARD

1943

KILL

Tonight there falls
A strange peace over Paris
A peace of blind eyes
Of dreams without color
That hurl themselves against the walls
A peace of useless arms
Of vanquished faces
Of absent men
Of women already faded
Pale cold and tearless

Tonight there falls
In the silence
A strange glow over Paris
Over the good old heart of Paris
The muffled glow of crime
Savage premeditated and pure
Crime against butchers
Against death.

LLOYD ALEXANDER

TUER

Il tombe cette nuit
Une étrange paix sur Paris
Une paix d'yeux aveugles

SOURCE NOTE: Paul Éluard (pseud. Jean du Haut), "Tuer," *Au Rendez-vous allemand, suivi de Poésie et vérité 1942* (Paris, Éditions de Minuit, 1945), p. 28.

De rêves sans couleur
Qui se cognent aux murs
Une paix de bras inutiles
De fronts vaincus
D'hommes absents
De femmes déjà passées
Pâles froides et sans larmes

Il tombe cette nuit
Dans le silence
Une étrange lueur sur Paris
Sur le bon vieux coeur de Paris
La lueur sourde du crime
Prémédité sauvage et pur
Du crime contre les bourreaux
Contre la mort.

ANDRÉ GIDE

1941

NOTE FOR JANUARY 12, 1941

"Neither victors nor vanquished!" I do not much like that slogan. It implies on both sides a pretense so flattering for our self-esteem that I am suspicious. A "collaboration" such as is proposed to us today could not be "loyal" when it is thus based on a lie. It is doubtless fine and noble and reassuring after a boxing match to see the opponents shake hands, but there is no question of denying that one has beaten the other. We are defeated. As soon as we showed any inclination to doubt this,

SOURCE NOTE: André Gide, "Note, le 12 janvier 1941," *Journal 1939–1942* (Paris, Gallimard, 1946) pp. 104–8.

our opponent would be able to remind us of the fact; let there be no doubt about it. And if he helps us to get to our feet today, this is only to allow us an effort from which he plans to reap the profit. He supposes quite rightly that our labor and the production we can supply will be better (or, to speak more clearly, that our output will be greater) if we are not reduced to slavery and if we keep the illusion of working freely and for ourselves.

"Is it therefore your opinion that we should refuse to play this game?"

"Perhaps be a party to it at first, and, if possible, without too much bitterness, but also without illusions, in order to avoid, subsequently, too bitter a disappointment. Shall I tell you just what I think? I believe it is good for France to bend for a time under the yoke of an enforced discipline. Just as she was not capable, in the depths of moral laxity and decay into which she had fallen, of winning a real victory over an enemy much better equipped than she, a united, resolute, tenacious, and pugnacious enemy skillfully led by a man with his mind made up to override all the scruples that weaken us, all the considerations that stand in our way; just so I do not believe France capable today of rising to her feet again all alone and solely by her own efforts. I say 'today' but as early as 1914 I wrote: 'We have everything to learn from Germany; she has everything to take from us.' I abide by that formula."

"Do you not feel something mortifying, insulting, and intolerable in what you are saying?"

"The most elementary wisdom consists in taking things, people, and events as they are and not as one would like, or would have liked, them to be. A wisdom we have often lacked, for we have a great tendency to take words for things that exist and we are satisfied with a bit of eloquence. One has to play with the cards one has."

"We hold excellent trumps."

"But they are scattered and we don't know how to use them properly. This is what keeps me from being too upset if the conqueror, with his fine method, assumes responsibility for our hand, temporarily."

"Those trumps will not endure giving up their freedom of self-determination."

"Too much liberty led to our downfall."

"And then you are leaving out the fact that the conqueror will not tolerate our revealing ourselves, in any domain whatever, as superior to him. He will manage in such a way as to subjugate our virtues and talents and to discredit those that will not submit; our virtues and talents, our men of virtue and talent."

"That may be, but what can we do about it? Besides, it occurs to me as we are talking that the only virtues and talents I really value are uncooperative."

"The uncooperative will be brought to heel. Yes, I recall that remark of yours that you quote. But I also recall another remark I have read in your *Journal*. It too comes from the period of the other war. 'I sometimes think,' you wrote, 'I think with horror' (and, to be sure, it was justified!) 'that the victory we are longing for is that of the past over the future.' Well, you must be satisfied: this time the forces of the future have triumphed."

"And, indeed, nothing saddens me more than seeing France at present expecting her salvation to come only from an attachment to everything about her that is oldest and most worn out. Their fine 'National Revolution'[1] gives me a pain in the neck. If our country is to be reborn (and I firmly believe that it will be), it will be in spite of that and against that. I expect our salvation to come from what is getting ready in the shadows and cannot emerge into the light of day until tomorrow."

JUSTIN O'BRIEN

NOTE

1. *"National Revolution"*: sociopolitical doctrine, much like National Socialism in Germany, elaborated at Vichy whose major premise was that the French defeat and the destruction of the

Republic had provided circumstances favorable to carrying out a reconstruction of France. The doctrine had its origins in the nationalist thought of the Action française and the "personalist" philosophies of government elaborated in the early thirties. Catholic and antidemocratic, it championed corporatism to guarantee professional freedom, since it was at once anticapitalistic and antisocialistic, and it favored a strong authoritarian central government as well as certan regional autonomy. It took as its motto, "Work-Family-Nation."

THE SIDES TAKEN

COLLABORATION OR RESISTANCE. In 1940, most people in France hesitated between the two positions, riddled with uncertainty. The antidemocratic extremists, nationalist or fascist, at first easily embraced collaboration, more or less aware of the built-in potential conflict between their real hopes for their country and the impact upon France of Nazi demands. The non-Communist left, of Jacobin tradition, inclined toward resistance. But the question of the best service one could render to a distraught country in a war whose issue seemed highly problematic was not easy to resolve. Stripped of all extraneous considerations it was a dramatic option for those few willing to become involved, a game of poker played with history for high stakes, with no guarantee of success.

The myth of Antigone as treated by Sophocles furnished the playwright Jean Anouilh with the dramatic framework in which to project the confrontation. The analogies between the situations of Thebes and of France needed little stressing. The action of Sophocles' play takes place at the end of a period of plague, followed by a devastating civil war brought about by the rival claim to the throne of Thebes of the two sons of Oedipus, Polynices and Eteocles. They are eventually found dead on the battlefield, locked in single combat. Creon, their uncle, on taking the reins of government in order to put an end to civil disorder, decrees that the body of Polynices, who led the attack on Thebes, be denied burial and left to rot—a terrible punishment—and that whoever disobeys the edict shall be stoned to death. Antigone, Polynices' sister, defies the edict in the name of a higher law, the law of the gods who require that burial be given the dead.

In Anouilh's play, Antigone does not appeal to a superior law to justify her act of civil disobedience, but to a kind of integrity based on an inner revulsion against the prevarications and equivocal calculations required of those who, like Creon, must maintain order by the use of force. Creon in Anouilh's play is not a petty tyrant, nor even an ambitious man, but one who sees that in times of chaos someone must steer the ship. In the scene below, the roles have been taken and must be played out. Antigone has challenged the decree on which Creon has staked his authority; no argument can bring about a reconciliation. Antigone will die, but in death she will destroy Creon.

By 1942 it was beginning to be clear that the "National Revolution" was foundering and that its attempt to unify the nation had failed. But the deadlock was still unbroken that opposed the Antigones and Creons of France. The real conflict was beginning.

JEAN ANOUILH

1944

From *ANTIGONE*

CREON And you still insist upon being put to death—merely because I refuse to let your brother go out with that grotesque passport; because I refuse his body the wretched consolation of that mass-production jibber-jabber, which you would have been the first to be embarrassed by if I had allowed it. The whole thing is absurd!

ANTIGONE Yes, it's absurd.

CREON Then why, Antigone, why? For whose sake? For the sake of them that believe in it? To raise them against me?

ANTIGONE No.

CREON For whom then if not for them and not for Polynices either?

ANTIGONE For nobody. For myself.

A pause as they stand looking at one another.

CREON You must want very much to die. You look like a trapped animal.

ANTIGONE Stop feeling sorry for me. Do as I do. Do your job. But if you are a human being, do it quickly. That is all I ask of you. I'm not going to be able to hold out forever.

CREON *(takes a step toward her)* I want to save you, Antigone.

ANTIGONE You are the king, and you are all-powerful. But

SOURCE NOTE: Jean Anouilh, *Antigone* (Paris, La Table Ronde, 1946), pp. 75–86. First performed at the Théâtre de l'Atelier in Paris on February 4, 1944.

that you cannot do.

CREON   You think not?

ANTIGONE   Neither save me nor stop me.

CREON   Prideful Antigone! Little Oedipus!

ANTIGONE   Only this can you do: have me put to death.

CREON   Have you tortured, perhaps?

ANTIGONE   Why would you do that? To see me cry? To hear me beg for mercy? Or swear whatever you wish, and then begin over again?

A pause.

CREON   You listen to me. You have cast me for the villain in this little play of yours, and yourself for the heroine. And you know it, you damned little mischief-maker. But don't you drive me too far! If I were one of your preposterous little tyrants that Greece is full of, you would be lying in a ditch this minute with your tongue pulled out and your body drawn and quartered. But you can see something in my face that makes me hesitate to send for the guards and turn you over to them. Instead, I let you go on arguing; and you taunt me, you take the offensive. *(He grasps her left wrist.)* What are you driving at, you she-devil?

ANTIGONE   Let me go. You are hurting my arm.

CREON *(gripping her tighter)*   I will not let you go.

ANTIGONE *(moans)*   Oh!

CREON   I was a fool to waste words. I should have done this from the beginning. *(He looks at her.)* I may be your uncle— but we are not a particularly affectionate family. Are we, eh? *(Through his teeth, as he twists)* Are we? (CREON *propels* ANTIGONE *around below him to his side.)* What fun for you, eh? To be able to spit in the face of a king who has all the power in the world; a man who has done his own killing in his

day; who has killed people just as pitiable as you are—and who
is still soft enough to go to all this trouble in order to keep you
from being killed.

A pause.

ANTIGONE Now you are squeezing my arm too tightly. It
doesn't hurt any more.

CREON *stares at her, then drops her arm.*

CREON I shall save you yet. *(He goes below the table to the
chair at end of table, takes off his coat, and places it on the
chair.)* God knows, I have things enough to do today without
wasting my time on an insect like you. There's plenty to do, I
assure you, when you've just put down a revolution. But urgent
things can wait. I am not going to let politics be the cause of
your death. For it is a fact that this whole business is nothing
but politics: the mournful shade of Polynices, the decomposing
corpse, the sentimental weeping, and the hysteria that you
mistake for heroism—nothing but politics.

Look here. I may not be soft, but I'm fastidious. I like
things clean, shipshape, well scrubbed. Don't think that I am
not just as offended as you are by the thought of that meat
rotting in the sun. In the evening, when the breeze comes in
off the sea, you can smell it in the palace, and it nauseates me.
But I refuse even to shut my window. It's vile; and I can tell
you what I wouldn't tell anybody else: it's stupid, monstrously
stupid. But the people of Thebes have got to have their noses
rubbed into it a little longer. My God! If it was up to me, I
should have had them bury your brother long ago as a mere
matter of public hygiene. I admit that what I am doing is
childish. But if the featherheaded rabble I govern are to understand what's what, that stench has got to fill the town for a
month!

ANTIGONE *(turns to him)* You are a loathsome man!

CREON I agree. My trade forces me to be. We could argue

whether I ought or ought not to follow my trade; but once I take on the job, I must do it properly.

ANTIGONE Why do you do it at all?

CREON My dear, I woke up one morning and found myself King of Thebes. God knows, there were other things I loved in life more than power.

ANTIGONE Then you should have said no.

CREON Yes, I could have done that. Only, I felt that it would have been cowardly. I should have been like a workman who turns down a job that has to be done. So I said yes.

ANTIGONE So much the worse for you, then. I didn't say yes. I can say no to anything I think vile, and I don't have to count the cost. But because you said yes, all that you can do, for all your crown and your trappings, and your guards—all that you can do is to have me killed.

CREON Listen to me.

ANTIGONE If I want to. I don't have to listen to you if I don't want to. You said your *yes*. There is nothing more you can tell me that I don't know. You stand there, drinking in my words. *(She moves behind chair.)* Why is it that you don't call your guards? I'll tell you why? You want to hear me out to the end; that's why.

CREON You amuse me.

ANTIGONE Oh, no, I don't. I frighten you. That is why you talk about saving me. Everything would be so much easier if you had a docile, tongue-tied little Antigone living in the palace. I'll tell you something, Uncle Creon: I'll give you back one of your own words. You are too fastidious to make a good tyrant. But you are going to have to put me to death today, and you know it. And that's what frightens you. God! Is there anything uglier than a frightened man!

CREON Very well. I am afraid, then. Does that satisfy you? I am afraid that if you insist upon it, I shall have to have you killed. And I don't want to.

ANTIGONE I don't have to do things that I think are wrong. If it comes to that, you didn't really want to leave my brother's body unburied, did you? Say it! Admit that you didn't.

CREON I have said it already.

ANTIGONE But you did it just the same. And now, though you don't want to do it, you are going to have me killed. And you call that being a king!

CREON Yes, I call that being a king.

ANTIGONE Poor Creon! My nails are broken, my fingers are bleeding, my arms are covered with the welts left by the paws of your guards—but I am a queen!

CREON Then why not have pity on me, and live? Isn't your brother's corpse, rotting there under my windows, payment enough for peace and order in Thebes? My son loves you. Don't make me add your life to the payment. I've paid enough.

ANTIGONE No, Creon! You said yes, and made yourself king. Now you will never stop paying.

CREON But God in heaven! Won't you try to understand me! I'm trying hard enough to understand you! There had to be one man who said yes. Somebody had to agree to captain the ship. She had sprung a hundred leaks; she was loaded to the water line with crime, ignorance, poverty. The wheel was swinging with the wind. The crew refused to work and were looting the cargo. The officers were building a raft, ready to slip overboard and desert the ship. The mast was splitting, the wind was howling, the sails were beginning to rip. Every man jack on board was about to drown—and only because the only thing they thought of was their own skins and their cheap little day-to-day traffic. Was that a time, do you think, for playing with

words like yes and no? Was that a time for a man to be weigh-
ing the pros and cons, wondering if he wasn't going to pay too
dearly later on; if he wasn't going to lose his life, or his family,
or his touch with other men? You grab the wheel, you right
the ship in the face of a mountain of water. You shout an order,
and if one man refuses to obey, you shoot straight into the mob.
Into the mob, I say! The beast as nameless as the wave that
crashes down upon your deck; as nameless as the whipping
wind. The thing that drops when you shoot may be someone
who poured you a drink the night before; but it has no name.
And you, braced at the wheel, you have no name, either. Nothing has a name—except the ship, and the storm. (A pause as
he looks at her.) Now do you understand?

ANTIGONE   I am not here to understand. That's all very well
for you. I am here to say no to you, and die.

CREON   It is easy to say no.

ANTIGONE   Not always.

                                              LEWIS GALENTIERE

   This is not the place to rehearse the long course of
French history. But it was the backdrop against which the
confrontations born of defeat were played out, confrontations more particularly focused on the conflicting attitudes
born of the French Revolution. Although the right-wing,
left-wing dichotomy is little more than a convenient oversimplification, it is nonetheless true that the positions of
the French writers grouped above are roughly polarized
along those lines: Montherlant's right-oriented aloofness,
with its obvious partiality to the Third Reich, is echoed
on the left by Gide's cool, urbane appraisal of the ambience in the country. An antidemocratic mystique, exacer-
bated by the all too obvious failures of the thirties; overt
admiration for the efficacy of the Third Reich; hatred of
Communist Russia and Marxist ideology and a recurrent

streak of more or less openly avowed anti-Semitism are common to those writers who, in some measure, accepted the premises of collaboration. But beyond that, each man's attitude coincided with the certainties to which he adhered. What becomes clear, retrospectively, is the myth-charged nature of their convictions. Not the least of these myths concerned the possibility that through some form of revolution or reorganization they might save their country. The illusion of control was to become increasingly hard to sustain in the face of reality, and as events forced the collaborators to jettison their myths, the best among them were to be caught in a tragic equivocation; they were publicly bound to play out a role that turned them inexorably from patriots to puppets to traitors exacerbating hatreds, working in exact opposition to their political goals.

The liberal-democratic left was at first on the defensive. The regime to which they had somewhat abstractly adhered had collapsed. Held responsible for France's defeat, it was on trial. Silenced, they debated the issues at first face to face with themselves in journals that register their doubts and uncertainties. Later, in the light of events, they reassessed principles that had been worn thin by glib repetition, until finally they joined battle with the passionate singleness of purpose voiced in Camus's letter to his erstwhile German friend. There is a new realism in that commitment that distinguishes it from Guéhenno's traditional stance, a heightened awareness of the exacting demands and ferocity of the fight but also a new mystique, a sense that in each man's conduct the whole world was in some measure concerned. "Commitment" then was an absolute, a fight to death against evil, a purifying struggle that could brook no intermediate formulas. But as one spans the spectrum of reaction it is clear that at first the basic motivation in the revolt against a Nazi-dominated universe was not essentially political in nature. It was

rather, as Mauriac exressed it, a revulsion against the
senseless barbarism of Nazi rule that united Frenchmen
beyond partisan passions. But the Nazi attack on Russia
and the full-scale participation of the Communist Party
in the underground struggle injected a new political
imperative into the fight. Paradoxically, the collaborators
had succeeded in bringing about what they most vocifer-
ously had fought. Communism, recovering from the pall
cast over it by its antinationalism in 1939, was soon
equated with the national struggle against oppression,
whereas their own myth of national regeneration was
irreparably eroded.

PART TWO

DAILY LIFE

THERE WOULD BE ample material to make a book recording the manner in which people conducted their daily life through the changing patterns of war, defeat, occupation, and liberation. It was a period when facts outstripped imagination. Poetry, diaries, fiction merge. Emotions, facts, impressions trivial, transitory, dramatic, were etched vividly on the mind in moments of intense awareness.

WAR AND DEFEAT

When war was declared on September 3, 1939, the decision was greeted on the whole with grim resignation by a population that had lived under its shadow since the outbreak of the Spanish Civil War and the Munich episode (September 25, 1938). No one could predict the future, but most anticipated the kind of attrition and wholesale massacre of men characteristic of World War I. Aragon's poem "The Time of Crossward Puzzles" catches the underlying mood of many inarticulate French people during the "phony" war and also, indirectly, the Communist Party member's opposition to it. The "broken world" of private human beings; the loneliness and heartache of separation; the gnawing fear and anxiety; the spasm of revolt against the senselessness of war itself; resignation and yet the hope of a return to an existence where lovers are united. Tarot cards speak of the future, and the crossword puzzle proposes its reassuring enigmas: these are the themes of *"les mots croisés."* The play on words in the title refers not only to the puzzles but to the two voices that alternately rise and respond to each other in the poem: the women's, the men's.

Céline's apocalyptic description of a bombardment as the German offensive swept across the Loire, Simone de Beauvoir's flat, staccato account of her return to Paris after the Armistice, vividly depict the chaotic, incoherent medley that the German blitzkrieg produced, uprooting hundreds of thousands of civilians fleeing the onslaught. A churning mass of human beings choked the roads of France where retreating Allied troops, advancing German units, deserters, prisoners of war, all desperately bent on making their way somewhere, hampered each other's movements, offering an easy target for bombing. Panic brought out simultaneously individual courage, unscrupulousness, cowardice, and despair.

The title of Aragon's "Song for a Barrel Organ," or "Song of the New Barbarism," is a play on words, the French designation for the barrel organ: *orgue de barbarie.* It is a lament describing the pattern of chaos in the north of France during the mid-May days in 1940 when, striking through Belgium, the panzer divisions drove the Allied troops to Dunkirk, encircling, fragmenting, and cutting off Allied units. To the dazed distress of the leaderless civilian population responds the sullen revolt of the "black" men of the north, the miners, returning home, refusing to leave France for the foreign country beyond the sea, namely England. Aragon shows his vivid sensitivity to the pathos of the situation and his immediate empathy with the emotions of the ordinary human being, shaping them in relation to the point of view of the Communist Party.

No more contrasting accounts could be found than Céline's savage and apocalyptic evocation of what the French called the exodus and Simone de Beauvoir's dazed, on-the-spot record of her subsequent return to Paris when, with the signing of the Armistice on June 22, the tedious, weary task of extricating oneself from the chaos began. Céline stamps what he writes with the mark of his own outraged emotions, transcribing not merely the event but its reverberation in his own mind, amplified into a cosmic calamity. Taunting, savage, emphatically infuriated by the discordant jangle of it all, lashing out against the human waste and human baseness, he transfers us into the very heart of his hyperbolic obsessive world by the wild, creative power of his revolt. One is at times almost shocked by the single-minded ferocity with which Simone de Beauvoir carries out her intent to reach Paris, by the cold, relentless dislike with which she observes others in like predicament —the Dutch family, for example, who gave her a lift. And she certainly gives us an insight into the painful lack of human solidarity which the defeat revealed and which so outraged Céline. But in the ambiguous zone between war and occupation, she gives a kaleidoscopic view of day-to-day experience, seen from the point of view of a participant and observer stunned by personal anxiety for the man she loves—Sartre, in this instance—and thereby detached, mechanically registering, as in a film, the unbelievable, the "absurd" configuration of events.

LOUIS ARAGON

October 1939

THE TIME OF CROSSWORD PUZZLES

O sun of sleepless midnight, solitude
Of husbandless houses where they lie awake
Spouses of terror, counting round their beds
The monsters that stand leering till daybreak

Who was it that unchained the banished fear
Put sand on the roof, insomnia in their hearts
And daubed the windowpanes with panic blue?
Nobody any more consults the cards

Keep dancing, wizards, on your briary heath
They will not seek your love-philters again
Love bowed their heads more humbly than a prayer
When the East Station swallowed up their men

Women who know at last as we ourselves
The paradise lost of our unknotted limbs
Do you hear the voice that murmurs, Only you
As lips bestow a kiss on the hollow winds?

SOURCE NOTE: Louis, Aragon, "Le Temps des mots croisés," *Le Crève-coeur* (Paris, Gallimard, 1941), pp. 14–16. Two hundred and fifty copies were published in France before the book was censored. Word of the poems got to England through Gide's "Imaginary Interviews," which were translated by Horizon (May and June 1942) from the Vichy *Figaro*. *Le Crève-coeur* was then published in England in 1942 by Éditions Horizon, La France Libre.

This poem first appeared in the *Nouvelle Revue française* on December 1, 1939, and it was read during the war at the Théâtre des Mathurins and the Théâtre Français.

Absence abominable, absinthe of the war
Once more we drink that bitter counterfeit
And yet our limbs were fused not long ago
I sensed for you whatever your body did

Too little have we prized those double hours
Too little asked if our dreams were counterparts
Too lightly probed the look in troubled eyes
Too seldom talked of our concurrent hearts

But only as a secret to share with you
Do I see the world in its other countenance
When rain-clouds grizzle the aging face of day
And now the midnight trees begin to dance

Listen. In the night my heartbeats call
I grope in bed for your presence unawares
And everything slips away. Except for you
Nothing else matters. I am not one of theirs

I am not theirs because I would have to be
Like Ligier's carved half-skeleton at Bar
Fleshless down to the waist, but holding up
To the high window his poor barbarous heart

I am not theirs because my human flesh
Is not a pastry to be cut with the knife
Because a river seeks and finds the sea
Because my living needs a sister life

I am not one of theirs because the shade
Exists for lovers, sunlight for the trees
Winds for the poplars scattering their seed
On the bee-encumbered, honey-laden breeze

I am yours. I am yours only. I adore
Your footprint and the hollow where you lay
Your slipper dropped, your handkerchief. Go sleep
My frightened child. I promise to lie awake

Here until dawn. The medieval night
Has draped this broken universe with black
If not for us, the storm will some day pass
The time of crossword puzzles will come back

                                        MALCOLM COWLEY

LE TEMPS DES MOTS CROISÉS

O soleil de minuit sans sommeil solitude
Dans les logis déserts d'hommes où vous veillez
Épouses d'épouvante elles font leur étude
Des monstres grimaçants autour de l'oreiller

Qui donc a déchainé la peur cette bannie
Et barbouillé de bleu panique les carreaux
Le sable sous le toit Dans le coeur l'insomnie
Personne ne lit plus le sort dans les tarots

Sorciers vous pouvez danser dans la bruyère
Elles ne veulent plus savoir si tu leur mens
Amour qui les courbas mieux qu'aucune prière
Quand la Gare de l'Est[1] eut mangé leurs amants

Femmes qui connaissez enfin comme nous-mêmes
Le paradis perdu de nos bras dénoués
Entendez-vous nos voix qui murmurent Je t'aime
Et votre lèvre à l'air donne un baiser troué

Absence abominable absinthe de la guerre
N'en es-tu pas encore amèrement grisée
Nos jambes se mêlaient t'en souviens-tu naguère
Et je savais pour toi ce que ton corps faisait

Nous n'avons pas assez chéri ces heures doubles
Pas assez partagé nos songes différents
Pas assez regardé le fond de nos yeux troubles
Et pas assez causé de nos coeurs concurrents

Si ce n'est pas pourtant pour que je te le dise
Pourquoi m'arrive-t-il d'entendre ou de penser
Si les nuages font au jour des mèches grises
Et si les arbres noirs se mettent à danser

Ecoute Dans la nuit mon sang bat et t'appelle
Je cherche dans le lit ton poids et ta couleur
Faut-il que tout m'échappe et si ce n'est pas elle
Que me fait tout cela Je ne suis pas des leurs

Je ne suis pas des leurs puisqu'il faut pour en être
S'arracher à sa peau vivante comme à Bar[2]
L'homme de Ligier[3] qui tend vers la fenêtre
Squelette par en haut son pauvre coeur barbare

Je ne suis pas des leurs puisque la chair humaine
N'est pas comme un gâteau qu'on tranche avec le fer
Et qu'il faut à ma vie une chaleur germaine
Qu'on ne peut détourner le fleuve de la mer

Je ne suis pas des leurs enfin parce que l'ombre
Est faite pour qu'on s'aime et l'arbre pour le ciel
Et que les peupliers de leur semence encombrent
Le vent porteur d'amour d'abeilles et de miel

Je suis à toi Je suis à toi seule J'adore
La trace de tes pas le creux ou tu te mis
Ta pantoufle perdue ou ton mouchoir Va dors
Dors mon enfant craintif Je veille c'est promis

Je veille Il se fait tard La nuit du moyen-âge
Couvre d'un manteau noir cet univers brisé
Peut-être pas pour nous mais cessera l'orage
Un jour et reviendra le temps des mots croisés

NOTES

1. *la Gare de L'Est*: point of departure for the eastern front.
2. *Bar*: Bar-le-Duc, town in eastern France near Lorraine.
3. *Ligier*: Ligier Richier (1500–1567), French sculptor, a pupil of Michelangelo. He carved the skeleton image referred to for the tomb of René de Châlons, Prince of Orange, in the church of Saint-Pierre at Bar-le-Duc. The effigy formerly bore in its hand a silver casket enclosing the prince's heart.

LOUIS-FERDINAND CÉLINE

1944

GUIGNOL'S BAND, I

Baroom! . . . Vroom! . . . They're razing the city! . . . The whole street caving in at the shore . . . Orleans collapsing and thunder at the Grand Café! . . . A table sails by and slices the air! . . . Marble bird! . . . twirls, smashes the window across the way into a thousand splinters! . . . A whole set of furniture teetering, bursting through the panes, scattering in a shower of flame! . . . The proud bridge, twelve towers, lurches, tumbles all at once into the slime. The mud from the river spatters everything! . . . churns, tosses the mob shrieking, gasping, spilling over the parapet! . . . What a mess . . .

Our rattletrap trembles, shakes pinned crossways at the curb between three trucks, swerves, sputters, it's dead! The motor's

SOURCE NOTE: Louis-Ferdinand Céline (real name Louis-Ferdinand Destouches), *Guignol's Band, I* (Paris, Denoël, 1944), pp. 521–6.

had it! Ever since Colombes it's been threatening to give out
on us! Wheezing to beat the band . . . It was designed for
modest efforts . . . not for chasing to hell and gone! . . . The
whole crowd's on our backs, bitching at us because we're
stalled! . . . because we're rotten bunglers! . . . That's a thought!
. . . 218,000 trucks, tanks, and pushcarts jammed smelted
together in terror leapfrogging each other stampeding to be the
first across the tottering bridge, lock horns, gore each other, and
smash themselves to a pulp as hard as they can . . . Only one
bike gets through, and without handlebars . . .

It's a horrible mess! . . . The world is crumbling! . . .

"Get the lead out, you brake-happy sonsabitches! Go shit in
your hats, you broken-down crumbums!"

That's not the end of it! Not finished! There's a lot left to
do! . . . We spin away! . . .

The Engineer Corps major gets ready to blast! Still another
thunderbolt! Sets a short fuse! . . . He's a fiend! . . . But
suddenly his machine flashes and sputters right between his
fingers! . . . The whole mob falls on him, engulfs him, snatches
him up, carries him off leaping furiously . . . The column starts
up, all the motors blast, backfire so loud you have to block your
ears! . . . Alarming remarks and blasphemies! . . .

Everything! meat! junk! tanks! hurtles into the big guns that
pound and scrape along on caterpillar treads, wrecking everything in their path at the command of a quartermaster sergeant!
It's the saraband of terror, a carnival amid the rumble of
crawling disruption! The rubber man wins! Long live the
cosmic villain, the unscrupulous bachelor with the corkscrew
bicycle, the iron-clad beast! . . .

Fritz is firing like hell at us, emerges up there from the cloud
bottoms! The bastard! He's mowing us down with his bang-
bang! He sprinkles us from the highest peaks, he's hemming us
in, he's buzzing around us! . . . It's the madness of slaughter,
crazed volleys and furious missiles! ricocheting all around! He
soaks us, floods us to death! And then he makes us dance again,
he really works at leading our bunny hop, diving viciously

darting all around us! We're really doomed! Shells! Three huge
ones! . . . It's a holy terror! And they're just so heavy! Blast
after blast! . . . The earth's turned upside down and gasping its
last! . . . weakens, trembles, groans far and wide, as far as you
can hear . . . all the way to the gentle hillocks down there!
Damn the echo! Damn the bomb! No mistake about it. It's all
getting worse! . . . we're going to die in a potato masher! . . .
a bedbug's end! . . . in suffocating sulfurations! rolled in salt-
peter, in destructive deflagrations! The dunghill's swarming! Up
there he's just bursting with zeal! . . . He's ticked off about our
misery! Horrible airplane! He's still peppering us! And three
loop-the-loops! It's a hailstorm! . . . Crackling Crisco in the air!
The paving-stones covered with bull's eyes! . . . The lady who
got one in the back has her arms around a sheep lying there,
she's going to twist her way under the axles, holding it, crawls
and convulses . . . a little way farther . . . winces, slides down,
falls with her arms out like a cross! . . . moans . . . stops
moving! . . .

The ambulance, our vessel of mercy, rocks and rolls, swerves,
shimmies back and forth over the largest paving-stones, loses
all its bolts, rams into a herd of animals, lands smack dab in
the middle of cattle, stallions, chickens . . . a tank barrel-assing
along smashes into it! . . . "Broing!" On the rebound it mashes
two tricycles, a nun, a police officer . . . It's time to say prayers
for the dead . . . All that on the bridge! Now the poor automobile is carried sixty feet ahead by the shock wave from the
bombs! Soaring inside the horrible blast! And then two steps
and two sputters . . . Look at it now? zigzagging down into
the whirlpool of slaughter . . . The crowd catches up with us
again . . . crushes us . . . we bolt every which way trying to
escape! . . . they try our weight like a housewife with a melon
and squeeze us violently! Our car blows its stack! . . . And
there we are hoisted up in triumph. Passed up over their
heads! Just perched up there on top of the crowd . . . Blam!
. . . Vloom! A hard-hitting hat trick for the bombardier! Down
we go! A twelve-ton truck full of railroad workers smacks us

from behind! . . . Phew! We won that round! . . . Banged back
and forth, pulled out of the surging crowd! In the middle of
the mess everywhere we turn we get torn apart! . . . The
ambulance loses its front wheels! . . . The crowd swells and
scatters us like wreckage! . . . Now it's the turn of a baby
carriage which is carried away over our heads! . . . A small
soldier reclines inside! his leg hanging over the side in tatters
. . . Nifty . . . He's a complete swine, this little dogface! He
makes dirty signs at us . . . We're really having fun with him!
We're all in the same boat together! . . . As the whirlpool comes
to a boil! . . . That bastard in the sky has it in for us . . . he's
back again . . . He stings us again swooping in on a tornado!
And there he comes again tobogganing at us, exploding, spurting out all his lightning . . . He's cutting our heads off, the
wild man! . . . the lousy bum! . . . He's whisking us off in his
stomach! Inside the bloody din! . . . He's climbing back to the
clouds, getting smaller and smaller! . . . He's turning around
up there, on the ceiling! a fly! . . .

Who's the corpse in the gutter? They're bumping and bang-
ing around in there against it, it's flabby! . . . There's a stomach
over there! wide open and the foot, with the leg twisted back,
folded in . . . That's one of Death's acrobats! . . . struck by
lightning right there!

Boom! Boom! There's no time to think things over! Two
enormous thuds . . . The big river getting pasted downstream!
. . . The smooth water laps up two giant bombs! . . . Which
produce two furious corollas! . . . Two marvelous volcano-water
flowers! . . . It all falls back again . . . cascades over the bridge
. . . We're flattened under the downpour, doused, rolled over,
smashed down again by the cyclone . . . vomited out again . . .
the mob grabs us, nabs us . . . and then the firing starts up once
more . . . The big guns are beating us up . . . The parapet's full
of explosions . . . They must be coming from the corners of the
tiny clouds just above the church! It's probably a reconnaissance
mission . . . More pilots aiming to kill us! . . . They don't give
a damn if it's men, cattle, or things! They're French or German!

... The situation is becoming critical ... my clothes feel damp and boiling hot ... The confusion is supreme! ... A mother in tears on the parapet is about to throw herself into the depths with her three little children! Seven Parisian transport workers hold her back, stand in her way ... brave men cool dedicated ... They finish their ham and head cheese first! ... Just let them try to touch her! she starts in shrieking with shouts so piercing, so dreadful they block out the rest of the noise! You can't help looking at her! ... a shell! ... Brraangg! ... that lands on the bridge! The main tower blows up, shatters! ... Hollows out a chasm in the roadway, a yawning gap ... a crater that sucks in everything! ... The people pour in, stuff the crevices! ... keel over from the acrid smoke ... in a hurricane of dust! ... We catch sight of a colonel, in the Zouaves I believe, who struggles in the cataract ... He goes down under the weight of the dead! ... tumbles right to the bottom ... "Vive la France!" he shouts at the end ... vanquished under the pile of corpses! ... There's others alive who grab onto the walls of the pit, they're in shreds because of the blast, they struggle wildly, fall back, they puke, they're done for ... They've been burned all over. A naked baby appears on the hood of a flaming truck. He's roasted, done to a turn ... "Good God! ... Shit! It ain't fair! ..." The father stands to the side in a sweat ... He says his piece ... Then he looks for something to drink! ... He grills me to find out if I've got anything ... Canteen? Canteen?

The concert's not over, another archangel's salting us, swooping full speed from the sky ... He wears us out with his onslaught ... We're so mashed together we can't budge ... The bridge rumbles ... quavers on its piers! ... and then click-clack! Rrrr! ... Rrrr! ... It's the music of big-time butchery! ... The sky rattles with rage against us! ... The water below ... now it's an abyss! ... Everything explodes! ...

It's true, the whole story I'm telling you ... There's still much more to it ... but my memory's out of breath! Too many people have walked over it ... like the bridge ... passed

through my memory . . . as they did through my life! Too many
people bawling about battle! And then the smoke again . . .
And I dived back under the car . . . I'm telling you the story
the way I remember it . . . Going down toward the lock it was
one big fantastic fun fair all the way to the Orleans ramp! . . .
They were dancing worse there than on the other one, a hundred thousand times worse than at Avignon! . . . in the forge
of God's thunder! . . . And boom! and zomp! and Holy Mary!
and dead and dead! in the Hurricane Dance Hall! . . . Hey! . . .
Hey! . . . doesn't matter! The world has even turned itself
upside down there, soft droopy old umbrella! It was drifting
with the cyclones! . . . Rough luck! . . . Whirr! And bang! . . .
Boom! . . . I saw it pass over the Grand Hotel! It was zipping
along nicely! I saw it glide . . . hover way up there . . . playing
in the clouds! . . . The bumbershoot and the main tower! They
were spinning in the squall . . . together! among the marauding,
purulent planes spurting machine-gun fire . . . Vraap! . . . Vra!
. . . Vraago! . . . Wha! . . . Wroong! . . . That's pretty close to
the way it sounds when a bomb goes off . . . the biggest kind!
. . . In the heart of a black and green volcano! . . . What a
burst of fire! . . . Another bomb that grazes us! . . . is going to
go off right in the water . . . Then the blast shakes us . . . Your
whole gut is wrenching you to death? . . . Your heart's in your
mouth! . . . thumping like a rabbit . . . What a disgrace, fright-
shit . . . crawling . . . under the caissons with three . . . four
. . . five legs in a tangle . . . Arms mixed up every which way
. . . smashed, sunk in the quivering mass! . . . in the mush of
terror-dung with men's shirts on fleeing in panic . . . Sprawling,
wallowing, gagging, you get hold of yourself as you're waved in
the air, pulled up by the roots, squashed, tossed to the back of
the crowd! Merry antics! There's a motor about to catch on
fire! . . . We climb up a mountain of wounded . . . They groan
heavily under our feet! . . . puke . . . We get all the breaks!
Somebody up there likes us! . . . We're coming out of it!
bewildered, smiling . . . Here's another one attacking us! He
dives on us like a death knell! He tears the clouds apart with

bullets! His tiny tongues of fire dart everywhere! . . . I see all
his flames pointed toward us . . . He's gray and black! . . . and
rotten from head to toe! . . . He's looking for us . . . He bursts
out of the sky like a slingshot pelting us with his unleashed
rage! . . . He bewitches us! . . . He damns us! . . . We throw
ourselves down on our knees . . . We beseech the Virgin Mary!
. . . with great fervent signs of the cross! . . . God the father . . .
The North Wind! The Asshole! . . . Mercy! that fails us in our
gurgling underpants . . . This is the downfall of the Spirits . . .
He doesn't stop firing at us volley after volley, that brute! hung
from the stars! . . . He flits here and there . . . rushes forward
. . . sways back and forth . . . He comes closer inside his cyclone
. . . Ffroo! . . . He's gliding along again! . . . He whirls over on
his back . . . with a silken rustle . . . We don't see him any
more . . . He's hexing us! . . . A sign of the cross! . . . and
three . . . four . . . five! . . . They don't stop the horrors!
. . . the assassin's atrocities! . . . You can't exorcise this demon!
. . . He's peppering us again from behind where the wind is!
. . . He's not leaving anything out, giving it all to us! . . . He's
really hit his stride . . . He's hailing on us . . . He's sending us
thunder . . . in mid-careen! . . . Here come the ricochets from
his massacre! . . . The rooftops are rattling . . . People begging
for mercy faint and fall down! . . . The mob topples over! . . .
The convoy collapses in a heap . . . The parapet breaks in half!
. . . The swarm of trucks shakes . . . quakes . . . somersaults
into the waves! . . . Well here I am spared once more! . . . I
got out of a nasty spot! . . . For twenty-two years it's been like
that! . . . It can't go on like this forever! . . . I lean up against
the car and steady myself next to Lisette, a girlfriend who
doesn't scare . . . between the wheels of the ambulance . . . from
there you can see the parade! . . . really all of it! and how it's
capsizing in all directions . . . You can also see Largot the
barber, he's been with us all the way from Bezons, he's been
following us with his bike . . . He's been drunk since we left
Juvisy; he wanted to kill a German, but he stopped talking
about it after Étampes . . . There he is against the parapet . . .

He's hugging an old woman . . . He kisses her every time there's
an explosion . . . while the motors roar . . . An old lady whose
hair is all white . . . in ringlets, braids, and curlpapers . . . She's
bleeding bright crimson from every part of her head . . . Largot
is tender toward her . . . He bends over her . . . He drinks her
blood . . . He's lost all sense of respect . . . but he's obstinate,
gluttonous . . .

"Mmm! . . . It's red wine!" he announces . . . "Mmm! It's
good!" . . . On top of everything else he laughs! . . . Not her!
. . . Grandma closes her eyes . . . Her head rocks back and forth
. . . She's cradled by the thunderclaps! . . . by the cloudbursts
that shake the rest of us! . . . Largot barks at me again . . .

"It's red wine! Hey, ambulance! . . . It's red wine! Hey!
Macadam! . . ."

That's what he calls me. Even though we're in the middle of
a disaster, his behavior upsets me . . . I don't like familiarity . . .
All those drunken carcasses around here have got me down . . .
I think I'm getting some pretty funny ideas myself . . . I'm not
drunk! . . . I never drink anything . . . It's my mind that's
making me wobble . . . jolted by what's happening! That's all!
by events that are too much for me! . . . And vroom! It's starting
up again lovelier than ever! . . .

Brutal, awful uproar is back again! . . . fantastic fireworks
three bombs together, a bouquet! . . . enough to shatter heaven
and earth! . . . shake up the elements until you can't recognize
them any more! . . . unhook the top of your head! . . . and then
your mind and your eyeballs! and your lungs until you're all
banged up inside, transpierced with horrible violence! . . . run
through with a dagger! . . . nailed to the door like a screech owl
. . . and that backfiring! . . . a thousand motors starting again
. . . assaulting the ramp! . . . ramming! . . . lunging! . . .
thundering mob! . . . and they squeal as they're trampled! flayed
alive by the lunatic line of vehicles . . . knocked about under
the wagons! . . . and the caterpillar with a hundred and twenty
thousand pulverating teeth! . . . gnawing the noise! . . . plowing
up the misery! under the three hundred thousand chains of its

belly that's stuffed with swinging steel . . . with spinning rings
for guts . . . and besides it squints at you from its crown . . .
with its whole big cannon-head ready to flatten you from the
distance! . . . From far off it catches sight of you lies in wait
for you! crazy you skittering down the road . . . wildly fleeing
the squalid pantomime of this freakish monstrosity! . . . Oh,
the tank, "The Dread Snapper" . . . Tell me a little about it!
Nostradamus-style! . . . how it's really impossible to survive this
disheartening din! . . . looking up at the syphmobiles, the oily
misery makers! . . . But the earth-shimmy is set to music . . .
there's no way to halt the dance! . . . This is the Divine
Thunder Ballroom! . . . And the daisy chain of a hundred
thousand dead, of a thousand birds squeaking, squealing in
flight, weaving the air . . .

And then comes another garland with soft accents and
muffled grenades . . . it's coming from the distance . . . out of
the hills . . . We sway to the echoes of the artillery . . . You
wouldn't think you could kick up your heels with your body
so weighed down by a saddle of cheap cold lead! . . . But you
get caught up in the rhythm again . . . the bottom of the bridge
chock-a-block with grenades stirs for you . . . You ought to play
your part too and beat your feet on the debris of men and
beasts . . . torn in quarters by the traffic . . . then shriveled to
the size of an egg with each burst of fright . . . Oh! A case of
rebellion arises amid all these stupefied gyrations . . . see how
Brigitte, the wife of District Attorney Sacagne, suddenly bounds
out of her car, breaks away from the anguished cries, picks up
her skirt with one good tug and jumps up on the parapet, from
there, towering above the mob, bawls angry words and insults
through all the torment.

                                        RAYMOND A. SOKOLOV

LOUIS ARAGON

August 1940

SONG FOR A BARREL ORGAN

The refugees the bombers stopped
Turned and came back in broad daylight
Touched in the head, so tired they dropped
    Turned and came back in broad daylight
    Under their loads the women bent
    The men were crazy with their plight

Under their loads the women bent
And children crying for lost toys
Looked without knowing what it meant
    And children crying for lost toys
    Opened their eyes too wide upon
    The shattered world of little boys
Opened their eyes too wide upon
The bakery at the corner burned
The crossroads with a Hotchkiss gun

    At the corner where the bakery burned
    Soldiers who count in an undertone
    And a colonel looking unconcerned
    The soldiers count in an undertone
    Their dead and wounded one by one
    From the schoolhouse comes a single groan
        The dead and wounded one by one
        The girls at home, what will they do?
        Oh, sweetheart, if I were not gone

SOURCE NOTE: Louis Aragon, "Complainte pour l'orgue de la nouvelle barbarie," *Le Crève-coeur* (Paris, Gallimard, 1941), pp. 46–49.

The girls at home, what will they do?
The men sleep with their photographs
The sky outlasts the swallows too
    The men sleep with their photographs
    On canvas stretchers head by head
    Each with a pictured girl who laughs
On canvas stretchers head by head
We'll take them away, the young men
Whose skin is gray, whose bellies red

    We'll take them away, the young men
    But who knows if it's worth our while
    Look, Sergeant, they'll be dead by then
And who knows if it's worth our while
Should they arrive at Saint-Omer
What will they find with every mile?
    Should they arrive at Saint-Omer
    The tanks have cut us from the sea
    They'll find the enemy is there

The tanks have cut us from the sea
We hear they've taken Abbeville
May all our sins forgiven be
    "We hear they've taken Abbeville"
    So said the gunners who passed by
    Seeing civilians at their heel
So said the gunners who passed by
Like painted ghosts they were so pale
The wild head and the starting eye

    Like painted ghosts they were so pale
    A fellow who came into view
    Laughed like a savage at their tale
A fellow who came into view
He was as dark as the mines
As dark as life itself in hue

He was as dark as the mines
This giant going home again
To Méricourt or Sallaumines
This giant going home again

Cried, "We return, no matter what
If it is bombs or only rain"
    Cried, "We return no matter what
    Better by far die where you are
    With one or two shots in the gut
Better by far die where you are
Than go into a strange country
Better a hundred times in war

    Die than go to a strange country.
    We're turning back, we're going home
    The heart full, the stomach empty
We're turning back, we're going home
All hope we lack and tears and arms
We found we're not allowed to roam
    All hope we lack and tears and arms
    Little they care in safety there
    Those people chased us with gendarmes

Little they care in safety there
They sent us back beneath the bombs
'You can't get by,' they told us. 'Bear
    Your lot. Go back beneath the bombs'
    We're going while as yet we live
    No need for us to dig our tombs
We're going while as yet we live
Still with our children, with our wives
Thanks to no one. No thanks we give"

Still with their children, with their wives
Saint Christophers of the hard road
They walked the way that cut like knives
Back to the flames, the burnt abode
Saint Christophers of the hard road
Giants outlined as they went by
  No staff in hand to help the load
  Giants outlined as they went by
Against the white rage of the sky.

SALLY WOOD

COMPLAINTE
POUR L'ORGUE DE LA NOUVELLE BARBARIE

Ceux qu'arrêtèrent les barrages
Sont revenus en plein midi
Morts de fatigue et fous de rages
        Sont revenus en plein midi
        Les femmes pliaient sous leur charge
        Les hommes semblaient des maudits
Les femmes pliaient sous leur charge
Et pleurant les jouets perdus
Leurs enfants ouvraient des yeux larges
        Et pleurant leurs jouets perdus
        Les enfants voyaient sans comprendre
        Leur horizon mal défendu
Les enfants voyaient sans comprendre
La mitrailleuse au carrefour
La grande épicerie en cendres
        La mitrailleuse au carrefour
        Les soldats parlaient à voix basse
        Un colonel dans une cour
Les soldats parlant à voix basse
Comptaient leurs blessés et leurs morts
A l'école dans une classe

   Comptaient leurs blessés et leurs morts
   Leurs promises que diront-elles
   O mon amie o mon remords
Leurs promises que diront-elles
Ils dorment avec leurs photos
Le ciel survit aux hirondelles
   Ils dorment avec leurs photos
   Sur les brancards de toile bise
   On les enterrera tantôt
Sur les brancards de toile bise
On emporte des jeunes gens
Le ventre rouge et la peau grise
   On emporte des jeunes gens
   Mais qui sait si c'est bien utile
   Ils vont mourir laissez Sergent
Mais qui sait si c'est bien utile
S'ils arrivent à Saint-Omer
Entre nous qu'y trouveront-ils
   S'ils arrivent à Saint-Omer
   Ils y trouveront l'ennemi
   Ses chars nous coupent de la mer
Ils y trouveront l'ennemi
On dit qu'ils ont pris Abbeville[1]
Que nos péchés nous soient remis
   On dit qu'ils ont pris Abbeville
   Ainsi parlaient des artilleurs
   Regardant passer les civils
Ainsi parlaient des artilleurs
Semblables à des ombres peintes
Les yeux ici la tête ailleurs
   Semblables à des ombres peintes
   Un passant qui soudain les vit
   Sauvagement rit de leurs plaintes
Un passant qui soudain les vit
Il était noir comme les mines
Il était noir comme la vie

Il était noir comme les mines
Ce géant qui rentrait chez lui
A Méricourt ou Sallaumines[2]
Ce géant qui rentrait chez lui
Leur cria Nous tant pis on rentre
Si c'est les obus ou la pluie
        Leur cria Nous tant pis on rentre
        Mieux vaut cent fois chez soi crever
        D'une ou deux balles dans le ventre
Mieux vaut cent fois chez soi crever
Que d'aller en terre étrangère
Mieux vaut la mort ou vous vivez
        Que d'aller en terre étrangère
        Nous revenons nous revenons
        Le coeur lourd la panse légère
Nous revenons nous revenons
Sans larmes sans espoir sans armes
Nous voulions partir mais non
        Sans larmes sans espoir sans armes
        Ceux qui vivent en paix là-bas
        Nous ont dépêché leurs gendarmes
Ceux qui vivent en paix là-bas
Nous out renvoyé sous les bombes
Nous ont dit On ne passe pas
        Nous ont renvoyé sous les bombes
        Eh bien nous revenons ici
        Pas besoin de creuser nos tombes
Eh bien nous revenons ici
Avec nos enfants et nos femmes
Pas besoin de dire merci
        Avec leurs enfants et leurs femmes
        Saints Christophes de grand chemin
        Sont partis du côté des flammes
Saints Christophes de grand chemin
Les géants qui se profilèrent
Sans même un bâton dans la main

Les géants qui se profilèrent
Sur le ciel blanc de colère

NOTES

1. *Saint-Omer, Abbeville*: towns near the north coast of France.
2. *Méricourt, Sallaumines*: towns in northern France in the
département of Pas-de-Calais.

SIMONE DE BEAUVOIR

1940

WAR JOURNAL

For four days I had been restless, unable to sit still. I had
convinced myself that Sartre[1] might well have returned to Paris
unexpectedly, and that in any case I should pick up some news
of him there. Besides, I wanted to see Paris under the Occupation, and I was getting bored. The Dutch family made up their
minds to go back, too, and said they'd give me a lift. Got up at
five o'clock, and made my farewells. I was upset at going,
agonized by the thought of the emptiness awaiting me in Paris,
but glad to be *doing* something. The Dutchman took an hour
to load the car. His calm, unhurried movements made me want
to murder him. He put a mattress on the roof and a pile of
cases in the back. His young wife stacked up a hoard of little
packages, not forgetting a jar of green beans left over from
dinner the night before, which she had no intention of letting
go to waste. On what remained of the rear seat went the
mother-in-law and me while the wife sat beside her husband:
both women wore hats and white satin blouses.

SOURCE NOTE: Simone de Beauvoir, "Journal de guerre," *La Force de l'âge*
(Paris, Gallimard, 1960), pp. 459–72.

All the roads were thick with traffic. Here and there I saw traces of a bombardment; along the way we passed an overturned tank, a truck, a German grave with a cross and the man's helmet on it, and any number of burned-out vehicles. When we reached La Flèche I found out that we had started with only 10 liters of gasoline: the Dutchman was relying on the Germans, who had promised to distribute gasoline all along the route. A few days earlier he could have had 25 liters, but he got tired of waiting in line, and had given up with only another half hour or so to wait. So at La Flèche he went off to the Kommandantur, which had been set up in a splendid riverside house. It was here that I first saw field-gray uniforms; the Germans in La Pouèze had all been wearing green. I took a turn around the town with the other two women: we bought a copy of *La Sarthe*[2] and read the conditions of the Armistice. I had already heard them over the air, and the only one I didn't know was that concerning the extradition of German refugees, which revolted me. I read the paragraph concerning prisoners with close attention, and it seemed certain to me that they would only hold those who were in Germany already. This conviction sustained me throughout the two days of my return journey, and made it possible for me to take some interest in it.

The Dutchman returned with the news that no one would be allowed more than 5 liters, and not before two o'clock anyway: it was now eleven. He decided to try for Le Mans, saying he "thought" he had enough gasoline to make it. About six miles short of our destination we were turned back: there was no gasoline in Le Mans, and three hundred cars had already formed a solid jam there. We had scarcely a drop left, and were really in the lurch; but we were lucky enough to try a farm, where there was a 5-liter can of reddish stuff that had been abandoned by the British.

At midday our car pulled up in Le Mans, between two large squares. In one of these stood the Kommandantur, and in the other the Préfecture. The entrance gates of the latter were still closed; about two hundred people were pressed up against them, clutching jugs, gasoline cans, or watering cans. Around the statue of some comically small public figure in a plumed hat (Levasseur,[3] I guess) a whole mass of cars had halted, not to mention some trucks loaded with mattresses and kitchenware. Refugees sat about, eating or dozing or just waiting for something to happen, very dirty and shabby-looking, surrounded by children and bundles, and grumbling away like mad. Someone said they'd been waiting eight days now, shuttled to and fro indefinitely between Préfecture and Kommandantur; there was also a rumor going about that Paris had no food supplies whatsoever. The Dutchman stood there in the midday sun and grinned in that idiotic way of his; he didn't want to stand in line at all, but his wife, with me supporting her, forced him to stay where he was. "Want eaties," she said, in a childish voice. She complained that the crowd smelled nasty, and made a paper hat to protect her husband's head. We were told that you first had to get a queue number; when you had this you could obtain a voucher; and once in possession of the voucher you could get some fuel—that is, on the day the gasoline arrived. At two thirty the iron gates were opened, and the crowd surged forward; but an official shooed everyone out again, telling them that at three o'clock a tanker was coming that held 10,000 liters, and there would be enough and to spare for everyone. Some people nevertheless stayed on, and obtained vouchers which entitled them to buy 5 liters from a nearby garage. The Dutchman, however, decided he was hungry. So we made our way to the main square, the atmosphere of which somewhat resembled a country fair, being dusty, overcrowded, and exposed to a killingly fierce sun. There were mobs of soldiers in field gray, numerous German cars, plus hundreds of trucks and other vehicles belonging to the refugees. All the cafés were packed with Germans. It was depressing to see them there, so well-groomed, cheerful, and courteous, while France was only represented by this miserable rabble. Military trucks, sound trucks, and motorcycles charged noisily around the island in the center of the square; a loudspeaker was blaring out some ear-splitting military march, and also a series of communiqués in French and German. It was absolutely hellish. Victory was written across every German face, while every French face proclaimed defeat aloud.

Nothing to eat in the cafés. We went back for our provisions and divided them among us. The Germans came and went, and saluted with much clicking of heels, and drank, and laughed. They also were very much on their best and most courteous behavior. When I dropped some small object one of them instantly picked it up for me. Then we sat down on the sidewalk beside our car, while the procession continued to and fro between Préfecture and Kommandantur, with people still clutching their empty watering cans. Some of them simply sat down on their gasoline cans and waited for a miracle, in the shape of that truck with its 10,000 liters of gasoline. An hour or two passed. Once again the Dutchman got tired of waiting in line and came back empty-handed. We found a small shop with a little bread and some pork for sale: the *pâtisseries* were crammed with young Germans, stuffing themselves on candy and ices. Further waiting. By eight o'clock the Dutchman had managed to get hold of 5 liters of gasoline. It was a relief to get clear of this baking caravanserai and be driving through open countryside. We found a farm, and slept in the hayloft.

The women woke up whining and complaining; the older one was having twinges in her sciatic nerve. "Those villainous Germans!" the younger one said, in that crappy voice of hers. "If we only had them in our power, we'd machine-gun every nasty little Boche in sight." Her husband started complaining because the straw had been pricking his knees. The farmer's wife sold us milk and eggs at a very reasonable price.

Once more we joined the procession of cars, wagons loaded with peasants and bales of hay, bicyclists, and the occasional footslogger. At La Ferté-Bernard there was a crowd of refugees who had got that far on German trucks, but had been put off and left just as night was drawing in. Now they were waiting for more trucks. Once again we saw empty watering cans and

heard the rumor that there would be "no gasoline today." I
was sick and tired of the whole business, and decided to get
home under my own steam. There was a train in the station
leaving for Paris, but it was reserved for railway employees who
were being repatriated, and though there were plenty of empty
compartments, no one else was allowed aboard. Orders were
that no travelers bound for Paris should be let on, only those
bound for Chartres, and even then you had to prove you were
domiciled there. Some people told me that they had been coming there every morning for the last few days, but it was never
any use. Paris was desperately short of food, they said, and this
was why refugees were not being repatriated. Yet despite this,
the papers and the radio exhorted them constantly to do so,
and German trucks gave them lifts home. In any case there was
no food at La Ferté either, and we were quite liable to sit there
till we starved to death. I walked back to the car in a dis-
heartened mood and sat down on the running board. Later I
tried to buy some food, but found nothing except a chunk of
coarse, oversalty bread which I swallowed with misery. No gasoline for three days at least, someone said. My heart sank into
my boots. I left my suitcase with the Dutch couple, determined
to get out of this place, no matter how.

It was nearly 110 miles to Paris. It's easy enough to say you'll
go on foot if you have to, but the thought of that distance on
a tarred road, with that sun blazing down on me, was decidedly
discouraging. So I went on sitting there on the sidewalk. I had
a thousand francs in my pocket, which was quite a lot—or
nothing at all; last night people had paid 1,500 francs for a
seat in a car, and today you couldn't get a seat at all, even at
that price. Two men had put on armbands and stood in the
middle of the road, stopping any car which looked as though
it had a little room left in it; but in reality they could never
squeeze another body in. Finally a German truck pulled up,
and I, together with two other women, made a dash for it. I
climbed aboard behind them, to find that the truck was going
as far as Mantes, only twenty-five miles short of Paris. This got

me well on the way to my objective. It was horribly hot under the tarpaulin roof: there was a crowd of people aboard, and a strong smell of gasoline. I was sitting near the back, on a suit-case, and shot up every time we went over a bump. To cap it all I was sitting facing the wrong way. Miserably I felt my stomach begin to rebel, and presently I brought up all the bread I had eaten. No one seemed so much as to notice this.

When the truck stopped I lay down on the embankment while the others were eating: a German tapped me on the shoulder and asked me if I would like some food. I said I wouldn't. Shortly afterward he woke me up, very politely. An old woman said that for the past two days the truck drivers had been showering cigarettes, food, and champagne on them. They were genuinely kind, she said; they seemed not to be obeying orders but rather possessed of a spontaneous urge to be helpful. Nogent-le-Rotrou looked as though it had been heavily damaged, Chartres seemed scarcely touched, and Dreux more or less intact too, though we passed a few shell holes along the road. We met large numbers of military trucks; the troops often shouted *"Heil!"* at us, and in one or two trucks they had all pinned the most gorgeous red roses to their gray uniforms. And still the long procession of refugees trailed on.

At Mantes I looked around, slightly bewildered, and finally approached a Red Cross car which seemed about to move off. I got in the back and found myself sitting between a really ultra-chic nurse—a certain Mademoiselle de Hérédia, and she didn't ever forget it, either—and some sort of senior Red Cross woman officer wearing glasses. In front we had another nurse, and a gentleman, whose name I've forgotten but who was driving. The women told me that all over France doctors had been among the first to flee, leaving the nurses at clinics and hospitals completely in the lurch. They described the fires that had raged around Paris, and the scene at Étampes, where two columns of jammed traffic had gone up in flames, and the great exodus, and the lack of proper first-aid, and the ridiculous inadequacy of the Civil Defense system; apparently the Ger-

mans split themselves laughing when they saw our slit trenches.
These women were rabidly anti-British. One of them said she
hadn't left her revolver out of her sight for three weeks now
because of French and English soldiers trying to commandeer
her car for a speedier getaway. We stopped for a while at
Saint-Germain; my head was splitting, and when I looked in
a glass I saw that my face was black with dust. We all drank
peppermint cordial, and around us the town was absolutely
dead. Not a sign of life from now onward, all the way to Paris.
I spotted some blown-up bridges across the Seine, and a little
farther on some bomb craters and ruined houses; and everywhere
that lunar silence reigned. On the Rue François Ier there was a
queue outside the Red Cross: people coming to get news of
prisoners. One or two people were waiting outside butcher
shops, too, but almost all other establishments were closed.
How empty the streets were! I had never expected to find such
a deserted wilderness.

On the Rue Vavin the landlady went into exclamations of
despair because she had thrown out all my belongings: I
couldn't have cared less. She gave me a letter from Sartre dated
June 9, still optimistic in tone. I cleaned myself up a bit and
decided to go and try to telephone from the post office. Spotted
my father sitting outside the Dumesnil, and had a sandwich
and a beer with him. There were a few Germans about, but one
was far less aware of them than in La Pouèze. My father told
me they were very polite, that as was to be expected Paris
now had German news bulletins only, that all foreign currency
had been frozen. He also expressed the opinion that POWs
were most unlikely to be released before the end of the war, and
that there were vast camps at Garches, Antony, etc., where they
were starving to death on a diet of "dead dog," as he put it.
Occupied France, he told me, had been "assimilated" into
Germany, and therefore they would all be held indefinitely.

The post office turned out to be closed. I went to see my
mother. When I left her, at eight thirty, she told me to hurry
because of the curfew. I don't think I have ever felt so utterly

depressed as I did during that walk back through the deserted
streets, under a stormy sky: my eyes were burning, my head on
fire, and the one thought in my mind was of Sartre, literally
and physically starving to death. The houses and shops and the
trees in the Luxembourg Gardens were all still standing; but
there were no men left, there never would be any men again,
and I had no idea why I myself so absurdly continued to survive. Went to bed in the grip of absolute despair.

                                                  June 30
     Will they or won't they come home? Stories go around
about soldiers turning up when they're least expected, dressed
in civilian clothes. To tell the truth I was still half expecting to
find Sartre waiting for me, all smiles, outside the Dôme; but no,
there's the same feeling of loneliness there as at La Pouèze,
only this time more hopeless. Still, there's one piece of slight
consolation in *Le Matin*, where they're asking if families
couldn't be allowed to communicate with their relatives in the
forces before the latter are demobilized. It now occurs to me
that perhaps the camps are holding our troops prior to releasing
them by stages. I can't give up hope.
     It's lovely weather. I resume my usual table at the Dôme,
close to the now almost deserted *terrasse*. There's a notice up
with information about the *plats du jour*, and I've seen shops
displaying magnificent fruit and good fresh ham; there's an
apparent air of prosperity abroad, very different from conditions
in Chartres or Le Mans. Almost no one about on the boulevard.
Two trucks full of young Germans in gray go past: this has
become so common a sight that now it hardly strikes me as
odd. Quite suddenly, and with my whole heart and soul, I find
myself believing the war will end, that there will be an "afterward." The proof of this is my purchase of a bottle of ink and
the notebook in which I'm writing an account of the past few
days. For three weeks now I have been in a sort of limbo: vast
public events brought their own individual, physiological agony,

but I wanted to become a *person* again, with a past and future
of my own. Perhaps here in Paris I shall achieve this aim. If
I can draw my salary, I shall stay put for a long while.

Paris is quite extraordinarily deserted, even more so than in
September. The weather is more or less the same, the air as
mild and calm as ever. Not many food stores are still open,
and those that are have queues outside them. We see a few
Germans around. But the real difference is of another sort. In
September something was *beginning*—something terrible perhaps, but nevertheless of all-absorbing interest. Now that's all
vanished, and the future stretches out before me in unremitting
stagnancy. I shall sit here and rot for years. Passy and Auteuil
are utterly dead; there's a smell of lime blossom and leafy
greenness about them that reminds me both of the coming
holidays and of time past. Even the concierges have packed up
and gone. Down the Boulevard de Grenelle I walk past the
former concentration camp for women. By the terms of the
Armistice all German refugees have to be returned to Germany.
No clause in the whole document fills me with greater horror.
I come back through the Latin Quarter and find it deserted.
But the cafés are open, and one or two people can be seen
sitting outside them. Hardly any Germans here.

I return to the Dôme. Now there are people around: a Swiss
sculptor, Hoggar's wife, a former beauty who wears odd golfing
plus fours and a funny little hood. And the Germans are in
evidence again: this strikes me as strange, but only in an abstract sort of way. They have dull faces, and look like tourists.
One isn't, as one was at Le Mans, conscious of their collective
power; and individually they are boring to look at. I observe
them but register nothing. Airplanes have been passing over the
city at rooftop level all day, with large black crosses painted on
their gleaming wings. Only three or four tarts out on the
terrasse, busy soliciting German clients—not without some
success.

. . .

July 1

Today the tarts have invaded the whole front part of the café—so much so, indeed, that it's like walking into a brothel. One of them's crying, and some of the others offer her consolation: "So he hasn't written—nobody's written; don't take on so." It's the same old story everywhere, in the Métro, on doorsteps, with women exchanging virtually identical lines: "Any news?" "No, he must be a prisoner." "When will the lists come out?" and so on. None of them, it now seems clear, will be released before peace is concluded; but still the stories keep circulating: "He got all the way to Paris before he was arrested. The Germans give them civilian clothes." So there is always the possibility of a miracle; and though it's as illusory and nerve-racking and irresistible as any lottery ticket, it provides every woman in Paris with one all-engrossing obsession. I used to think that this sort of uncertainty was quite unbearable, but even here patience can be acquired. In a week, perhaps, there will be some news, or a letter, or the lists will be published. So you prepare to wait for a week; time has little value.

Took a long walk through the suburbs to kill some time. People were coming back home. All the way I heard the same thing everywhere: "Just back from Montauban—if I'd known what things were like I'd never have gone!" A cyclist stopped by one group: "Your mother is back already!"—and then they all crowded around to give him the latest news about his mother and his house. Much milling around and greetings between neighbors. There are gardens full of roses and currant bushes, cornfields dappled with red poppies, and sweet-smelling clover along the embankments—all the elements of country living spread out around prim suburban villas. Certain of these carry a sign reading *"Maison habitée"* or, more often, *"Bewohnt."*[4] I thumb a lift back, get picked up by a small and ancient car, the driver of which was just making the return trip from Agen. He too was saying, "If only I'd known!" He'd driven nearly five hundred miles with his wife aboard, she having a fractured spine at the time. He tells me how frightful this was for both of them: "I can tell you, madame, you're a mature woman;"—here gesturing toward his private parts—"I feel it *there*, I feel it really badly!" The authorities in the nonoccupied *départements* were preventing people leaving, and some said we'd be arrested at Vierzon, but Vierzon came and went without our being stopped. Followed the Seine most of the way back. People swimming and boating in the Grand-Jatte: holiday atmosphere, though somewhat oppressive. When the car stopped close to a bridge a German soldier threw us a bar of chocolate from a truck. Some of them standing beside the road, chatting very cheerfully with a group of pretty girls. "There'll be plenty of little Germans on the way soon," the driver remarked to me. I've heard this phrase a dozen times, never with any hint of censure attached to it. "It's just human nature," said the driver. "You don't need to talk the same language for *that*." I haven't seen the symptoms of real hatred in anyone yet, only a wave of panicky fear among the country villagers, followed by a wide and wary eye when that first alarm had worn off.

I meet Lise again. She tried to get out of Paris by bicycle last Thursday, and found herself pedaling along beside a German car. Afterward she was held up in a long line of crawling trucks and told to turn back. She and her bicycle were both bundled into the back of a truck and given a ride. Now she wants to teach me to ride a bicycle.

My parents complain about the dearth of adequate food. Dinner consists of soup and macaroni: I haven't had a good square meal for days. Seems that Paris really is short of supplies. My father tells me of the menu offered by one big restaurant on the Place Gaillon: cucumber salad, 8 fr., cheese omelette, 12 fr., crab pilaf, 20 fr., noodles, 8 fr., strawberries, 18 fr. No other dishes. I think of Magny's dinners at Braibant's during the siege of Paris.[5]

July 2

A gray day with a chill in the air. Everywhere deserted. Just six people around the newsstand by the Métro station. I bought two papers. What a wasteland—sentimental pro-German propaganda—a "compassionate" tone, a mixture of sorrow, superiority, and brotherly regard for the wretched population of France. And promises: the railways will be running again, postal service will be resumed.

Telephoned Camille's house. Madame J. told me she and Zina left on foot, with rucksacks, since when nothing has been heard of them. Dullin[6] too has had some adventures: am going to see him tomorrow. Also phoned one of Bost's[7] sisters, who says he's been evacuated to Avignon, and his brother is a prisoner.

I went to the Sorbonne to find out about my salary. Was filling in some forms when a schools inspector pounced on me. "Teacher of philosophy?[8] Exactly what we need." He put a call through to Duruy, and I'm to report there tomorrow. Eight hours of work a week; it might be much worse.

July 3

Have had a bicycling lesson with Lise through the small quiet back streets around the Rue Vavin. Kept my balance on the seat right away. Have even learned to mount by myself and to turn corners. Start classes at Duruy.[9]

At 4:15 I go see Dullin at the Atelier. Find Montmartre depressingly dead. The concierge wouldn't let me in at first, saying that Monsieur Dullin was "not in a state to receive visitors"; but then she came back, visibly astonished, with the information that I was lucky—he was expecting me right away. I found him in his shirt sleeves, with an apron tied around him, surrounded by a mass of old papers and torn photographs, and looking rather haggard. He shook hands with me effusively, and said how worried he was about Camille. He had left on Tuesday to see old Madame J. at Ferrolles, and about the same time Camille and Zina were to have caught a train down from the Gare d'Orsay. They had arranged to meet in Tours, but Dullin had been unable to get there, and now had no idea of

Camille's whereabouts. Crécy was already completely evacuated by the time Madame J. climbed into his trap. They set off in the direction of the Loire, but got caught up in a flood of refugees and wandered around for thirteen days, sleeping in the trap, eating practically nothing, and on several occasions being machine-gunned from the air—all without ever managing to get across the river. He had also taken an old servant-woman with him, who proceeded to go crazy. She spent all one day wandering vaguely round in search of food, and finally vanished into a wood, saying she was looking for eggs. He never saw her again. Finally the Germans picked them up and made them turn back. He was very scared of being recognized by the Germans, and tried to pass himself off as a peasant. Once he passed a convoy of prisoners who greeted him by name: this caused him great annoyance.

July 5

The newspapers are quite unspeakable: it turns my stomach to read them and they put me in a black mood. Lise and I went to the Palais-Royal to check through the lists of prisoners. Found the place closed, with a fantastic queue outside, and in any case information is available only about camps in the Paris area. Anyway I know Sartre is a prisoner: the only thing I'm interested in is the date of his release. Afterward we had a drink in the Café de la Paix: full of extremely dandified German officers, and no one else there at all. Most depressing. Have moved into my grandmother's flat, she being at present with my parents. The postal services have been restored, and I've written some letters, but still feel a desperate sense of isolation.

July 6

Notice posted up in the Dôme saying the place is out of bounds to Germans: I wonder why? Anyway it's a relief not to have to look at those uniforms any longer.

I went to the Bibliothèque Nationale and took a reader's
ticket. I have embarked upon Hegel's *Phenomenology of Mind*;
at present can scarcely make head or tail of a word of it. Have
decided to work at Hegel every afternoon from two till five; it's
the most soothing occupation I can imagine.

I telephoned Dullin. When he reached Crécy he found there
had been widespread looting—by Frenchmen. Someone told
him Camille was in the Tours area, and he's determined to get
a lift down there in a truck.

After this year's events the thought of dying no longer seems
quite so frightful. Anyway I know only too well that all life is
nothing but a brief reprieve from death.

July 7
A bicycle ride around Paris with Lise. I passed a column
of armored cars, full of black-uniformed Germans, their heavy
berets blowing in the breeze: a fine yet depressing spectacle.
Back to the Bibliothèque Nationale, and read more Hegel. Still
find him extremely hard to understand. Have come across one
passage that would make a wonderful epigraph for my novel.[10]
Copied it out.

Potatoes are once more available, in unlimited quantities, in
Paris, and meat, and even butter. Meals are back to normal at
the Dôme; there's no feeling of scarcity at all. What I really
miss is the cinema, but they're only putting on quite impossible
films.

What with the clocks being set to German time, and a curfew at eleven o'clock, find myself cooped up in my room while
it's still quite light. Most peculiar. I stand outside on my
balcony for a long while, unable to believe my eyes.

July 11
A penciled note from Sartre, in an open envelope that's
been canceled twice—once by the postal authorities and once
by the Government of Paris. For a moment I don't recognize

the handwriting; then I stare uncomprehendingly at the letter itself, which looks as though it's been delivered by hand. He says he may, repeat *may*, be home before the end of the month; he asks for news of me (though I'm by no means sure a letter will reach him); he says he's not badly treated, and that's about all he's allowed to say. I have no real idea of *how* he is. This note is of unbelievable importance, yet its content is nil. All the same, I breathe a little easier now.

July 14

Paris in the rain: most depressing. Felt an overwhelming need to talk to someone, anyone, so phoned Dullin. To my amazement Camille answered: went over to see her at six o'clock. Found her wearing indoor clothes; a little puffy around the eyes, but otherwise flourishing. Dullin was there too, similarly dressed and all in black, very cheerful and expansive. Madame J. and Vandéric were also present. Vandéric had served with the Belgian Army: he told us they were sent up to the front line completely unarmed, and left there. Three days later they were told to move out again, still without having been issued any arms. Camille told me about her own exodus: on Tuesday she forwarded her luggage to Tours—it has almost certainly been lost, and there was a mass of manuscript material and notes in it—after which she and Zina set off together, each of them wearing a rucksack, and Camille herself also carrying the two dolls, Friedrich and Albrecht, in a suitcase. They reached Nevers in two days, by train. After that they tried to go on to Tours by truck; it was a tough job, but they managed it. Tours was deserted. The bridges were being mined, and air raids took place every night. Their rendezvous with Dullin was at the *poste restante*, and the post office was closed. Accordingly, they moved out into the country, where they found an engineless train that had been standing in a siding for days, and climbed aboard it. Everyone was very disturbed, expecting the Germans to arrive during the night. Camille and Zina finally sought refuge with the railroad-crossing attendant, who rented

them a room. There they stayed, dressed as peasant women and
bored stiff. Meanwhile the occupants of the train gradually
drifted away. One evening a colonel turned up and warned
them that there would be a "small artillery battle" next day,
and they should all take shelter. They accordingly went into a
cave, and when the "small battle" was over they returned home.
Camille passed herself off as the gatekeeper's sister-in-law, being
improbably convinced that the Germans had some dreadful fate
in store for all refugees. She contrived to send a letter off to
Dullin; and when Dullin learned about this letter, he dropped
all the parcels he was holding, and began to tremble so violently
that Madame J. thought he was on the point of passing out. It
all ended with Camille getting a lift back on a truck.

PETER GREEN

NOTES

1. *Sartre*: Jean-Paul Sartre was taken prisoner by the Germans
on June 21, 1940; he was released in the spring of 1941.
2. *La Sarthe*: local newspaper.
3. *Levasseur*: René Levasseur (1747–1834), deputy to the Con-
vention in 1792 and enthusiastic Montagnard politician.
4. *Bewohnt*: "occupied."
5. *Magny's dinners . . . siege of Paris*: between 1862 and c. 1875
men of letters and painters dined every two weeks at the Magny
restaurant in the Latin Quarter of Paris. Among them were
Flaubert, Gautier, Renan, Sainte-Beuve, Taine, Turgenev, and the
brothers Goncourt. The siege of Paris here referred to is that which
ended the Franco-Prussian War, 1870–1871.
6. *Dullin*: Charles Dullin (1885-1949), French actor and stage
designer who, after working with Copeau at the Vieux Colombier
Theater, founded in 1920 the Atelier Theater in the old Théâtre de
Montparnasse. He directed the first presentation of Sartre's *Les
Mouches* in 1943. Camille is his wife.
7. *Bost*: French journalist, friend of Sartre and Beauvoir.
8. *teacher of philosophy*: Simone de Beauvoir received her
Agrégation de philosophie in 1929. She taught philosophy on the
secondary-school level at Marseilles (1931–1932), Rouen (1933–
1937), and Paris (1938–1943).
9. *Duruy*: girls' *lycée* in Paris.
10. *my novel*: *L'Invitée* (1943); the epigraph from Hegel being,
"Every conscience desires the death of the other."

THE OCCUPATION:
GENERAL CONCERNS

WHEN THE CHAOS OF DEFEAT had subsided, certain basic preoccupations underlay the most uninvolved lives: the fate of the more than two million French prisoners of war touched almost all French families, as did also the increasingly stringent rationing, reaching almost famine proportions in certain zones. Coexistence with the all-pervasive occupiers in the Occupied Zone; the separations, hardships, and often divergent moods created by the demarcation line established by the Armistice; the dichotomy, fully exploited by the occupier, between the occupied north and the Vichy-governed south, which was to end on November 11, 1942, immediately after the United States' invasion of North Africa.

The prisoners of war were magnificent pawns in the hands of the Germans, who used them to great advantage in negociations with Vichy. They promised their liberation in return for French economic cooperation, and later for contingents of French workers sent to Germany for obligatory service there. Small token contingents of prisoners were in fact released, whether for reasons of health, as in Sartre's case, or, as in Brasillach's, because their prewar, fascist position designated them as potential allies for the Germans. But for most of the men, captivity was

162   DEFEAT AND BEYOND

to last for an interminable five years, until the end of hostilities. The prisoners were Brasillach's constant concern. Marked though it is by some of Brasillach's idiosyncrasies (the romantic cult of his past youth, of the camaraderie of adolescence), his attempt, after liberation, truthfully to plumb the peculiar nature of the experience is a valuable document. True, conditions in the camps varied immensely and eventually deteriorated. But Brasillach's account of his experience, brief though it was, not only gives a glimpse of the camps—albeit rosy, since he was an officer and a pro-German—but of the peculiar introversions and the physical and emotional attritions of camp life, an experience widely shared by young and vigorous men the world over.

Rationing began very early, in August 1940, in a desperate attempt to keep prices down and to assure an equitable distribution of food between the rich agricultural regions of France, the cities, and the least productive sections such as the Riviera. The defeat had taken a heavy toll of France's peasant population, some 80,000 killed, with 700,000 more in German prisoner-of-war camps. Herds abandoned during the panic of the exodus had been depleted; furthermore, the Germans regularly requisitioned considerable stocks of food for their own use as stipulated in the clauses of the Armistice. The well-known tedious round of food hunting began. As the lists of rationed goods lengthened, items like meat began to disappear and the bread became coarser and coarser. Tickets, pink, blue, or green, lettered according to population categories, varied the ration with the category. Rules, regulations, and counterregulations were all emitted with considerable zeal. Queues and endless searches for supplies became the lot of the housewife. Concurrently and inevitably a thriving black market developed—both in goods and in tickets—so vigorous that in October 1941 a death penalty was imposed on ticket counterfeiters. Food

became an obsession, the unscrupulous among the rich
bourgeoisie literally overstuffing themselves daily to the
detriment of those poorer than they, or more scrupulous,
who attempted to subsist on legal rations. Thriving doubly,
France's peasants and black marketeers piled up large
fortunes. No further comment need be made on Marcel
Aymé's sardonic short story, a proof that in their predicament people could still lucidly mock themselves. Black
humor with its realistic cynicism was one of the forms of
defense against despair and demoralization, a corrective to
the overly inflated moral tone of both officialdom and
propaganda from abroad.

Perhaps the most poignant picture of the insuperable
barrier raised between sensitive individuals by the roles of
occupier and occupied thrust upon them was given in
early 1942 by the well-known *Silence of the Sea,* the first
work published under the pseudonym Vercors by the
Éditions de Minuit, a clandestine press. The image of
the German officer Vercors presented was the image we
have glimpsed throughout the texts collected heretofore
from Montherlant to Simone de Beauvoir: the courteous,
humane, disciplined soldier of the first contacts. By 1943,
after the German defeats in Russia and North Africa, his
silhouette has changed. There is a strange mixture of
grudging compassion, contempt, disgust, and irritation in
Guéhenno's view of him as the end of the war approaches,
in spite of Guéhenno's efforts to assert his humanitarian
creed rather than his revulsion. The cohabitation of
occupier and occupied, even where as gentle and lucid a
man as Guéhenno was concerned, had proved to be
corrosive.

The same weary irritation is clearly present in Guéhenno's impatience with the easier climate of nonoccupied
France, sheltered from too brutal a confrontation with
reality and, in Guéhenno's eyes, emasculated and befuddled by the myth of Vichy. The collaborationist versus

the noncollaborationist; the exile versus the man facing
the situation on his native soil; the prisoners versus the
rest of the nation; the rich versus the poor; the inhabitants
of the northern zone versus the inhabitants of the southern:
fragmentation, not the unity proclaimed by Maurras, was
the reality the French people faced.

ROBERT BRASILLACH

May 1940–January 1945

REFLECTIONS OF A PRISONER

We like to ask a Frenchman who has been imprisoned in Germany what he has gained from his captivity. This experience, shared for various periods of time by almost two million men, must, we think, have taught him some lesson and contained something of extraordinary value for everybody. And yet men who distrust generalizations do not know what to reply to the first questions: an officer's idle life is different from that of a soldier who works; life in one camp is different from another; life in an *Arbeitskommando*[1] is not the same as life in the main prison. Thousands of differences spring to mind, thousands of contradictions which seem insoluble and inexplicable to those who have not been in prison camps. "You've come to ask me what I think of Germany?" one will say, "and never have I seen so few Germans as in those months." "You've come to know if we thought of the future," another will say, "and we only thought of the past." And a third man will say: "What did the past matter? We were only interested in the future that the past couldn't foretell." Yet there is a prisoner's truth which gradually emerges from the mists of memory, against the background of watchtowers and barbed-wire fences.

I am writing these lines in Paris, before the images of the camp have faded from the horizon. Will they ever fade? I'm sure it will take many months, even years. A summer has already gone by during which I returned to a way of life superficially closer to my former life. But will there ever be anything like my former life again? I don't think so.

I can make the gestures I used to make, or gestures more

SOURCE NOTE: Robert Brasillach, "Réflexions d'un prisonnier," *Journal d'un homme occupé* (Paris, Les Sept Couleurs, 1955), pp. 137–45.

like them than those I made last winter, behind the barbed
wire of Westphalia. I can read newspapers at sidewalk cafés
and, if I want to, go to the theater or the cinema—but I don't
go any more. I can see old friends and indulge in a myriad of
pleasures. Why not admit that everything now seems slightly
fictitious to me?

Does that mean that I feel nostalgic about those hours I
spent in Germany, hours from which I certainly gained something? For weeks and months the camp obsessed me. It is no
longer completely mine because time passes, that's inevitable.
In the daytime I still sometimes think of the red *Marschfeld*[2]
where men are still marching around under the eye of the
guards. I automatically think that it's time for the roll call,
time for the canteen to open. But that no longer matters.

Six months later the experience seems decisive enough for
me to realize that what does matter is the conviction that
captivity—like the trenches in the last war—leaves such a deep
scar in one's mind as to transform things for a long time.

On my return I was lucky enough to find almost everything
the way I left it: my family, my job, my friends. I could have
resumed my prewar life, which had simply been interrupted,
and on the surface I did so. But it all remains far, far away
from me. The tasks to which I devote most of my energy have
drifted away, a whole world seems to divide me from my former
friends, whom I remain as fond of as ever. Why? I can hardly
understand. If I had suffered intolerably in prison I might
understand better; but I did not suffer. No, the present, like
the past, is far away from me, that's all. I have abandoned all
that I valued.

But I cannot go on living in the memory of the camp, which
has now also disappeared for me. I have seen other friends of
mine, not just chance comrades who have returned, and they
have nothing to say to me. The best and the dearest friends,
once stripped of the uniform we used to wear, seem to lead a
life which is no longer my life. Captivity, like school, is a form
of promiscuity, but it is also a form of proximity. The uni-

formity of the setting allows discussions, friendships, and permanent contacts which may be a source of irritation or pleasure, but which do not normally occur in one's life. Life rids us of them after the age of eighteen. We suddenly find them again in our thirties, and when we leave them, it is like another farewell to our youth. My friends of yesterday, my friends in captivity, each in his own way, have drifed from me and left me to myself. Captivity separates me from my life before the war like a vast chasm, and from now on liberty separates me from captivity.

In the extraordinary world of today, to the sound of warring armies, the small fate of a single individual does not much matter. But that is all we have. And since nothing valid links me to a double past, dear to me but severed from me, I too must start afresh in the present. I sometimes feel almost happy, or at any rate curious to be alive among the few new friends whom I did not know before the war and who offer me some novelty. Strangers give me part of that strangeness, that availability, that youth which I felt in captivity. I cannot always attune myself to the others, whether they come from the camps or from my more distant past, even if we had shared the same experiences. Captivity is a rift.

If you have been as fond of your past as I was, this rift can only be painful. But it also has an advantage which mysteriously attunes itself to the new world born around us. We had already thought of this in the camp, and I used to stay so to my friends. "We shall never find our past again," we claimed, "and we shall never be able to transfer the camp into our future." So what remains if not novelty, the call of the open sea, the future? We may suffer when we leave what we loved. But when we have no alternative, when we find no stability in the various periods of our past, we must break adrift. Everything about us is new: we shall never see the Europe of Versailles,[3] let alone the Europe of 1914, its monarchies dying under gold and jewels, its democracies in top hats smiling at the races in the spring. But everything can also be new in ourselves: we can no more resume our previous lives than the men who returned from four years combat in 1918 could find the decrepit universe which had crumbled about them. A rift can mean rebirth: and if it were to mean that, captivity would have been beneficial.

If we remove all the superfluities, however important they may be, what is the essence of captivity, for every prisoner, whatever his background? It is to have isolated him from his past and all his natural ties, from his family, friendships, loves, home, job, and country. It is to have cut him off from all the groups which he chose—even from his regiment and from the war, for the troops were usually split up. It is to have formed a man alone in a crowd. Although you are never physically alone, captivity is solitude. When the prisoner goes home he must seek advice from this solitude, and to a similar solitude he returns.

When Robinson Crusoe was cast on his desert island he was alone, he was naked, and he knew nothing. He gradually built himself a house from the sticks and stones which he gathered at random: he became that expert odd-job man whom children are taught to admire; he made friends with the plants and the animals, and one day, he made friends with Friday, before he met the other shipwrecked Europeans.

Crusoe's story is the story of a prisoner. Alone and abandoned, the prisoner gradually conquers his universe of sticks and stones; he gradually finds his Man Friday and makes friends with him. In prison, comradeship compensates for solitude and one wants to make it the image of the future. One needs a very good memory and a very bad mind to remember that once he left his island Crusoe started traveling feverishly, that Friday was nothing but a companion who disappeared at the turn of a page, and that Crusoe's former life no longer counted after the rift which captivity in the solitude of the island had made in his days. All he retained was a taste for the new world, which is probably the only kind of taste left to us in the future.

What the prisoners are particularly aware of is time elapsing *outside them*. Men usually age with time, they age with their wives, and they age while their children grow up. The prisoners know that far away from them their wives and children are growing older, but they have remained on that warm spring day when they were captured, and one day they suddenly find themselves back in an older universe in which they have had no share. So, in this lull in time, they think, they plan for the future so as to make up for it on the double when they return and catch up with the time that has fled from them. This is why their solitude and experiences are not useless: they have constructed something invisible deep inside themselves.

Returning prisoners always talk of the comradeship of the camp in a way which often surprises people who have not shared their experiences. For the Frenchmen of this war there was nothing like that comradeship in combat of 1914: it has been replaced by comradeship in captivity, with fewer risks, of course, more like school comradeship and therefore more *rejuvenating*. It did not exist everywhere, or for everybody. Nothing is worse than the metaphysic and myth of comradeship at all costs. Like all qualities comradeship is not as common as optimists maintain. But when you find it, it has a flavor which nothing can replace. Even if the future separates us from them, strips them of their value and their charm, the friends of our prison days remain in our minds like the rare friends of youth, of a free and wonderful time on the slopes of adolescence, under the sun on the hills and beaches. We knew them in mourning, monotony, and empty days, and they gave us their support and fraternity. With them we shared, materially and morally, all we had. We created a community and we sometimes vaguely hoped that this community could later become the model of a national or universal community. If all that remains on our return is the memory of these days, that at least will be productive and worthwhile.

In double isolation we watched our own country in our hearts and the country where we were imprisoned in our minds. As a prisoner I did not have the impression that I was any less informed about the world than my free countrymen. I was often better informed, I saw when I came home. In our letters, newspapers, and books we saw a history of France and the world being written day by day. It did not lack precision. Even Germany appeared to us only from behind the bars of her newspapers and what we felt of her immense presence around us. At night I talked a couple of times to a German interpreter, about his country, his youth, the party struggles, and the future of Europe—strange conversations under the grayish lamps of our room, between a soldier of the Reich and some French officers, trying to find in their common concerns ways of understanding and fulfilling each other. I remember it clearly, like the symbol of many future conversations, like an attempt to understand and learn, paradoxically performed in this forced retreat. All that was human and material seemed to have disappeared, leaving only a purified figure, a colorless design with a barely perceptible trace of the future. So it happens that men isolate themselves, shut themselves up with their books, with a companion, or alone, before entering into action, and in those mysterious hours they gather their strength for the future. But when they do enter into action, they forget their retreat.

A wise man gets something out of whatever may befall him. I feel sorry for the prisoner who gains nothing from his captivity other than moral suffering and boredom, no secret nourishment for the future, no deep source within himself. But this enormous rift which isolation left between Robinson Crusoe and his past is, if he can accept it, the greatest and bitterest benefit that captivity can provide. The prisoner must not vainly try to relive the joys of yesterday, he must not try to revive that comradeship which cannot survive without those flat fields on the horizon, seen through barbed wire. But he should try to produce the material necessary for constructing a ..new joy within himself and a new world around him after this period of reflection and contemplation. If he cannot do this, I have not got the courage to cast the first stone, because I know well the weight which the memory of those weeks can impose. At night, last year, every single night, I dreamed of my return, and now, in the dark, I still sometimes wake up and imagine that unforgettable setting, or hear an imaginary footstep in the long gray corridor. But all that must be forgotten, and each prisoner must take a new footing, like the swimmer who leaves the sea.

When you are a prisoner it is difficult to *understand* your captivity. When you are free everything gets deformed. And yet nothing will be done, all will be lost if the understanding of captivity has not been mastered by him who has experienced it. To understand your captivity is not to be hypnotized by it, in a pale magnetic slumber—it is to search for the most valid motives for your own *liberation*.

ALASTAIR HAMILTON

NOTES

1. *Arbeitskommando*: labor brigade.
2. *Marschfeld*: parade grounds.
3. *Europe of Versailles*: i.e., of the Treaty of Versailles following the First World War (1919).

MARCEL AYMÉ

1943

THE LIFE RATION

A Wartime Fable

(Extracts from the diary of Jules Flegmon)

10th February. An absurd rumor about new restrictions is
going round the neighborhood. In order to avoid the risk of
serious shortages, and to ensure a high margin of productivity,
the Government, so people are saying, intends to abolish all
unproductive and useless elements in the population—old and
retired people, *rentiers*, unemployables, and so forth. Basically,
I must say, I think it would not be a bad idea. I ran into
Roquenton this morning, that preposterous, impetuous old
party, seventy if he's a day, who married a young woman of
twenty-four last year. He was almost speechless with fury.
"What has age got to do with it," he shouted, "if I make my
dear girl happy?" I told him, in well-chosen words, that he
should be proud to sacrifice himself for the good of the community.

12th February. No smoke without fire. Lunched today with
my old friend Maleffroi, a commissioner on the Préfecture
de la Seine. I loosened him up with a bottle of claret and then
pumped him adroitly. Of course there's no question of actually
putting useless mouths to death. The idea is simply to ration
their living time. They're to be entitled to so many days of

SOURCE NOTE: Marcel Aymé, "La Carte," *Le Passe-muraille* (Paris,
Gallimard, 1943), pp. 71–95.

existence a month, Maleffroi explained, according to their
degree of uselessness. It seems that appropriate ration cards—
life cards as they are to be called—have already been printed.
I find the scheme both sensible and conceived in a spirit of
poetic justice, and I seem to remember saying some quite witty
things about it. Maleffroi, affected no doubt by the excellent
wine, gazed at me with eyes brimming with friendship.

13th February. An infamy! An abomination! A monstrous denial
of justice! The new decree is published in this morning's papers,
and lo and behold, among the elements whose consumption is
not counterbalanced by any material productivity of goods and
services are included artists and writers! I could at a pinch
understand the measure being applied to painters, sculptors,
and musicians—but writers! There is an illogic in this, a disregard of basic values, that will remain an eternal blot on our
civilization. Clearly the usefulness of writers and least of all my
own writings—I say it in all modesty—is not something that
can be measured or weighed or demonstrated by any uncouth
yardstick such as the bureaucratic mind may be expected to
devise. So, then, I am in future to be entitled to only fifteen
days of existence a month!

16th February. Since the new decree comes into force on the
1st March, and registration must be completed by the 18th of
this month, the people condemned by their present position in
society to.a part-time existence are all rushing frantically round
in search of any kind of employment which will enable them
to be classified as whole-time livers. But the Government, with
diabolical foresight, has issued an order forbidding any changes
of address before the 25th.
    I had the notion of telephoning Maleffroi to ask him if he
could find me a job as a house porter or museum attendant or
something of the sort within the next forty-eight hours. I was

too late. He had just given away the last office boy's job at his
disposal.

"Why on earth did you wait so long before getting in touch
with me?"

"But how was I to know that I should be affected? You
never told me when we lunched together that—"

"Indeed I did. I said quite definitely that the decree would
embrace all useless sections of the population."

17th February. My concierge evidently considers me half dead
already, a ghost, a shade occasionally emerging from the nether
regions, for this morning she forgot to bring me my mail. I gave
her a severe telling-off when I went downstairs. "It is for the
sake of pampering idlers of your sort," I said, "that many of the
cream of the nation are being compelled to sacrifice a part of
their existence." A profoundly true observation. The more I
think about it, the more monstrously unjust this decree seems
to me to be.

Met Roquenton and his young wife. Really I felt sorry for
him. He is only getting six days of life a month; and what is
even worse, Madame Roquenton, because of her youth, is getting fifteen. The thought of this interlude has plunged the poor
old boy in despair. The lady seems more philosophical about it.

During the day I met several people who are unaffected by
the decree. Their lack of understanding, and their indifference
to the sacrifices of others, fill me with disgust. They treat this
abomination as though it were the most natural thing in the
world, and even seem to be delighted by it. The egotism of
the human race is beyond belief.

18th February. Queued for three hours at the Mairie of the
Eighteenth Arrondissement to get my life card. There were
about two thousand of us in double file—pitiful victims of the
insatiable greed of the working class. And this was only a first

example. From what I could see the proportion of elderly people was only about half. There were pretty young women with saddened faces who seemed to be sighing, "I don't want to die yet." The professionals of love were numerous. The decree has hit them very hard in limiting their life ration to seven days a month. One of them complained in my hearing that the effect would condemn her to remain a prostitute for the rest of her life. A week was not long enough for a man to grow attached to a girl, she said. I am not so sure of that. Among those in the queue I noticed (not unmoved; and indeed, I must confess, with a secret satisfaction) a good many of my Montmartre friends, writers, and painters—Céline, Gen Paul, Daragnès, Fauchois, Soupault, Tintin, D'Esparbès and others.[1] Céline was in one of his black moods. He said that the whole thing was just another Jewish conspiracy, but in this I think his ill-temper has led him astray. The decree specifically states that all Jews, irrespective of age, sex, or calling, are to be allowed only one half-day of life a month. In general the crowd was bad-tempered and rowdy. The large number of police keeping order treated us with the utmost contempt, evidently regarding us as no more than the dregs of humanity. More than one of us got booted on the bottom for complaining about the time we were kept waiting. I endured this humiliation with silent dignity, but I looked hard at one particular sergeant while my whole being cried out in protest. It is we who today are the damned upon earth.

At last I got my life card, a book of coupons each of which entitles the holder to twenty-four hours of existence. The coupons are a delicate periwinkle blue, so soft and tender that it brought tears to my eyes.

24th February. I wrote to the competent authority a week ago asking for my case to be reconsidered. I have been granted a supplementary life ration of twenty-four hours. Better than nothing.

5th March. For ten days I have been living a life of feverish activity which has caused me to neglect my diary. In order to waste nothing of my curtailed existence I have practically gone without sleep. During the past four days I have written as much as I would normally do in three weeks, yet my style has lost none of its brilliance nor my thinking any of its profundity. I have grasped at every pleasure with an equal frenzy. I would like to possess every pretty woman I set eyes on, if the thing were possible. Partly from a desire to make the most of every moment, but perhaps also in a spirit of revenge, I make a point of eating two large black-market meals every day. Today for lunch I had three dozen oysters, two poached eggs, a wing of goose, a plate of roast beef, vegetables, salad, cheese, a sweet with chocolate sauce, a grapefruit, and three tangerines. Although I did not for a moment forget my melancholy fate, I drank my coffee at the end with a certain feeling of contentment. Shall I end by becoming a complete stoic? Just after leaving the restaurant I ran into the Roquentons. It is poor Roquenton's last day for March. Tonight at midnight, having used his last coupon, he will lapse into a state of nonbeing for twenty-five days.

7th March. Called upon young Madame Roquenton, a grass widow since midnight. She received me with a graciousness which her unhappy state made even more charming. We talked of all kinds of things, including her husband. She told me how he had vanished into nothingness. They were both in bed. At a minute to midnight Roquenton took her hand and gave her his last instructions. As the hour struck she felt his hand melt, so to speak, in hers. There was no longer anything at her side but an empty pair of pajamas and a set of false teeth on the pillow. We were both deeply moved by her recital, and when I saw the tears brimming in Lucette's eyes I took her in my arms.

                                 . . .

12th March. Went yesterday evening to have a drink at the flat
of Perruque, the Academician. In order to preserve the myth
that those artistic throwouts are "immortal" the Government
has put them all in the whole-time life category. Perruque's
complacency and hypocrisy were really revolting. There were
about fifteen of us there, all rationed and using up our last
coupons for the month. Perruque was the only whole-lifer. He
patronized us as though we were hospital cases, full of sympathy, but with a malicious twinkle in his eye, and overflowing
with promises to look after our interests in our absence. The
old mountebank was so obviously delighted at being one up on
us that it was all I could do to stop myself telling him what I
think of him and the dreary, turgid rubbish he puts on paper.
I'd have done it too, if I didn't hope to succeed him one of
these days in the Academy.

13th March. Lunched with the Dumonts. They quarreled as
usual. Dumont cried: "My God, if only I could use my life
coupons in the second half of the month, so as not to be alive
at the same time as you!" He obviously meant it, and Madame
Dumont wept.

16th March. Lucette Roquenton vanished into limbo last night.
She was very frightened and so I thought I had better be there
to comfort her. I arrived at about half past nine to find her
already in bed. To spare her the anguish of the last moments I
managed to put the bedside clock back a quarter of an hour.
Five minutes before the plunge she burst into tears, but thinking that she still had twenty minutes to go she recovered and
insisted on powdering her nose, which I thought rather touching. As the moment approached I did not take my eyes off her.
She was laughing at something I had said, and suddenly the
laugh was cut short and she vanished beneath my gaze as
though it were a conjuring trick. I touched the warm place

where her body had lain and was gripped by the silence that overtakes us in the presence of death. It was very painful. Even now, as I write these lines by the light of morning, I still feel acutely distressed. From the moment I awoke I have been counting the hours that remain to me. My turn comes at midnight . . .

I add these lines with a quarter of an hour to go. I have got into bed, and I wish my temporary death to find me pen in hand, exercising my profession. This seems to me a suitably courageous attitude. It is the kind of gallantry I prefer, elegant and unostentatious. After all, how do I know whether this death is really temporary, or whether it will be simply death? The promise of resurrection does not convince me. I find myself wondering whether, after all, it is merely an ingenious official device for concealing the truth. If none of the rationed returns to life in a fortnight's time, who will stand up for their rights? Not their heirs, of that we can be certain! And what good would it do if they did stand up for them? The thought has suddenly occurred to me that the official date of our resurrection is the first of next month—April Fool's Day! I am terrified—I believe I am go . . .

1st April. I'm alive! Not an April fool after all! And I had no sense whatever of the passing of time. I woke up in bed in the same state of panic that overtook me just before my death. My diary was lying on the coverlet, but when I tried to finish the sentence I had been writing I found that my fountain pen was dry. When I saw that the clock had stopped at ten past four, and my watch at about the same time, I began to realize what had happened. I rang up Maleffroi to ask him the date. He was not best pleased at being woken up in the middle of the night and my delight at being restored to life left him tolerably unmoved. But I had to talk to someone.

"You see," I said, "the distinction between spatial time and experienced time is not merely a metaphysical fantasy. I am the living proof. The fact is, there's no such thing as absolute time."

"Possibly. But that doesn't alter the fact that it's half past twelve. If you don't mind—"

"It's a very comforting thought. The fortnight I haven't lived is not necessarily lost to me. I expect to make it up later on."

"Well, good luck to you," said Maleffroi, "and good night."

When I went out at about nine o'clock this morning I had a sense of abrupt change. The season had made a leap forward. The trees were breaking into leaf, the air was fresher, the streets had a new look. The idea that the world had been able to get on without me for a fortnight caused me some dismay and still does. I met a number of people also resuscitated during the night, and we exchanged notes. Old Madame Bordier button-holed me for twenty minutes while she told me how she had lived through fifteen days of ecstasy detached from her body. But Bouchardon was the funniest of all. He went off in his sleep on the night of the fifteenth, and woke up this morning convinced that he had somehow been overlooked and that nothing had happened. When I met him he was on his way to attend a wedding which must have been celebrated a fortnight ago. I did not undeceive him.

2nd April. Went to tea with the Roquentons. The old man was in high spirits. Since he had no sensation of the passing of time, the events which occurred during his absence have no reality for him; and he is quite incapable of imagining that his wife could have been unfaithful during the nine days she was left alone. Well, so much the better. Lucette kept gazing at me with languishing eyes. I dislike these furtive demonstrations behind other people's backs.

3rd April. I can't get over my fury. While I was dead Perruque contrived to have the opening of the Mérimée Museum postponed till the 18th. As the old scoundrel knows perfectly well, I was to have delivered an important speech which might have done a great deal to assist my election to the Academy. But by the 18th I shall be back in limbo.

7th April. Roquenton has gone off again, this time with perfect good humor. He invited me to dinner, and when midnight struck we were drinking champagne in the salon. Roquenton was actually standing up, and suddenly we saw his clothes collapse in a heap on the floor. The effect was comical, I must say, but I thought Lucette's wild burst of gaiety somewhat excessive.

12th April. Today I received a most harrowing visit from a man of about forty, extremely poor, nervous, and obviously ill. He was a workman with a wife and three children, and he wanted to sell me some of his life coupons to buy food for his family. His wife was a semi-invalid, he told me, and he himself was not well enough at present to do a full-time job. His earnings and sickness allowance were barely enough to keep them above the starvation line. It was a pathetic case, but the idea of buying his coupons filled me with embarrassment. It made me feel like an ogre, a fabulous monster exacting a tribute of human flesh. I said I couldn't accept them and offered him a sum of money for nothing; but this touched his pride, and he refused to take it except in exchange for one or more days of existence. In the end, since I could not persuade him, I bought one coupon, and after he had left I put it away in a drawer, resolved not to use it. To take a day of another man's life seems to me odious.

14th April. Met Maleffroi in the Métro. He told me that the system of life rationing is beginning to give results. Since the well-to-do are particularly hard hit, business is a great deal less brisk on the black market and prices are coming down in consequence. They are hoping, in high places, that the black market will finally disappear altogether. It seems that the people as a whole are getting more food, and Maleffroi remarked that the Parisians are beginning to look healthier, a statement which I received with mixed feelings.

"And what is no less remarkable," said Maleffroi, "is the tranquil and relaxed atmosphere in which we live when the life-rationed people are out of the way. It makes one realize what a danger the rich are to society, to say nothing of the unemployed, the intellectuals, and the tarts. They do nothing but stir up trouble, agitation, disorder, and a yearning for the impossible."

15th April. Refused an invitation to the Cardonnets' "passing-out" party. It is becoming fashionable, among the jazz set, to hold parties on the night of their temporary death, and I am told that these often develop into orgies. Disgusting.

16th April. I go off this evening. No alarm.

1st May. On coming to life again at midnight I had a slight shock. My provisional death (this is the expression in current use) came upon me while I was dressed and on my feet, and I returned to find myself naked with my clothes on the floor. The same thing happened to the painter, Roudot, who was giving a party to a number of friends of both sexes, all due to pass out at midnight. The effect must have been rather funny. This month of May promises to be so beautiful that I hate having to miss the second half.

5th May. During my last life spell I had the feeling that some antagonism was springing up between the whole-time lifers and the rest of us. This seems to have grown more acute, and certainly no one can now deny that it exists. It is a matter of jealousy, which, surprisingly, appears to be mutual. That the people who are rationed should be jealous and even deeply resentful of the privileged class is perfectly understandable. But as I am beginning to realize there is jealousy on the other side as well. The whole-time lifers secretly envy the rest of us as the initiates of a mystery, a flight into the unknown, in which they have no share; and the feeling is heightened by the fact that this barrier of limbo is something which is far more obvious to them than to us, since we have no awareness of it. To them our relative death seems like a holiday, while they are compelled to keep their noses to the grindstone. The general effect is to make them gloomy and bad-tempered, whereas we on the other hand, always conscious of the swift passing of time and the need to make the most of what is allowed us, are altogether better humored. I thought of this today while I was lunching with Maleffroi. Disillusioned and sardonic, and at moments positively aggressive, he went out of his way to sympathize with me in my hard fate and to stress his own good fortune—obviously in an attempt to convince himself. He talked as one might do to a friend belonging to an enemy country.

8th May. Today a very questionable-looking individual knocked at the door and offered to sell me life coupons at 200 francs each. He had fifty to dispose of. I kicked him out, and only the fact that he was rather large saved him from being kicked downstairs.

10th May. Roquenton went off four days ago, for the third time. I haven't seen Lucette since he went. I gather she has taken up with some nondescript blond young man. I can imagine the type—some young jazz-loving oaf. Anyway I couldn't care less. The silly little creature never had any sense or good taste, a thing I realized from the first.

. . .

12th May. The black market in life coupons is growing on an immense scale. The spivs go to the poorer working people and talk them into selling a few days of life so as to be able to buy extra food for their families. Old men with nothing but workers' pensions and the wives of prisoners of war are also easy game. The present rate varies between 200 francs and 250. I doubt if it will go much higher, because the number of wealthy or even well-off people is small compared with the number of the poor. Apart from which, a great many people refuse to treat human life as a thing to be bought and sold like merchandise. I shall not compromise with my conscience.

14th May. Madame Dumont has lost her life card. It's a most awkward thing to happen because to get a new one takes about two months. She accuses her husband of having hidden it so as to get rid of her. I don't think he would do anything so disgraceful. The spring has never been so beautiful as it is this year. I regret having to die the day after tomorrow.

16th May. Dined last night at Baroness Klim's. The only whole-time lifer among the guests was Monseigneur Delabonne. There was talk of the black market in life coupons, and I said that I considered it an infamous business. I was completely sincere, but perhaps I also hoped to make a good impression on the Bishop, who has great influence in the elections to the Academy. I felt a certain chilliness in the gathering, and Monseigneur smiled indulgently at me as though I were a youthful priest carried away by apostolic zeal. The subject was dropped, but after dinner the Baroness broached it again to me in confidence. She told me she thought I was mistaken, and that my immense and widely recognized talent as a writer, the depth of my views and the important part I had to play, imposed on me the moral obligation to prolong an active life devoted to the enrichment of thought and the service of the nation. Seeing me much moved, she invoked the support of the assembled company. They were unanimous in reproaching me with high-minded but sentimental scruples which run counter to the true spirit of the Decree. Monseigneur, being asked his opinion, refused to commit himself but replied with a far-reaching parable. A hard-working and capable farmer is short of land, whereas his neighbors let theirs go to waste. So he buys some of their fields and plows and sows and reaps rich harvests for the benefit of everyone.

I allowed the brilliant gathering to talk me round, and this morning was still sufficiently convinced to buy five additional life coupons. I intend to go into the country and justify this supplementary spell of life by working like mad on my book.

20th May. Have been in Normandy for the last four days. Except for an occasional stroll I have done nothing but work. The local farming population scarcely knows of the existence of life cards. Even the old people get twenty-five days life a month. I asked an elderly peasant to sell me a coupon, since I need an extra day to finish a chapter, and I said that the price in Paris is 200 francs. He positively laughed at me. "Only two hundred! Do you know what we get for pork on the hoof?" So there was no deal. I'm catching the train to Paris tomorrow afternoon so as to be able to die in comfort in my own home.

3rd June. What a business! The train was late and my provisional death overtook me a few minutes before we reached Paris. I came to life again in the same compartment, but the train was on a railway siding in Nantes. Of course I was stark naked. The embarrassment and trouble it caused me have left me feeling quite ill. Fortunately I had been traveling with an acquaintance who had my clothes sent to my flat.

4th June. Ran into Melina Badin, the actress, who told me a most preposterous story. It seems that some of her admirers

clubbed together to give her an extra spell of life, with the
result that on the 15th May last she found herself with twenty-
one coupons in hand. And she claims that she used the lot,
meaning that last month she lived thirty-six days. I thought
it well to adopt a frivolous attitude.

"May was a truly gallant month," I said, "since it prolonged
itself solely for your sake."

Melina seemed genuinely put out by my refusal to believe
her. I think she must have gone off her head.

11th June. Dramatic events have taken place at the Roquentons'. I only heard about it this afternoon. On the fifteenth of
last month Lucette was visited by her blond-haired jazz fan and
at midnight they went into limbo together. When they came
back to life they were still in bed but no longer alone. There
was Roquenton, also resuscitated, between the two of them!
Lucette and the young man pretended not to know one
another, but it seems that Roquenton considers this highly
improbable.

12th June. Life coupons are now selling at fantastic prices and
it's impossible to get one under 500 francs. It seems that the
poor are becoming more miserly with their lives and the rich
more greedy. I bought ten at the beginning of the month,
when the price was still round about 200, and the next day I
had a letter from my Uncle Antoine, in Orleans, sending me
nine more. The poor man was having such a bad bout of
rheumatism that he preferred to go into limbo while he got
over it. So now I have nineteen coupons, five more than I need,
since there are only thirty days in the month. I shall have no
trouble in selling them.

15th June. Maleffroi dropped in on me yesterday in the best
of humors. The fact that some people are paying large sums of

money in order to be able to live all through the month, like
he does, has quite restored his hopeful outlook. It was all that
was needed to convince him that the whole-time lifers are to
be envied.

20th June. Am working at high pressure. If rumor is to be
believed Melina Badin was not as mad as she sounded. Any
number of people claim to have lived more than thirty-one days
last month. I have met several myself. Well, of course, there
are people who will believe anything.

22nd June. To pay Lucette out, Roquenton spent ten thousand
francs on life coupons which he kept for his own use. She has
been in limbo for a week. But I think he now regrets it.
Solitude seems to weigh heavily on him. I find him very much
changed, scarcely recognizable.

27th June. The story that last month was increased in length
for people possessing sufficient coupons is gaining ground.
Laverdon, a man whose word one would ordinarily accept,
assures me that he lived thirty-five days. I am afraid this life
rationing must be affecting people's minds.

28th June. Roquenton died yesterday morning—not provisional
death but the real thing, probably due to grief. The funeral is
tomorrow. When Lucette comes back on the 1st July she will
find herself a widow.

32nd June. It seems, after all, that time has dimensions of which
we knew nothing. The whole thing is more confusing. Yesterday
I bought a newspaper at a kiosk and found that it was dated
the 31st June.

"Hullo!" I said. "Has the month got thirty-one days?"

The woman in the kiosk, whom I know, stared uncomprehendingly at me. I glanced at the headlines and read: "Mr. Churchill to visit New York from the 39th to the 45th."

In the street I heard two men talking. "I've got to be in Orleans on the thirty-seventh," one of them said.

A few minutes later I ran into Bonrivage, drifting along with a haggard look. He told me of his bewilderment and I said what I could to comfort him. We have simply got to take things as they come. But in the course of the afternoon a thought suddenly struck me. The whole-time lifers are quite unaware of any anomaly in the unfolding of time. It is only the people in my category, who have fraudulently procured for themselves the prolongation of this month of June, who are dumbfounded by what is happening. Maleffroi, when I told him about it, did not understand a word I said and thought I was raving. But what do I care how long time lasts! Since last night I have been madly in love. We met at Maleffroi's apartment as it happens, and fell in love at first sight. Adorable Elisa!

34th June. Saw Elisa yesterday and again today. I have found the right woman at last. We're engaged. She is leaving tomorrow to spend three weeks with relatives in the Unoccupied Zone and we are to be married when she gets back. My heart is too overflowing with happiness for me to be able to speak of it, even in this diary.

35th June. Took Elisa to the station. As she got into the train she said, "I'll do my very best to be back before the 60th." Upon reflection this rather perturbs me. I've used up my last life coupon today. What will the date be for me tomorrow?

1st July. People to whom I mention the 35th June don't know what I'm talking about. Those five days have left no trace in their memory. Fortunately I met a few people who had lived them fraudulently, as I did, and I could talk to them about them. But they were queer conversations. For me yesterday was the 35th June, but for some people it was the 32nd or the 45th. I met a man in a restaurant who had lived to June 66th, which called for thirty-six black-market coupons.

2nd July. At first I thought that I would not trouble to go out, assuming that Elisa was away. But then a doubt assailed me and I rang her up. She said she didn't know me and had never set eyes on me. I did my utmost to explain that without realizing it she had lived through days of rapture in my company. Amused but by no means convinced, she agreed to meet me on Thursday. Desperately apprehensive.

4th July. The newspapers are full of the "Life-coupon Racket," which looks like being the biggest scandal of the season. The rich have bought up so many life coupons that the saving in food and the increased productivity which the decree was designed to bring about are practically negligible. Apart from this there are special cases which have aroused great indignation. One is that of Monsieur Wadé, the multimillionaire, who appears to have lived 1,967 days between June 30th and July 1st —in other words, five years and four months! I met the celebrated philosopher, Yves Mironneau. He explained to me that every individual lives countless millenniums but that our consciousness only has brief, intermittent glimpses of that infinity, and that it is these, put together, which constitute our lives. He said other things, even more profound and subtle, but I must confess I did not follow him very well. The truth is, my thoughts were elsewhere. I call upon Elisa tomorrow.

5th July. I have seen Elisa. All is over and I have nothing more to hope for. She admitted finally that she remembered having met me at Maleffroi's. She did not seem to doubt my sincerity and perhaps was even touched by it, but it evoked no tenderness on her side, nor even any sympathy. I suspect that Maleffroi is the one she's interested in. Anyway, all my eloquence was in vain. The spark that was struck between us that evening of the 31st June was due to nothing but chance, the mood of the moment. And then people talk about the affinity of souls. I am suffering the tortures of the damned. Well, perhaps it will inspire me to write a best-seller.

6th July. Life cards have been abolished. As if I cared!

NORMAN DENNY

NOTE

1. *Céline*: pseudonym of Louis-Ferdinand Destouches, novelist whose visceral language and darkly pessimistic vision effected a kind of linguistic and stylistic revolution in French literature. He was especially known during the war years, in spite of his personally very gentle nature, for his violent, almost propagandistic writings against the Jews, especially *Les Beaux Draps*, to which Aymé ironically alludes here. *Soupault*: Philippe Soupault (1897–   ), French writer, poet associated for a while with the Dadaist movement, close collaborator of André Breton and contributor to the Surrealist review *Littérature*, who later turned to journalism; like the other persons, mentioned here, he was a friend of Céline's.

TO THE GERMAN I PASS IN THE STREET

I don't really know what I feel when I'm near you. I don't hate you, I don't hate you any more. I know you will never be my master. I pretend not to see you. I pretend you don't exist. I promised myself never to talk to you. I speak your language, but if you talk to me I shrug my shoulders and pretend not to understand. And yet the other day, in the Place du Châtelet, you came up to me. You were wandering around like any lost soldier, looking for Notre-Dame. I deigned to understand, and with a gesture, without a word, I pointed to the towers stretching up into the sky, staring you in the face on the other side of the river. You felt stupid, you blushed, and I was pleased. That's how far we've got.

What do you think you look like in your green uniform, in our streets and squares? In Paris, in France, a soldier is blue or gray. You are too buttoned up. And those elegant gloves of yours? You're too neat. And your dagger? Your revolver? Gloved executioner! And your boots? How many pairs of shoes could be cut from them for those who now go about barefoot?

I don't hate you. I can't hate. When you get into the Métro we squeeze together to let you on. You are untouchable. I lower my head a little so that you can't see my eyes, so that you won't have the warmth of a glance exchanged. You are there in our midst, like an object, in a circle of silence and frost. I can see you from head to foot, in your slightly crumpled uniform, a little threadbare around the knees and elbows, and that belt plate over your navel with its inscription which always surprises me: *Gott mit uns*[1] . . . It makes me muse: *Gott mit uns*! I wonder which God is with you. An odd God.

SOURCE NOTE: Jean Guéhenno (pseud. Cévennes), *Dans la prison* (Paris, Éditions de Minuit, 1944), pp. 54–61.

Is he still there when you shoot? Was he there when you pinned that scrap of white paper on my friend's chest in order to aim better? Because you like things to be done properly. But don't you see that I can't look at you. I mean, what if it were you? And if I were to see in your eyes that little spark which makes you shoot so well? There are not many of you in Paris, and six hundred and seventy Parisians have already been shot. With ten men to a firing squad that makes six thousand seven hundred executioners. How do I know you're not one of them?

I tell myself there is every sort among you, as there is among us. There are some pretty low sorts. There are those officers we see near the Madeleine and the Opéra, in their fine coats, with their conceited caps, that proud stupidity on their faces, those plated daggers dangling on their behinds. Then there are those busy little women, those post office employees and telephonists, looking like Valkyries,[2] so vain and empty. The other day, in the Place de la Concorde, before the Naval Ministry, I stopped to watch the sentries, those two immobile puppets standing on either side of the door, as they have stood for over two years, without drinking, eating, or sleeping, the symbol, in mid-Paris, of your mechanical and funereal order. For a moment I watched them do their puppets' turns. But one gets tired of the Nuremberg clock, and I was leaving in disgust when I bumped into somebody as I turned. I apologized. I raised my eyes. Who was it? One of those Valkyrie telephonists, red with rage, foaming at the mouth, ready to call a guard to avenge her honor. But my apologies had disconcerted her. She recovered, and with a look of triumph she said: "*Ach!* . . . So . . ." I regretted my apologies.

But you are not all like that. I see you every Wednesday on my way to work, in the square before my office. For what legalized looting there every week? When I arrive at eight your wagons are standing under the trees at the edge of the road. Most of the men are in the nearby factories picking up the goods. Only a few remain to look after the wagons and the horses. I sit on a bench, some way away, waiting for my office to open. Most of them are peasants, reservists, some very young ones

too, but deformed and ill-built. Among them is a sort of dwarf,
with the ends of his trousers dragging along the ground, who
seems to be the drudge of the squad. They talk, but I'm too far
away to hear them. They look sad and nostalgic, and that
makes me want to look at them. The dwarf is not the one who
interests me most, though: I am more interested in an old
man who has been standing by the wagon level with my bench
for at least six months—German regularity! I observe his worn
jacket, his trousers, his boots. He is at the head of the team,
leaning against the shaft. He seems so lonely, so resigned, so
desolate. *Zum Befehl*,[3] as I hear him shout, clicking his heels,
each time a *Feldwebel*[4] talks to him. *Zum Befehl* forever. He
smokes a porcelain pipe like a proverbial German. The dwarf
sometimes comes up to him, but he doesn't pay much attention
to him. He only has one comrade. His comrade, in exile and
war, for all the years they have been trudging along the roads of
Europe, from East to West, from West to East, in the sun and
the rain, the dust and the snow, ever since they set off together
without knowing why, *zum Befehl, zum Befehl*, his comrade
is a horse—the horse on the left of the team, an old black
horse, who looks like quite a veteran too. Every Wednesday I
watch their display of affection. The old horse pulls on his
halter until he can touch his companion with his nose and
gently nibbles his shoulder until the old soldier turns around
and rubs his nostrils with his big fingers. Those two are
kindred spirits.

  That old man, left to himself and his friendship for his
horse in the miseries of war and exile, helps me think of you
with some compassion and imagine you to be human. He and
I are probably the same age and he makes me look back on
our past of lost Europeans who have tried vainly for forty years
to reconcile the demands of our honor and our hunger. It
seems that one man's hunger can only be satisfied by another
man's famine, that one man's honor must always be at the price
of another man's degradation. That is not true. But go home,
old man, go home . . .

                                              ALASTAIR HAMILTON

NOTES

1. *Gott mit uns*: "God with us," German miltary motto dating from World War I, which has its equivalent in most languages.
2. *Valkyries*: lesser goddesses of Scandinavian mythology who personified heroic virtue and were believed to pour beer and hydromel on those who died in combat.
3. *Zum Befehl*: "At your command!"
4. *Feldwebel*: German military officer.

JEAN GUÉHENNO

August, 25, 1941

THE SOUTHERN ZONE

The Southern Zone—The great problem of Vichy is that the people have no idea what is going on in the other zone. To facilitate betrayal opinion has to be devitalized. Above all, nobody must know what the requisitions were like, or that thousands of Frenchmen have been shot. Saying it as I do, pushing a copy of *L'Oeuvre*[1] under people's noses with the latest measures taken by the SS,[2] not only do I make myself suspect and provoke the village spies, but I feel that I embarrass everybody. People hesitate to believe me: the figures have become so enormous as to be unbelievable. People prefer not to know, and have got into the habit of it. The politicians of Vichy have created a double France, and they degrade one half so that the Germans can slaughter the other with greater ease.

ALASTAIR HAMILTON

NOTES

1. *L'Oeuvre*: daily paper of the Radical Socialists.
2. *SS*: Schutzstaffel, an elite military unit of the Nazi Party, serving as a special police force. The SS controlled the concentration camps, and its subsidiary agencies combatted resistance in the occupied countries.

SOURCE NOTE: Jean Guéhenno (pseud. Cévennes), "Zone-sud," *Dans la prison* (Paris, Éditions de Minuit, 1944), 51–52.

RESISTANCE

THE WORD "RESISTANCE" was first pronounced in London by General de Gaulle in his second appeal to the French nation on June 22, 1940. However, his appeal seemed at first to reach only a handful of Frenchmen outside France, those who were already abroad or who had been evacuated from Dunkirk or had made their way out of France by other means. These "Free French" formed the nucleus of the Gaullist "Fighting French Forces."

Within France itself, still numbed by the military collapse and by the flood of refugees—an estimated ten million French as well as a couple of million Belgians and Dutch—the General's appeal had at the time only a minor effect. Numerous Frenchmen who, though uncommitted ideologically, were keenly aware of their country's weakness and deeply concerned for its plight, rallied to what seemed to them the more immediate task at hand: to restore some form of order to France itself. Some of these temporarily joined Vichy rather than abandon the country to its fate. The great majority of people, like Simone de Beauvoir, regained their homes to reorganize their existence as best they could.

But scattered individuals had immediately felt the inner distress and revulsion that Simone de Beauvoir registers when confronted by such stipulations in the Armistice agreements as the return to German authority of the many German refugees on French soil—a majority of them Jewish. It is to this undertow of personal feeling that such poems as Paul Éluard's "Courage" are addressed. Éluard's "Seven Poems of Love in War," in which the themes of love, indignation, shame, anger, and eventual triumph are interwoven, create an inner mood of confidence and generosity. It was an antidote to the debased image of a bedraggled, panic-stricken, self-centered people that had haunted French minds since the days of the exodus. Poetry, in the hands of Aragon, Éluard, and many other poets, became the language of emotional liberation for the French and a source of inner strength and control.

The diverse German security forces—of which there were a variety, often engaged in bitter rivalries—spread their networks over France, camouflaged to some degree in the southern zone, with headquarters in Paris. Vying with each other for the center of the stage, each of the small splinter groups of active collaborationists, in north and south, recruited and organized its own paramilitary groups, not greatly to the satisfaction of the occupiers. Of these the most notorious was the Milice, a tactical police force, officially organized under the orders of Laval in February 1943, essentially to maintain order in southern France. The *miliciens* worked closely with the Gestapo, whose methods they emulated.

In the meantime, the collaborationist press and radio in the north, the Vichy-controlled press and radio in the south blanketed out all news media. The French had no outside information other than the rigorously outlawed BBC broadcasts. The authorized press was rather differently colored at first, according to the balance struck by the editor between ideological conviction, illusion, and a realistic appraisal of fact. Brasillach's *Je suis partout*, Déat's *L'Oeuvre*, Doriot's *Gringoire* were often at odds

with each other and with the occupier, and were frequently censored. Severe though the well-known repressive
measures of the occupiers proved to be, and increasingly so
as their military situation deteriorated, the ambiguities
inherent in the French collaboration seem to have imposed
some restraints on the Germans themselves.

Nonetheless, two months after the Montoire interviews
the Gestapo was arresting hostages in retaliation for
sporadic acts of violence. The inevitable cycle of terrorism
and counterterrorism had begun. The credibility gap
between the language of collaboration and the realities
of France's situation widened the inner dissensions. The
impotence of the Vichy government, even of its most
carefully thought out and best-justified initiatives and
policies, became apparent. Against a slowly mounting tide
of skepticism and anti-Nazi feeling, Vichy began to function in a void. It was in Paris, among the intellectuals and
the students, who attempted to organize a mass protest
demonstration as early as November 11, 1940, at the
Tomb of the Unknown Soldier, that the first sporadic
resistance groups took shape toward the end of 1940. By
the time the war was over, Resistance, its reality, its
contradictions, its myths, had swept over the country.
More than in other occupied countries, where resistance
was perhaps even more desperate and heroic, the French
Resistance created its own legend, no doubt because of
the articulateness of France's intellectuals. The creation
of a legend indeed seems a necessity if an underground
movement is to grow, a condition of its efficacity. However great the discrepancy often proved to be between
the heroic legend and the facts, nonetheless the many
individual and collective acts of courage and the price
paid in human lives are above question. Torture and
death in extermination camps were the fate the resistants
confronted. It is estimated that by the time Paris was
liberated and the Resistance groups were disarmed and

integrated into the regular French Army by General de
Gaulle, approximately 30,000 resistants had been executed
and 115,000 deported, of whom only about 40,000 sur-
vived. They included a particularly high proportion of
France's intellectuals and men of letters.

One of the first aims of the early Resistance groups was
to counteract the double propaganda of the Nazi and
collaborationist information services and press, to maintain
contact with the free world, and to voice and crystallize
reactions that remained inoperative as long as they were
individual and unformulated. The nuclei of these early
groups formed around small, scattered, mimeographed
clandestine sheets put out by amateurs, often at first quite
recklessly distributed and consequently short-lived. These
early times were the most heroic ones of the Resistance,
the most costly too in terms of human beings. These
publications proliferated and gained in diversity and efficiency. The catalogue of the Bibliothèque Nationale
devoted to the clandestine press lists 1,015 titles of such
sheets, newspapers, and periodicals. By 1944, some, like
Défense de la France, L'Humanité, or *Combat,* were
distributing up to half a million copies. Most of them
reflected ideological positions that ran the gamut from
Marxism to the extreme right. The most widely circulated
favored some form of socialism for the future. Besides
these, there were innumerable clandestine reviews, purely
literary in content, Jean Lescure's *Messages,* Noel Arrand's
Éditions la Main à plume, Pierre Seghers' press in the
South among the best known. In 1943, when Resistance
networks covered France and the clandestine press had
gained in experience and power, Aragon, one of whose
many pseudonyms was "The Witness of the Martyrs,"
recalled the history of one such early group, that of the
"Musée de l'Homme" in Paris. Aveline recalled their spirit.
In Lyons toward the end of 1941, a young writer, Pierre
de Lescure, and an engraver, Jean Bruller, alias Vercors,

were able to set up a more ambitious clandestine press, "Midnight Editions," that over the years of occupation put out some thirty-three titles, first among them Vercors's famous anticollaborationist *Silence of the Sea;* under the pseudonym Forez, Mauriac's *Black Notebook;* and under the pseudonym Auxois, Edith Thomas's *Contes d'Auxois.* In Paris, the gentle, urbane writer Jean Paulhan—former director of France's literary review *La Nouvelle Revue française,* which had been taken over by Drieu La Rochelle, the collaborationist—had been involved in clandestine activities since 1940, founding early in 1942 the Resistance sheet of the literati, *Les Lettres françaises,* which became the rallying point of the "National Committee of Resistance Writers." It was he who in 1943 furnished Aragon the documents concerning the fate of the "Musée de l'Homme" group.

On June 22, 1941, the German armies attacked along the whole Eastern Front, invading Russia. The French Communist Party, quiescent until, then, one might even say acquiescent, came out from under the shadow that had fallen upon it since its defense of the prewar Hitler-Stalin pact. From then on, the Resistance changed character. Disciplined, well organized, and trained, the Communist forces, familiar with the techniques of underground guerrilla warfare, began to dominate the Resistance. Violent action—sabotage, assassination, terrorism in all its forms—rapidly increased. Whereas in 1940 the French railroads reported seven acts of sabotage, by 1941 the count was one hundred and thirty, plus forty-one with explosives and nine trains derailed. The perturbation created by the growing violence is clearly apparent in Brasillach's reflections at that date and the near panic that underlies the new rhetorical cast of his style. From early 1943 on, increasingly short of manpower, the Nazis put a good deal of pressure on the French to send men to work either on the Atlantic Wall or in German industries.

Many young men then joined the guerrilla forces in the *maquis*. These had begun to appear in the winter of 1942–43 and by March 1944 comprised some 35,000 men, often engaged in active warfare.

One of the functions of the clandestine press was to impose and keep alive the heroic legend of the underground in the face of the adversary's stigmatization of their acts and the reprisals they drew. Such is the function of a tale like Edith Thomas's. Voluntarily linked to the medieval national epic, as the reference to the medieval *Song of Roland* indicates, it has a balladlike simplicity. Very close in spirit is Dominique Aury's evocation of the *maquis*. Gestures, words, attitudes are exemplary; literary preoccupations are secondary. These are in fact icons, in pattern not unlike the bulk of short stories that have appeared in similar situations the world over. They aim at counteracting the sense of futility and horror with simple images of heroism.

Deprivation, daily anxiety, black-market banditry, terrorism, uncertainty, fratricidal divisiveness in purpose, heroism, cruelty, violence: such is the fate of all occupied countries. The French, however, knew one great alleviation: the translation of their experience into language.

LOUIS ARAGON

THE RESEDA AND THE ROSE

He who believed in heaven
He who did not believe
Adored the lovely captive
The booted soldiers grieve
Which of them climbed the ladder
Which of them watched below
The one who believed in heaven
The one who did not know
What does it matter
What name is given
To the light that guided their feet
Both of them died that she shall live
In the dawn that we shall greet
He who believed in heaven
And he who did not believe
One turned in at the chapel door
One of them turned aside
But both were true to a faith denied
And held to the oath they swore
That she should live who was said had died
Both of them, salt and leaven
Of hope that cannot deceive
He who believed in heaven
And he who did not believe
When the wheat is slashed by the hail
Bickerings wrong or right

SOURCE NOTE: Louis Aragon, "La Rose et le Réséda," *La Diane française* (Paris, Seghers, 1946). Aragon dedicated this poem to four heroes of the Resistance, two of them Catholics, the others Communists.

Are drowned in the howl of the gale
Side by side in the fight
Stand he who believes in heaven
And he who holds to his doubt
A footstep crunched in the snow
From the wall of the citadel
A sentry's shots rang out
One of them staggered one of them fell
Which died? which crawled through the field below
Staunching his blood with his sleeve?
The one who believed in heaven
Or the one who did not believe?

Which of them in their prison
Sleeps on the softer stone?
Which cares for the rat's derision?
Which suffers the more alone
When the dank cold bites to the bone
He who believes in a heaven
Or he who believes in none?

A rebel is a rebel
At the break of the cruelest dawn
Our sobs for both are a single knell
Our grief for them both is one
For him who believed in heaven
And him who believed in none
As the eastern sky grows grey
They utter a single name
The name of the captive they both may say
Who never brought her shame
He who believed in heaven
And he who believed in none
Their life that was freely given
Their life and their death were one
And the red of their blood is the same
As it seeps in the soil they love

Though one held his faith to the earth alone
And one to heaven above
One of them—which of them—who can say?
One of them runs and one has wings
From Brittany or the Franche-Comté
When once again the cricket sings

Call it flute or call it cello
In their double love that glows
Crocus or jonquil, lark or swallow,
Dark or fair, peach or pear,
Who shall quibble Who shall care
If she who was a captive wear
At her bosom, in her hair
The reseda and the rose?

RAMON GUTHRIE

LA ROSE ET LE RÉSÉDA

Celui qui croyait au ciel
Celui qui n'y croyait pas
Tous deux adoraient la belle
Prisonnière des soldats
Lequel montait à l'échelle
Et lequel guettait en bas
Celui qui croyait au ciel
Celui qui n'y croyait pas
Qu'importe comment s'appelle
Cette clarté sur leur pas
Que l'un fût de la chapelle
Et l'autre s'y dérobât
Celui qui croyait au ciel
Celui qui n'y croyait pas
Tous les deux étaient fidèles

Des lèvres du coeur des bras
Et tous les deux disaient qu'elle
Vive et qui vivra verra
Celui qui croyait au ciel
Celui qui n'y croyait pas
Quand les blés sont sous la grêle
Fou qui fait le délicat
Fou qui songe à ses querelles
Au coeur du commun combat
Celui qui croyait au ciel
Celui qui n'y croyait pas
Du haut de la citadelle
La sentinelle tira
Par deux fois et l'un chancelle
L'autre tombe qui mourra
Celui qui croyait au ciel
Celui qui n'y croyait pas
Ils sont en prison Lequel
A le plus triste grabat
Lequel plus que l'autre gèle
Lequel préfère les rats
Celui qui croyait au ciel
Celui qui n'y croyait pas
Un rebelle est un rebelle
Nos sanglots font un seul glas
Et quand vient l'aube cruelle
Passent de vie à trépas
Celui qui croyait au ciel
Celui qui n'y croyait pas
Répétant le nom de celle
Qu'aucun des deux ne trompa
Et leur sang rouge ruisselle
Même couleur même éclat
Celui qui croyait au ciel
Celui qui n'y croyait pas
Il coule il coule et se mêle

A la terre qu'il aima
Pour qu'à la saison nouvelle
Mûrisse un raisin muscat
Celui qui croyait au ciel
Celui qui n'y croyait pas
L'un court et l'autre a des ailes
De Bretagne ou du Jura
Et framboise ou mirabelle
Le grillon rechantera
Dites flûte ou violoncelle
Le double amour qui brûla
L'alouette et l'hirondelle
La rose et le réséda

LOUIS ARAGON

1943

THE CASE OF THE MUSÉE DE L'HOMME

In the "case of the Musée de l'Homme"[1] most of the arrests were made in January 1941. But the main defendant, the ethnologist Vildé, who had worked in the Resistance since July 1940, was only caught in March 1941. The sentence was passed in December 1941. The execution took place on February 23, 1942. Do we realize what these dates meant for the accused? From the arrest to the sentence, long months of Nazi prison, incessant interrogations, tortures to obtain evidence, and after the death sentence, more than two months delay, what Villiers

SOURCE NOTE: Louis Aragon (pseud. Le Témoin des Martyrs), "L'Affaire du Musée de l'Homme," *Le Crime contre l'esprit* (Paris, Éditions de Minuit, 1944), pp. 19–28. The manuscript was received by the editors in December of 1943 and published on February 26, 1944.

de l'Isle-Adam[2] called "torture by hope," to end on the Calvary of Paris, the Mont Valérien.[3]

All we know is that the lawyer L.-M. Nordmann, and the ethnologists Anatole Lévitzky and Boris Vildé from the Musée de l'Homme, were atrociously tortured in the Cherche-Midi prison.[4] Vildé was tortured for three months—he never broke. He assumed the responsibility for all the facts of which the others were accused. Maybe we should say what these "questions" were, which our patriots suffered at the hands of the Gestapo. It was said that at the Cherche-Midi the cell of a sixteen-year-old Jew who had been tortured for several weeks without saying a word stank so strongly of pus that even the torturers objected to the smell and had it disinfected. But it made no difference. The stench persisted. To our shame we must admit that the "French" prisons are just as bad as the German jails and that the same cries which induce the Gestapo to prevent people approaching the cellars where they torture in Lyons are also heard in the Paris quarters of Pétain's judicial police. Needles under fingernails, testicles pricked, male organs squeezed to bursting point, victims suffocated until they faint in the middle of interrogations, appalling flagellations, blows purposely inflicted on open, suppurating wounds, hair burned, soles of the feet roasted, men literally flayed by ox-hide thongs, broken bones . . . all these and many other things in dreadful conditions of filth, among excrement, vermin, and microbes, are performed—though not only—by the Gestapo to punish the French for the crime of being French. But at least the defendants of the Musée de l'Homme had the bitter satisfaction of being tortured by the enemy and not by those Frenchmen who compete with the Germans in cruelty and refinement, by those Frenchmen who seem to take pride in living up to the Schadenfreude, the malicious joy of the Parisians.

Two of the accused were acquitted: another was sentenced to four months in prison; Agnès Humbert, Muller, and Héricault, to five years. But ten others, Boris Vildé, Anatole Lévitzky, L.-M. Nordmann, Sénéchal, Pierre Walter, Ithier,

Andrieux, Madame Simonet, Leleu, and Odon were condemned
to death. The seven men were executed on February 23, 1942.
We can't describe each one of them. Here are just a few facts
to acquaint ourselves with those who died.

Maître Nordmann, a Parisian lawyer, was one of the first to
be arrested. A double agent denounced him as he tried to get to
England from Brittany. This Frenchman, whom the Germans
had taught the French to regard as a Jew wanted by the French
police, was arrested, "questioned," and sentenced by the Germans for editing and distributing a clandestine paper. It was
only later that his dossier was joined to that of the scientists
from the Musée de l'Homme. All that was held against him
was giving money to help an aviator escape to England. The
Paris bar had tried to intervene in his favor.

The father of the law student Sénéchal died of wounds
received in the 1914–1918 war. His son, accused of giving food
to the English and helping them escape to the free zone, died,
like his father, from German bullets. That is how the French
tradition is founded from one generation to another.

The 1914–1918 war had also prepared the defendant Ithier
for martyrdom: he had been gassed. He was a widower and he
leaves a fifteen-year-old daughter. The schoolteacher Andrieux
was also a war casualty. He had been declared totally disabled,
and, also a widower, he leaves his two daughters, nineteen and
seventeen, in a France where the foreign invader had tried to
murder him twice in twenty years.

Like Nordmann, the photographer Pierre Walter, an Alsatian
and a Catholic living in Nice, was denounced by an *agent
provocateur* and found himself among the defendants of the
Musée de l'Homme. The German judge Roskopen, who considered all Alsatians good Germans, was upset that he should
be from Alsace. "Did you ever hesitate on the choice of your
country?" he asked him hopefully. And Pierre Walter replied:
"I never hesitated to serve France." He was a widower and he
wanted to remarry at the age of thirty-six. He had a fiancée
who had also been arrested and was liberated shortly before his
execution.

One should read the letters which Walter wrote his fiancée. They are the best expression of the state of mind of this courageous Frenchman (if Herr Justizprasident Roskopen permits).

"Don't think I am being Spartan, but I really am happy . . . You see, it is really out of cowardice that I do not weep. A word of advice for you both" (his brother and his fiancée). "Remember that I don't mind having no hope left. This will help you. And remember that I am out of pain and that I died for a finer image than I have seen since our defeat" (the French flag on the spire of the pink cathedral). "I am departing in the belief that it is still possible, and this hope will not die with me." He told his fiancée about the chaplain, "a splendid, charming fellow who knows France well," of what he had been reading, and he recommended books by Fernand Vandérem and Henri Duvernois.[5] "Am I too tolerant? But it is enchanting. And yet I used not to like Duvernois. Finally, I have Saint Augustine's *Confessions*, but I admit that I have nothing of the devil who becomes a hermit. I think God is full of mercy and understands that all his children, as he created them, cannot be saints . . ." And he told her of his regrets: "I wanted a small photograph of you and my brother in his free-shooter's cap. I have a paper knife with a picture of Nice. To start with, it was cruel. Now no longer . . ." A little later on the same day he wrote: "Life is beautiful, my little Lise, and fun: make the most of it (I don't want to give you bad advice) . . . Oh no, I can't stand bores! And then you've already suffered enough as it is . . . Now that you are my fiancée there are masses of things I can no longer tell you. Too bad! 'Wrap up your troubles . . .' "

This letter was dated Sunday, "my best Sunday for years." It had a postscript written on Monday at eleven o'clock: "Charged by the public prosecutor and the interpreter, change of cell, it'll be for five. *Vive la France!* I feel sorry for my comrades Ithier, René, Boris, all of them and you who remain. A thousand kisses to you all from your Pierrot."

At about five o'clock in the afternoon a truck drove them to the Mont Valérien. The chaplain whom Walter had mentioned

and the German public prosecutor, Dr. Gottlob, accompanied
them. All the way they spoke of death, trying to find the best
philosophical definition for it. Like Judge Roskopen, who had
frequently commented on the dignity of the accused and their
loyalty to each other during the trial, Dr. Gottlob said that the
seven men died like heroes. They were told that they could not
all be shot together. Vildé, Ithier, and Lévitzky asked to die
last. Their request was granted and they fell with their hands
and eyes unbound.

I have left the portraits of the main protagonists, Vildé and
Lévitzky, to the end. Both were ethnologists, both worked at
the Musée de l'Homme. Both were Russians, both fled from
Soviet Russia and became French. They illustrate the lies of
Dr. Goebbels'[6] propaganda: the lie of racist science, and the lie
of anti-Bolshevism.

Anatole Lévitzky was the older of the two. Born on August
22, 1901, in Bogorodsk near Moscow, an Orthodox Christian,
the son of a Czarist senator and of a family inscribed for
several centuries in the register of nobility, he emigrated with
his family to Switzerland, where they kept a Russian pension at
Montreux. As a young man in Paris he worked as a taxi driver to
be able to attend lectures at the Sorbonne. It was owing to the
psychoanalyst Otto Rank[7] that he could continue his studies.
He took a degree in literature in 1931, studied at the Institute
of Ethnology, and entered the Ethnographical Museum as an
attendant. This attendant was to impose himself as an equal on
the professors for whom he worked. Soon his masters themselves
asked him to give lessons at the School of Advanced Studies[8]
where he was studying as a specialist in North African ethnology, and when the Musée de l'Homme was organized in 1937
he was the main founder of a museum to be the pride of Paris.
He directed the department of comparative technology. In
1938 he represented France at the International Congress of
Anthropological and Ethnological Science in Copenhagen. Just
before the war he scoured Europe, visiting museums in Germany, Holland, and England. He was already famous for his

studies on shamanism,[9] and he prepared a long general work
on the subject.

He took French nationality, volunteered for the infantry, and
became an officer in 1939 after a course at the Officers' Training College: his regiment is said to have distinguished itself.

Boris Vildé was born in St. Petersburg in 1908. After studying chemistry and making his literary debut (poems and short
stories), he left his country, and lived first in Germany. Here,
from 1930 to 1932, he lectured at the universities of Jena and
Hamburg, published articles on modern German literature, and
wrote further short stories in Russian. In 1932 he arrived in
Paris. Having taken a degree in German, he turned to scien-
tific research, took a diploma in Japanese at the School of
Oriental Languages, and started studying linguistics and eth-
nography. He took French nationality in 1936, did his military
service, and married the daughter of Ferdinand Lot, history
professor at the Sorbonne, a member of the French Institute
and winner of the Prix Osiris in 1939. After going on an official
mission to Estonia in 1937, he entered the Musée de l'Homme,
where he was put in charge of the European section and took
a particular interest in the northern Arctic civilizations. A
member of the Linguistic Society, the author of a remarkable
report on the artificial creation of words in Estonian, he went
on a mission to Finland in 1939 and established contact between the Museum of Helsinki and the Musée de l'Homme.
Boris Vildé wrote for the review *Races et Racisme*; he was one
of the authors of the collection devoted to Finland by *Les
Horizons de France* in April 1940; he translated some Estonian
short stories published in the *Anthology of Estonian Narrative*,
and rapidly and silently attained world fame as a linguist and
ethnologist. He became an artillery corporal, then a sergeant
major during the 1939–1940 war, and he wanted to join the
air force and volunteer for Finland.

This is the man, an Orthodox Christian and an *émigré*, whom
the Vichy press, hardly concerned by an extra lie or two, described on several occasions as a Jew and a Bolshevik. A note

delivered by various eminent people in the Place Beauvau says: "He was once in favor of the National Socialist doctrines, then violently opposed them. However severe his punishment, he will receive it with resignation and nobility. We want his life to be spared because he is a great scientist who will not be easily replaceable, and also because, when the hour of peace and mercy arrives, he will be one of the men able to unite the scientists and peoples of Europe and arrange for the collaboration between France and Germany and Eastern Europe."

No, it is not by chance that these two men who had fled from Bolshevism in their country became French, increased their awareness of human reality through the study of ethnology, the science of men and peoples, and opposed Hitler's racism, which for an instant had attracted at least one of them. It is not by chance that they founded this Musée de l'Homme, whose teaching is opposed to false Nazi science, which is nothing but an instrument of conquest. It is not by chance that they became the victims of those who loudly declared war on Bolshevism. The Vildé and Lévitzky case is concrete proof of the absurdity of Hitler's propaganda, which represents him as the defender of civilization. It shows what ends' the anti-Bolshevik *myth*, the racist *myth*, really serve. It was quite natural that the men of the swastika, the executioners of Europe, should come across these two European minds whom France had enabled to become great scientists ready to counteract the lies of racism and anti-Bolshevism with both French science and the calm courage of two French citizens. Seven Frenchmen sang *La Marseillaise* as the German guns went off at the end of that February afternoon in 1942, at dusk on the Mont Valérien.

ALASTAIR HAMILTON

NOTES

1. *Musée de l'Homme*: institute for research in ethnology and anthropology founded in Paris in 1938. The group whose fate Aragon describes was one of the first to actively oppose the Germans but, lacking experience, was quickly decimated.

2. *Villiers de l'Isle-Adam*: Philippe-Auguste, Comte de (1838–1889), French writer with a flair for the fantastic and symbolic. The short story alluded to here takes place in the prisons of the Inquisition where the condemned rabbi is allowed to think he can make an escape.

3. *Mont Valérien*: fort in a western suburb of Paris in which thousands of Frenchmen were executed during the Occupation.

4. *Cherche-Midi prison*: military prison in Paris.

5. *Fernand Vandérem and Henri Duvernois*: Vandérem (1864–1939) was a writer, critic, and reporter; Duvernois (1875–1937), a novelist, playwright, and short-story writer.

6. *Dr. Goebbels*: Joseph Goebbels (1897–1945), Minister of Propaganda for Hitler.

7. *Otto Rank*: Viennese psychoanalyst, one of Freud's first pupils.

8. *School of Advanced Studies (l'Ecole des Hautes Études)*: attached to the university, this institution offers supplementary studies in the sciences with an emphasis on lab work.

9. *shamanism*: religion of Ural-Altaic peoples in western Siberia, based on a cult of nature and supernatural spirits who are in communication with the priests, or shamans.

CLAUDE AVELINE

September 1943

THE RESURRECTION OF FRANCE

July 1940. In a capital dazed by the ruin of her nation, silent, deaf, blind, and powerless, some friends proudly decided to revive the sight and hearing of their compatriots. As an echo to the little France libre[1] which had just been founded across the Channel, they called themselves the Free Frenchmen of France. They wrote and typed their pamphlets themselves.

SOURCE NOTE: Claude Aveline, "Résurrection de la France," in Jean Paulhan and Dominique Aury, *La Patrie se fait tous les jours* (Paris, Éditions de Minuit, 1947), pp. 144–46. Reprinted from *Cahiers de la Libération*, date unknown.

They appealed to the workers, the students, the man in the street and the Métro—the empty street and the crowded Métro where, their coat pockets stuffed full of incendiary leaflets, they enjoyed brushing against the nauseating tunics of the conqueror —enthusiastic, they were still inexperienced at the job. By the autumn a new group had joined them. It had one, then several portable copying machines, trained rudimentary troops. It procured Swiss, English, and American newspapers and listened in to broadcasts so as to enable our friends to gather enough information to issue a real news bulletin which we thought would be the avant-garde of the clandestine French press, *Résistance*, and it was to have its martyrs, its prisoners, its outlaws. I tell what I know, and I don't know everything. The pessimists could claim that our obscure means were like fistfuls of salt thrown into a lake to change it into a sea. And we did sometimes feel curiously lost in the midst of this immense, agonizing apathy which showed no indulgence for the victor but had no faith in itself. The provinces of the Occupied Zone hoped for nothing more. And the other zone was not mentioned. It hoped only to consecrate its defeat. It greedily enjoyed its provisional liberty. And with half a dozen bugles and drums it saluted the grubby French flag which flapped over it like a slap. Nevertheless we performed our task. Other groups arose, leading parallel or similar activities. And one day . . .

No, it didn't happen *one day*. And we modestly admit that the miracle did not occur solely as a result of the first inner refusal. The Allies had something to do with it, and so did the enemy. The enemy most of all, who first realized the meaning of "collaboration" according to Hitler's gospel: the victor may kill and loot, as much as he likes, each day. Then there were the Allies. By resisting the enemy, by expanding each year over the world, they made the word "victory" a prospect, a possibility, a probability, a conviction, a certitude. The military units who rumble through our villages at night do not bear the swastika. Fascism is dead and National Socialism is taking a last breath of fetid air before suffocating. Vichy trembles, and

the whole of France, who has arisen despite her chains, awaits
deliverance, the liberation which will give her the first taste of
a slogan hitherto imprisoned like herself: Liberty! Is it merely
another form of submission, an incurable inertia which will only
change camp with victory? But if it stands under our walls,
victory hasn't yet breached them. Behind the ramparts of flesh
and concrete which surround our prison, the enemy keeps his
army of spies and executioners awake. He murders, tortures,
and deports. Despite constant terror France now dares arise with
one thunderous murmur; the real voice of combat bursts from
every open window; at every crossroads, in every square, faces
laughed with joy when Stalingrad was freed, Tunisia liberated
Sicily conquered. These were not only the signs of impatience;
they were a provocation, the intentional, calculated defiance of
a new pride. It was not so difficult to change the lake into a
sea. It was enough for us no longer to be a few dozen Frenchmen standing on its banks with our fists full of salt, but a few
million—the whole of France. And the sea is gradually preparing for the storm. It must succeed! There must be no
quarter for those who gave none! No piece of rotten wood must
remain afloat, no buoys, no wreck! France must be relentless!
Only then will her resurrection not only lead her to victory but
also establish her in peacetime.

ALASTAIR HAMILTON

NOTE

1. *France libre*: Gaullist forces organized outside of France in
1940, including a provisionary "government in exile." They published a review, *La France libre*.

PAUL ÉLUARD

SEVEN POEMS OF LOVE IN WAR

> *I am writing in this land where they pen up men*
> *In offal and thirst, silence and starvation . . .*
> ARAGON, *Le Musée Grévin*

I

A ship in your eyes
Became master of the wind
And your eyes were the country
Found again in an instant

Patient your eyes waited for us

Under the trees of the forests
In rain in torment
On the snow of mountain peaks
Among the eyes and the games of children

Patient your eyes waited for us

They were a valley
More tender than a single blade of grass
Their sunlight gave substance
To the lean human harvest

SOURCE NOTE: Paul Éluard (pseud. Jean du Haut), "Les Sept Poèmes d'amour en guerre," *Au Rendez-vous allemand* (Paris, Éditions de Minuit, 1945), pp. 13–18. The original clandestine edition of these poems was published in 1943 at Saint-Flour (Cantal) in booklet form, by the Bibliothèque Française.

They waited to see us
Always
For we brought love
The youth of love

And the reason of love
The wisdom of love
And immortality.

II

Light of our eyes more populous
Than the greatest battles

Towns and suburbs villages
Of our eyes conquerors of time

In the cool valley the sun
Burns bright and fluid

And the rose flesh of springtime
Struts upon the grass

Evening has folded its wings
Over a Paris without hope
But our lamp sustains the night
As a captive liberty.

III

The spring flowing sweet and naked
Night stretches everywhere
The night when we join together
In a mad and feeble struggle

And the night which curses us
The night when the empty bed
Of solitude is dug
The future of an agony.

IV

A flower knocks
At the gates of the earth

A child knocks
At the door of his mother
The rain and sunlight
Born with the child
Growing with the flower
Flowering with the child

I hear reasoning and laughter.

They have calculated the sorrow
That a child can bear
So much shame without vomiting
So many tears without dying
There is a sound of footsteps under the archways
Black and blest with horror
They are coming to uproot the flower
They are coming to vilify the child

With misery and weariness.

V

The heart's corner they said softly
The corner of love and hate and glory
We answered and our eyes reflected
The truth which was our sanctuary

We have never begun
But we have always been in love
And because we are in love
We want to free others
From their icy solitude

We want and I say I want
I say that you want and we want
Light to perpetuate
Couples shining with virtue
Couples armed with audacity
Because they look into each other's eyes

And their goal is in the lives of others.

VI

We do not trumpet our misfortune
The better to show you our unhappiness
Such as it is very great very stupid
And all the more stupid because it is complete

We claimed that death alone
That earth alone could limit us
But now it is shame
That walls us up alive

Shame of unbounded evil
Shame of our absurd butchers
Always the same always
The same lovers of themselves

Shame of the trainloads of the tortured
Shame of the words scorched earth
But we are not ashamed of our suffering
We are not ashamed of our shame

Not even a bird is left alive
In the wake of these coward warriors
The air is empty of sobbing
Empty of our innocence

Resounding with hate and vengeance.

VII

In the name of the perfect profound face
In the name of the eyes I look at
And the mouth I kiss
For today and for always

In the name of buried hope
In the name of tears in the darkness
In the name of sorrow that brings laughter
In the name of laughter that brings fear

In the name of laughter in the street
Of the gentleness that links our hands
In the name of fruits covering flowers
On an earth good and beautiful

In the name of the men in prison
In the name of the women deported
In the name of all our comrades
Martyred and massacred
For not accepting the shadow

We must drain our rage
And make the iron rise up
To preserve the high image
Of the innocent everywhere hunted
And who will triumph everywhere.

LLOYD ALEXANDER

LES SEPT POEMES D'AMOUR EN GUERRE

> *J'écris dans ce pays où l'on parque les hommes*
> *Dans l'ordure et la soif le silence et la faim . . .*
> ARAGON, Le Musée Grévin [1]

I

Un navire dans tes yeux
Se rendait maître du vent
Tes yeux étaient le pays
Que l'on retrouve en un instant
Patients tes yeux nous attendaient

Sous les arbres des forêts
Dans la pluie dans la tourmente
Sur la neige des sommets
Entre les yeux et les jeux des enfants

Patients tes yeux nous attendaient

Ils étaient une vallée
Plus tendre qu'un seul brin d'herbe
Leur soleil donnait du poids
Aux maigres moissons humaines

Nous attendaient pour nous voir
Toujours
Car nous apportions l'amour
La jeunesse de l'amour
Et la raison de l'amour
La sagesse de l'amour
Et l'immortalité.

II

Jour de nos yeux mieux peuplés
Que les plus grandes batailles

Villes et banlieues villages
De nos yeux vainqueurs du temps

Dans la fraîche vallée brûle
Le soleil fluide et fort

Et sur l'herbe se pavane
La chair rose du printemps

Le soir a fermé ses ailes
Sur Paris désespéré
Notre lampe soutient la nuit
Comme un captif la liberté.

III

La source coulant douce et nue
La nuit partout épanouie
La nuit où nous nous unissons
Dans une lutte faible et folle

Et la nuit qui nous fait injure
La nuit où se creuse le lit
Vide de la solitude
L'avenir d'une agonie.

IV

C'est une plante qui frappe
A la porte de la terre
Et c'est un enfant qui frappe
A la porte de sa mère
C'est la pluie et le soleil
Qui naissent avec l'enfant
Grandissent avec la plante
Fleurissent avec l'enfant

J'entends raisonner et rire.

On a calculé la peine
Qu'on peut faire à un enfant
Tant de honte sans vomir
Tant de larmes sans périr

Un bruit de pas sous la voûte
Noire et béate d'horreur
On vient déterrer la plante
On vient avilir l'enfant

Par la misère et l'ennui.

V

Le coin du coeur disaient-ils gentiment
Le coin d'amour et de haine et de gloire
Répondions-nous et nos yeux reflétaient
La vérité qui nous servait d'asile

Nous n'avons jamais commencé
Nous nous sommes toujours aimés
Et parce que nous nous aimons
Nous voulons libérer les autres
De leur solitude glacée

Nous voulons et je dis je veux
Je dis tu veux et nous voulons
Que la lumière perpétue
Des couples brillants de vertu
Des couples cuirassés d'audace
Parce que leurs yeux se font face

Et qu'ils ont leur but dans la vie des autres.

VI

Nous ne vous chantons pas trompettes
Pour mieux vous montrer le malheur
Tel qu'il est très grand très bête
Et plus bête d'être entier

Nous prétendions seule la mort
Seule la terre nous limite
Mais maintenant c'est la honte
Qui nous mure tout vivants

Honte du mal illimité
Honte de nos bourreaux absurdes
Toujours les mêmes toujours
Les mêmes amants d'eux-mêmes

Honte des trains de suppliciés
Honte des mots terre brûlée
Mais nous n'avons pas honte de notre souffrance
Mais nous n'avons pas honte d'avoir honte

Derrière les guerriers fuyards
Même plus ne vit un oiseau
L'air est vide de sanglots
Vide de notre innocence

Retentissant de haine et de vengeance

VII

Au nom du front parfait profond
Au nom des yeux que je regarde
Et de la bouche que j'embrasse
Pour aujourd'hui et pour toujours

Au nom de l'espoir enterré
Au nom des larmes dans le noir
Au nom des plaintes qui font rire
Au nom des rires qui font peur

Au nom des rires dans la rue
De la douceur qui lie nos mains
Au nom des fruits couvrant les fleurs
Sur une terre belle et bonne

Au nom des hommes en prison
Au nom des femmes déportées
Au nom de tous nos camarades
Martyrisés et massacrés
Pour n'avoir pas accepté l'ombre

Il nous faut drainer la colère
Et faire se lever le fer
Pour préserver l'image haute
Des innocents partout traqués
Et qui partout vont triompher.

NOTE

1. *Le Musée Grévin*: long, anti-German poem written early
during the Occupation by Aragon and published by the Editions
de Minuit, which also published Éluard's poetry clandestinely.

EDITH THOMAS

1944

FTP

He was told: "A train full of Germans will be passing
tonight at eleven thirty-four."

It was hardly five minutes from the station to the forest. So
the Germans would pass at eleven thirty-nine. But he went
to the *bistrot* near the station where René usually had lunch.
René was eating with the stationmaster in a corner of the
room. They greeted each other nonchalantly and talked about
the weather.

René said: "Aren't you eating here? There's some rabbit and
potatoes. It's fabulous." He replied: "No, my wife's expecting
me. She'll be livid if I'm late." So René got up and said: "I'll
go a little way with you. I'll be back for my coffee in a minute,"
he shouted to the stationmaster.

They went out as nonchalantly as ever and lit a cigarette on
the doorstep.

After a few steps they turned down a side street. Grass was
growing between the cobbles. From time to time an old

SOURCE NOTE: Edith Thomas (pseud. d'Auxois), "FTP," *Contes
d'Auxois (transcrit du réel)* (Paris, Éditions de Minuit, 1944), pp. 51–60.
The initials of the title stand for Francs-Tireurs Partisans, a Communist
Resistance group founded in the unoccupied zone in late 1940 to set up
maquis in the countryside where French workers who were to be deported
could find refuge, and also to perpetrate other subversive activities against
the Germans and the Vichy government.

woman raised a curtain and dropped it again. Familiar faces—
they were part of the street. It's René who works at the station,
and Paul, the bank clerk, they've always been pals. They did
their military service together and they were in prison together
during the "phony war." But they managed to escape before
being sent to Germany. And I know Paul's mother: we went to
school together. He married a schoolteacher, a little brunette
from Paris, rather proud, but better than one thinks. René's
still a bachelor. It's too bad he doesn't marry: he could make
a girl happy. Paul's going home: he lives at the end of the
road, nearly in the fields, a house with one story, and a flower
garden in front, but he's planted some potatoes and spinach
in it.

They dropped the curtains: Nothing ever happens in this
street worth looking at. It's not as if I were living in the Grand
Place with all the movement of the market and the *Kommandantur* in the town hall; or even the Rue de la République,
which is now called the Rue du Maréchal Pétain.

Paul's going home and René's with him because they're two
old pals, that's all.

Paul asked: "Is it true that a train full of Germans is passing
at eleven thirty-four this evening? Have you checked?"

"Yes," said René, "I've checked."

"What time is the last train before it?" asked Paul.

"It's a freight train. It passes at ten and doesn't stop."

"Five minutes from the station to the forest," calculated
Paul. "That's five past ten. You need ten good minutes to go
from Pierre Levée to the railroad. So you must be at Pierre
Levée at five to ten. You'd better come directly to make sure
the freight train has passed. Tell Louis and Alain. I'll tell Big
Paul" (because he was bigger than Paul and Robert).

They stopped to light a cigarette—"I smoke a mixture of
tobacco and cornsilk"—someone passed them. The road inspector. They greeted him.

"All right," said René.

"All right," said Paul.

And Paul pushed open the garden gate, making the bell tinkle in the empty lane. His steps creaked on the gravel path.

Paul went home for lunch while René went back to the station. "That boy should get himself a wife, Madame Gentillon, I'm telling you."

And now he told Alice.

"This afternoon you must warn Big Paul and Robert: tonight, five to ten, at Pierre Levée."

She paled slightly: her skin turned gray. She didn't ask anything. She waited.

"Tell them not to forget their notebooks."

She knew what "their notebooks" meant. But the blood returned to her cheeks. She didn't say anything. She waited. He added:

"It's for a train."

She threw her coat over her shoulders and went off to school.

She was training her class for the school certificate,[1] and she was sure that at least fifteen of her pupils would pass. She made sure no one could detect her anxiety. Then she went to get a book from the school library. It was the *Song of Roland*.[2] She slipped a note into it. At four o'clock she kept back her best pupil, Marie-Catherine, for a few seconds. She said: "Here, Marie-Catherine, give your father this book. He asked me for it. Don't forget, Marie-Catherine."

But she knew that Marie-Catherine never forgot anything.

On her way back she stopped at the cobbler's. There were some people in the shop. She asked:

"When can I bring you my clogs to repair? The sole has broken again."

"That's all junk," said Big Paul.

"And please, would you remove a nail from this shoe immediately. It hurts."

She was sitting on a low chair and had started to take off her shoe. In the meantime the other customers had left. She said very quickly:

"This evening, at five to ten, at Pierre Levée. You won't forget your notebook."

Then she put on her shoe again.

He smiled with all the wrinkles in his face which lined his mouth and eyes. He was about fifty, well built, but lined.

"So when can I bring my clogs?"

"Not before next week," he replied. "I've got too much work."

They had dinner. They listened to the radio. He pretended to be calm. But she sensed his anxiety. No, it wasn't anxiety, it was interest, great interest in everything. But for her it was anxiety. She watched him as she dried the dishes and said to herself: "If this were the last time I were to see him." And she felt her heart. She wasn't made to be a hero's wife. She wasn't made to hand a shield to her husband or her son, and say, "Come back on top of it, or beneath it." She was made for everyday life and peace, reading and writing lessons, dictation, domestic problems, coming home to clean the house and cook at night. She was made to have a child and cradle it, to have a husband she loved and love him to the end.

What was missing for them to be happy? But she knew that happiness was impossible, that you had to forget the rest and that every moment reminds you there is no happiness, even the simplest, even the humblest, *now*, without lies or selfishness. So much the worse: happiness will be for tomorrow and maybe for others. But not for us, for tomorrow.

He must go if he wants to be on time. And he mustn't be late. But Paul never knows the time.

"It's nearly a quarter to ten," she said.

He kissed her vaguely. And what if it were the last time, she wondered. She heard his steps on the gravel path. But the bell didn't tinkle. She unhooked it at night so that nobody could hear who was coming or going. She put it back early in the morning.

. . .

She took her knitting, and her hands worked fast. Then her hands fell onto her knees again and there was nothing but waiting and the anguish of waiting.

There was no moon, but there were stars. A warm night which forecast summer nights. A fine night, and who were you under it?

First he had to leave the town. That's easy: at this time of night one doesn't meet anybody. And even if he did meet someone he could say he was going to smoke a cigarette on this fine night before going to bed. And his papers were in order: he was a conscientious employee who did his job and was well known in town. What's so strange about smoking a cigarette on such a fine night?

He took a lane which passed behind the wall of the gasworks. After the fences came the fields and his feet sank into the soft earth.

Pierre Levée was where the paths crossed: there was a large beech tree and no stones. Long ago there may have been a standing stone, a menhir,[3] or something like that, as Alice would say, who knew all the old stories and old names. He thought of Alice, of what he'd acquired since she had been his wife. And if she hadn't been his wife he might not have had the courage and faith to be here tonight: a man.

A shadow, two shadows, were glued to the trees. He went up to them: there was Big Paul, there was Alain. There was Louis, then Robert.

"René's expecting us over there. Have you got the machine guns? Have you got the sleeper screws?"

They said "Yes, yes," one after the other.

Why were they here tonight, all six of them, instead of being asleep in the dismal slumber of the little town?

There was Big Paul, walking ahead. He had once believed in the peaceful transformation of the earth, the disappearance of injustice, abundance, peace, joy; that you only had to stretch out your hand and talk of justice; that the rich would renounce their riches and share them. And then he gradually discovered that you only earn by toil. And that was why he was with those who knew what they wanted and wanted the means of what they wanted.

There was Paul. His wife Alice had taught him that man created history by his will and that his will of liberation continued, today as it had yesterday, through the history of every day, and that history isn't something you submit to; it's something you accomplish.

And there was Robert who was here because he wouldn't admit that his country could be conquered and do nothing to gain its independence. And that was why he sided with those who no longer expected help from elsewhere, and fought for the liberation of his country.

And there was Louis, the tanner. He was here to be together with the workers and peasants of the U.S.S.R., who had accomplished their liberation and knew what they were defending and why they died.

And there was Alain who wasn't seventeen yet, because he liked to be near the fighters, because he liked blows—giving them and if need be receiving them—because he liked courage, without even knowing its name.

And there was René walking in the distance, alone, along the track to meet them. René who was from the Public Assistance[4] and had never known his parents. He knew how hard the world was if you had no parents, and that working in a station was a success for him. "You see that anybody can do anything in our society." But he knew it was a lie and that there was a terrible handicap at the start which settled the future, and that this future should at last be settled justly.

And so these six men walked in silence on the empty earth under the naked sky, and because these six men were there together in an act of will and liberty, something had been changed in the history of men, something in the Europe bruised by the blows of jackboots, in the bleeding Europe without a face or a voice.

And because these six men were there, and others like them in France and other European countries, men who wouldn't yield, who refused to be dupes, who committed themselves entirely, something was changed, a step had been made which moved man from the abyss and put him closer to that other Man, the Man he would be tomorrow.

They got to the main road which cut the forest. They stopped a moment, listening to the noises— frogs croaked. Then the wind blew and the still, leafless branches waved. That squeak was one pine grating against another.

Above the noise of the sky and the forest they tried to hear the sound of men: the steps of a patrol, the imperceptible tinkle of a bicycle, the distant roar of a car. But there was nothing.

Then, rapidly, they crossed the road and assembled under the trees on the other side. A few yards on and there was the railroad. A kneeling shadow was already working on it. They went onto the ballast. And now, crouching or bent over the rails, they looked like odd gnomes curiously lit by electric lights.

Paul looked at his watch.

"Is it done?" he asked.

They replied in a whisper: "Yes, it's done."

Then they met again under the trees with their machine guns.

They heard the train in the distance. It had gathered speed since the station, and in a few more minutes it would be there.

They saw the engine heel over and the tender follow it in a crash of iron. The other cars stayed on the track. They saw frightened Germans get out of the cars.

And calmly the six men started shooting. With no more hatred than a surgeon.

With no more hatred.

ALASTAIR HAMILTON

NOTES

1. *school certificate*: a primary school diploma.
2. *Chanson de Roland*: twelfth-century French epic of Charle-
magne, his valiant nephew Roland, and their battle against the
Saracens in Spain.
3. *Menhir*: large upright stone of a type that can be seen in
Brittany today and which was perhaps linked to a Druid cult.
4. *Public Assistance*: governmental department for the assistance of the needy.

PAUL ÉLUARD

1942

COURAGE

Paris is cold Paris is hungry
Paris no longer eats chestnuts in the street
Paris has put on the old clothes of an old woman
Paris sleeps standing in the airless Métro
Still more suffering is imposed on the poor
And the wisdom and the folly
Of unhappy Paris
Is the pure air the fire
The beauty the goodness
Of her famished workers
Do not cry help Paris
You are living a life without equal
And behind the nakedness
Of your pallor of your lean bodies

SOURCE NOTE: Paul Éluard (pseud. Maurice Hervent), *Au Rendez-vous allemand* (Paris, Éditions de Minuit, 1945), p. 10. The poem appeared in *Les Lettres françaises*, No. 5, 1943, and in *L'Honneur des poètes*, Vol. I, a collection of poems received by the Éditions de Minuit in May of 1943 and published on July 14, 1943.

All that is human is revealed in your eyes
Paris my lovely city
Fine as a needle strong as a sword
Simple and knowing
You tolerate no injustice
For you it is the sole disorder
You shall free yourself Paris
Paris trembling as a star
Our hope surviving
You shall free yourself from weariness and mire
Brothers let us have courage
We who wear no helmet
Neither shod nor gloved nor well brought up
A ray of light shines in our veins
Our light comes back to us
The best of us have died for us
Now their blood finds our heart again
And once again it is morning a Paris morning
The point of deliverance
The space of a nascent springtime
Idiot force has the worst of it
These slaves our enemies
If they have understood
If they are able to understand
Will rise.

                                        LLOYD ALEXANDER

COURAGE

Paris a froid Paris a faim
Paris ne mange plus de marrons dans la rue
Paris a mis de vieux vêtements de vieille
Paris dort tout debout sans air dans le métro
Plus de malheur encore est imposé aux pauvres
Et la sagesse et la folie
De Paris malheureux

C'est l'air pur c'est le feu
C'est la beauté c'est la bonté
De ses travailleurs affamés
Ne crie pas au secours Paris
Tu es vivant d'une vie sans égale
Et derrière la nudité
De ta pâleur de ta maigreur
Tout ce qui est humain se révèle en tes yeux
Paris ma belle ville
Fine comme une aiguille forte comme une épée
Ingénue et savante
Tu ne supportes pas l'injustice
Pour toi c'est le seul désordre
Tu vas te libérer Paris
Paris tremblant comme une étoile
Notre espoir survivant
Tu vas te libérer de la fatigue et de la boue
Frères ayons du courage
Nous qui ne sommes pas casqués
Ni bottés ni gantés ni bien élevés
Un rayon s'allume en nos veines
Notre lumière nous revient
Les meilleurs d'entre nous sont morts pour nous
Et voici que leur sang retrouve notre coeur
Et c'est de nouveau le matin un matin de Paris
La pointe de la délivrance
L'espace du printemps naissant
La force idiote a le dessous
Ces esclaves nos ennemis
S'ils ont compris
S'ils sont capables de comprendre
Vont se lever.

DOMINIQUE AURY

DEPARTURE

I didn't see what became of those men that night when they left for the *maquis*. But some of them will tell their story for a long time, as they told it to me: how they met up, the men from all the neighboring villages and the little town which is the center of the district; how they reached the old quarry where they were to meet, on that night which fell so softly, so warm and yet so cool. They each thought there'd only be about ten of them; each man thought he would find a group of strangers apart from the leader, but each man found his pals. The abandoned town built itself up around farm lads and deserters who had been in hiding: the grocer, the truck driver, the schoolteacher, the policeman, men from this district and from the next, men from the water's edge and men from the farms lost in the plains—over eighty men in all.

This tiny battalion of volunteers was led by volunteers, and as in every revolution, this miniature army was composed of very young men, men known as territorials in the other war. One of the organizers was thirty: everyone had seen him in the town pharmacy; everyone knew his clever, quiet face, his good humor, his false indignation. Only his friends knew what calm and lasting courage, what determination Marcel had been hiding for four years now behind his smile and his banter. But now the worst was over: the men were there, the arms were there. This was his last night of secrecy.

When all the groups had formed and the daylight had

SOURCE NOTE: Dominique Aury, "Le Départ," in Jean Paulhan and D. Aury, *La Patrie se fait tous les jours* (Paris, Éditions de Minuit, 1947), pp. 407–9. Reprint of "Un Village et son maquis," *Les Lettres françaises*, October 1944.

faded, they groped their way back to the village. These silent
shapes followed other shapes who carried machine guns and
stopped at the crossroads to let the men pass. It would be easy
to illustrate this story: it is so full of symbols. The arms of the
Liberation were hidden in a tomb, and the volunteers went to
fetch them at night, close to their sleeping wives and children.
They received them from the hands of their men, the hands of
Henri the locksmith, half hidden by the tomb like a tradesman
at his counter. But to be there one day, he had risked his life
for four years, like Marcel.

And then what happened? The men only vaguely recalled
the rest of that anxious night. With heavy weapons on their
shoulders they trudged across the woods, over roots, across the
fields, over furrows and stones. A little before dawn they
arrived in a strange wood, where a copse hid a miniature
clearing and some vast marl grottoes. They grew proud of
these grottoes. They made the *maquis* an inaccessible lair, a
timeless refuge. They formed high vaults, hollowed in a white
and fragile sandstone used to soften the clay soil. They were
deep and the rough walls hid dark recesses. A copse grew over
them. They say you should have seen the largest grotto at night,
by the white light of an acetylene lamp. The men lay on the
ground, rolled in their blankets. Whenever one of them stirred,
great sections of shadow moved over the walls. Two lads with
machine guns stood guard night and day, and as the wood was
in a huge plain the wind rustled the leaves of the chestnuts and
beeches and shook the canvas of the tents outside. On stormy
days the mud was slippery and the clearing was so small that
the cooks thought they'd set the copse alight when they lit a
fire between two rocks. One had to bend down to pass along
the paths leading there. It was so well protected, so secret, that
the Germans could stand two hundred yards away and not
notice anything.

On the dawn of the first day, while they were settling in and
posting the first sentries, a rear-guard team wiped out the footsteps in the cemetery, put back the tombstone, and closed the

gates. At the same time German convoys started to furrow the roads. So when the little town awoke, its best defenders had left and the enemy was there. It was the moment of truth, exposed and sincere. The French no longer hid before the French. Hope was no longer a secret.

ALASTAIR HAMILTON

COLLABORATIONIST POINT OF VIEW

ROBERT BRASILLACH

1941

JUNE 23 AND OCTOBER 25

June 23, 1941

"Frenchmen, you have a short memory!"[1] In these terms
Marshal Pétain, in one of his best and most vigorous speeches,
reminded our countrymen of the tragic days of last year and
the evening when we heard he had asked the Germans for an
armistice. Since then it would be folly to say that we have had
an agreeable time, and I do not suppose anybody would dare
do so. But when we think of those weeks of 1940, of those
spectacles witnessed by so many Frenchmen, of the broken and
abandoned nation, we tell ourselves that our country exists and
that it is arising again. One must have a short memory not to
prefer this June to last June. With firmness and good sense the
Marshal told us this simple truth, and every Frenchman had
tears in his eyes as he heard it, for below this firmness they all
felt the trace of an invincible hope.

. . . We had been waiting for years. To be more precise, we
had been waiting ever since the beginning of this war which
we knew he did not want and which he considered badly conducted. We had been expecting him since March 20, a cata-
strophic day for our country, when Paul Reynaud[2] came to

SOURCE NOTE: Robert Brasillach, *Journal d'un homme occupé* (Paris, Les
Sept Couleurs, 1955), pp. 161–62, 193–94.

power with a majority of one vote, amidst the undisguised disapproval of the Chamber and the independent press. We had been expecting him since Reynaud lied to us about Norway.[3] Ever since the French front yielded, the most intelligent people had realized that all was in vain: the fight was lost. And we still did not know that the commander in chief had told the government three times to request an armistice. His only mistake was his respect for legality, which had so often thwarted the efforts of French officers: he should have had Reynaud and Mandel[4] arrested. We had been expecting him ever since the evacuation and fall of Paris. His first act was one which anybody who was neither blind nor mad had forseen since May 14—the act which saved the essential part of the country. On June 17, 1940, Marshal Pétain, victor of Verdun,[5] asked the German High Command for an armistice.

. . . We forget what the Armistice then meant for a country about to be condemned, lost, invaded from end to end, where shelters were being dug before the *Préfecture* of Perpignan.[6] We forget the human lives which this act has saved, the children who could breathe again, the millions of people who could once more look up at a harmless sky no longer filled with murderous lead. That was the advantage.

October 25, 1941

Every Frenchman will have understood that each time the much jeopardized Franco-German reconciliation is about to be proclaimed London, supported by Moscow, gets in the way. Each time there is talk of negotiations and hope of a new return of prisoners, our plans are upset by elements which *on no account* want the survival and welfare of France.

Do you want our comrades, more than a million men of under forty, to stay behind the barbed wire of prison camps for months and years, so that there should be no danger of their supporting a hostile country?

Do you want France, bereft of a large part of her territory and empire, to become a vague subprovince of greater Europe?

Do you want every day of next winter to be harder for you? Do you want your life disrupted at every moment because of this state of emergency? Don't you want anybody, for any reason, however serious, to be allowed in the street between dusk and dawn?

Do you want your children brought up in fear and misery, with no future but to become laborers and mercenaries?

Do you want our country, France, the firstborn of Western nations, torn by rival antagonisms because she has been unable to discern the truth about her future, to drift away slowly and miserably, leaving nothing but a luminous trace in the minds of men, like the races which have disappeared?

Do you want to suffer both morally and materially? Do you want to endanger your selves, your homes, and those whom you love? Do you want your countrymen exiled? Do you want the end of everything that makes life worth living?

Or do you simply want to live?

ALASTAIR HAMILTON

NOTES

1. *"Frenchmen . . . memory!"*: speech by Pétain, June 16, 1941.

2. *Paul Reynaud*: on March 20, 1940, Reynaud succeeded Daladier, in whose government he had served as Minister of Finance.

3. *Norway*: allusion to the landing of Franco-British troops at Narvik in northern Norway (April 1940) that ended in disaster and the occupation of Norway by German forces.

4. *Mandel*: see above, page 79, note 5.

5. *Verdun*: from February to November 1916, the French forces commanded by Pétain withstood strong German offensives on the Verdun front, a turning point in the war that won for Pétain the name of *"vainqueur de Verdun."*

6. *Perpignan*: southern French town on the Mediterranean, close to the Spanish border.

By late 1943, for the average person experiencing the attrition of war, the terrorism and counterterrorism of the Occupation, the balance had shifted in favor of the Allies. The Resistance movement, costly though it was, now made sense. Beneath the mystique of resistance—which had absorbed the more appealing traits of the early mystique of collaboration—a deadly struggle for power in the postwar world was being waged at all levels, from the summit talks at Teheran to the *maquis*. It echoed within the ranks of the French intellectuals involved in the struggle, even as they raised the banner of unity. To a greater or lesser degree the majority of France's writers were by now connected with the writers' national Resistance group. But politically, they nonetheless envisaged the future from very different points of view. It is not our purpose here to discuss the political maneuvers either within the Resistance groups in France or between these and the Gaullists in London. But beyond the practical problems of everyday living and for those more directly engaged in the struggle, beyond the intricate requirements of tactical efficacy and eventual political action, many writers felt the need to appraise the bitter reality they were confronting from a more detached, more universal point of view. With or without the permission of the German and French censorship, they continued to publish. Believing that spiritual attrition could destroy as relentlessly as physical deprivation, they were determined not to let the great literary tradition of France die.

Many of the themes that became almost obsessive in those years had always been latent in Western thought, becoming more insistently predominant in the last hundred years. Common to the post-World War I generations —of whatever political hue—was a nagging doubt, fed on Hegel, Marx, and Nietzsche, concerning the course and character of Western civilization, the relation between its professed values and its real orientation as manifest in the shape of its history. The frame of reference of the literary works of consequence that appeared in those years is a confrontation with the culture of the past, the "yes" or "no" its values could elicit in the present from minds intent on facing their experience with integrity. For the writers of the early forties, one of the major questions raised by the violence and sadism of the Nazi methods of conquest was how to counteract the brutalizing effect of the struggle upon the resistants themselves, upon the French nation and the Western world as a whole. Hence the high value of the literary endeavor in those years, and its tone. Literature was considered not merely as an adjunct in the fight or, as the poet Henri Michaux called it, an "exorcism," but as a privileged way of maintaining and communicating a certain measure of integrity, humanity, and freedom of mind even at the heart of chaos.

PART THREE

THE LITERARY SCENE: MAN'S FATE

LITERATURE AND
COMMITMENT

THE FIRST OPTION of the noncollaborationist writers had often been to remain silent, in protest. When they were confronted with the literature of the collaboration, however, they felt that silence would be tantamount to acquiescence in a monstrous mystification, which would debase the literary endeavor as a whole. The fight, then, must be joined and waged even unto death.

The spirit behind the clandestine Éditions de Minuit is clearly apparent in Pierre de Lescure's initial statement of purpose. It could hardly be more flatly opposed to the deliberately simplistic position expressed in Aragon's "The Poet to His Party." De Lescure's protest is here directed against Nazi censorship and its endorsement by French publishers and booksellers. But it could just as aptly have been directed against the absolute commitment to political directives enthusiastically professed by Aragon. Spiritual freedom and creativity—for De Lescure synonymous with life—and submission to political dictates are, and always have been, mortal enemies. Aragon's little poem, with its facile rhythms and simple vocabulary, is clearly didactic. The Communist Party is praised as a "light," a source of revelation that "gives back" what was lost: the eyes, the memory, and the songs, in other words the power to see, to understand the significance of France's heroic past, and joyously to act. Commitment to the party is the absolute value from which all others derive, including the value of the poet's own activity as songmaker.

Both the politically committed Aragon and the non-committed De Lescure clashed with the Nazis, but the "yes" and "no" were differently engaged. In the realm of the creative arts, both positions rested on individual acts of faith that could not rationally be either corroborated or refuted. *

* The debate flared openly in 1945, when, from Mexico, Benjamin Péret, true to his surrealist creed, reiterated Pierre de Lescure's position in his *Le Déshonneur des poètes*, a bitter rejection of Paul Éluard's communist stance in *L'Honneur des poètes*. The issue is still open.

PIERRE DE LESCURE

January 1942

MANIFESTO OF THE ÉDITIONS DE MINUIT

There was a time when people were exiled if they preferred Euripides to Racine. For the glory of France, the tyrant claimed. Today the physics of Einstein, the psychology of Freud, and the Book of Isaiah are banned. We are not allowed to reprint Meredith, Thomas Hardy, Katherine Mansfield, Virginia Woolf, Henry James, Faulkner, and all the other writers we admire. "Don't put works by Shakespeare, Milton, Keats, Shelley, or any of the English poets and novelists in your window," says the booksellers' union, by order of the Ministry of Propaganda. And French literature is "sorted out" when it enters Belgium, Holland, Greece, or any other part of "New Europe."[1] In September 1940 the publishers' union signed an agreement of censorship with the authorities in occupation. A notice proclaimed: "By signing this agreement the German authorities wanted to show their trust in the publishers. The publishers' one desire is to enable French thought to continue its mission, and at the same time respect the victor's rights," and "The German authorities were satisfied with the publishers' initiative."

At another period[2] in French history the prefects "eliminated" writers who refused to praise their master. The master said of the others: "I opened the doors of my anteroom, and in they rushed."

In France there still are some writers who do not rush to the anterooms and who refuse to obey orders. They feel that they must express themselves. To influence others, perhaps, but

SOURCE NOTE: Pierre de Lescure, "Manifeste des Éditions de Minuit," in Jean Paulhan and Dominique Aury, *La Patrie se fait tous les jours* (Paris, Éditions de Minuit, 1947), pp. 121–22.

above all because if they don't express themselves the mind will die.

That is the aim of the Éditions de Minuit. Propaganda is not our field. We want to safeguard our inner life and serve our art in freedom. Names are unimportant. It is no longer a matter of personal reputation. It is a matter of man's spiritual purity.

ALASTAIR HAMILTON

NOTES

1. *"New Europe"*: fascist-controlled Europe, Nazi slogan expressing the official Nazi mystique.

2. *another period*: reference to censorship in seventeenth- and eighteenth-century France.

LOUIS ARAGON

1943

THE POET TO HIS PARTY

My party has restored my eyes and my memory
I had forgotten what every child knows
That my blood was so red and my heart a French heart
All I knew was that the night was dark
My party has restored my eyes and my memory

My party has restored my belief in heroism
I see Joan of Arc I hear Roland's horn
An age of heroes is reborn in the Vercors
The simplest words ring out like swords
My party has restored my belief in heroism

SOURCE NOTE: Louis Aragon, "Du Poète à son parti," in *La Diane française, 1942–1944* (Paris, Seghers, 1946), p. 87.

My party has restored the colors of my France
My party my party thank you for what you have
    taught me
For ever since everything comes to me by way of songs
My party has restored the colors of my France

LOUIS ARAGON

DU POETE A SON PARTI

Mon parti m'a rendu mes yeux et ma mémoire
Je ne savais plus rien de ce qu'un enfant sait
Que mon sang fût si rouge et mon coeur fût français
Je savais seulement que la nuit était noire
Mon parti m'a rendu mes yeux et ma mémoire

Mon parti m'a rendu le sens de l'épopée
Je vois Jeanne filer Roland sonne le cor
C'est le temps des héros qui renaît au Vercors
Les plus simples des mots font le bruit des épées
Mon parti m'a rendu le sens de l'épopée

Mon parti m'a rendu les couleurs de la France
Mon parti mon parti merci de tes leçons
Et depuis ce temps-là tout me vient en chansons
La colère et l'amour la joie et la souffrance
Mon parti m'a rendu les couleurs de la France

CONFRONTATION AND CONTESTATION

THE GREATER LITERARY WORKS—and they were surprisingly numerous—that came out in France during the war years were seldom hit by censorship. They evolved naturally out of the literary patterns of the prewar years. Nonetheless their success hinged on their readers' and their own awareness of the tragic realities of the hour, too overpowering to be disregarded. In literature, an intense preoccupation with historical events of vast proportions is often accompanied by the use of myth, whether old myths reshaped or myths newly created according to some—in a broad sense—philosophical perspective. During the Occupation years, myth, besides the advantages of distancing it offered, could also serve as a vehicle for the appraisal of the present situation while eluding the rigors of censorship.

It is impossible here to do justice to these intricate and multileveled works, which have already elicited considerable critical commentary. Like much modern art, all are concerned with a redefinition of man's perception of himself, society, and the world and with the creation of a new awareness. In keeping with the atmosphere, situations are "extreme," stark, set in a dramatic ambience. Yet the literature of the Occupation years often speaks of the possibility that human beings might in some measure counter a seemingly overpowering adverse fate. Lucidity, awareness, revolt, freedom, responsibility are key words in these years.

THE ABSURD

"Labyrinth," the poem by Henri Michaux, projects in the slow, heavy tones of ancient lore a nightmarish vision of life as a maze which in some manner all the texts collected here confront and contest—whether with *Angst*, nausea, or a sense of the absurd. And it is Michaux too who, in his derisive, blasphemous onomatopoeia "Immense Voix," expresses the quasi-visceral revolt that rings like a challenge in all the texts below with the single exception of Simone Weil's, which is no less eloquent for its objectivity. Confrontation and contestation are the two pivots of a debate that centers on man's fate, freedom, and responsibility.

The Biblical tale of the destruction of Sodom and Gomorrah by fire and brimstone sent as a punishment from heaven is the backdrop Giraudoux chose for a highly modern play. As the curtain goes up the angels, God's messengers, have already appeared bringing God's ultimatum to men: if they can find a single human couple living in harmony with each other and God's law, the cities will be saved; otherwise they will suffer total destruction. Two couples are singled out to deflect the impending holocaust: John and Leah, James and Ruth, typically unfaithful each to the other. In the scene below Ruth makes her last-ditch plea to an unmoved John, begging him to save the city by playing the role God demands. The two voices arise, intertwined, John's with its lucid vision of the irrational violence of God's creation, Ruth's with its desperate aspiration toward harmony. They are witnesses to the duplicity and irrationality of the human lot: God has stacked the cards against his creature. The allegory is clear. There is no ideal order that presides over man's fate, meting out punishment in the form of disaster. Violence is inherent in a cosmos against which human aspirations—voiced by Ruth—rise in ineffectual protest, for human beings partake in the violence done them.

Camus's *The Stranger* is too well know for comment. Beneath the surface simplicity of the story, an archetypal pattern is discernible: from his purely physical immersion in existence Meursault, in the course of his adventure, accedes to an awareness of what it is to be a human being. This awareness change, not the facts of his existence, but his relation to them, to himself, to others, to the world. Drawn by chance into another man's quarrel, Meursault kills a man in a moment of quasi-hallucination, impelled by the violence of the sun that encompasses him on all sides. In contrast to the vast, lawless solitude of the beach, his trial—a purely human affair—takes place in the crowded, stuffy courtroom. In the scene given below, prosecutor and attorney for the defense confront each other in a rhetorical duel that leaves Meursault bewildered yet intact. The terms of the double argument simply do not fit the facts. Meursault's world does not mesh with the world of words that supposedly deals with it. A stranger to his act, a stranger to the man on trial, Meursault listens in, as it were, on his trial—and the experience is one stage in his itinerary toward a final awareness.

What Camus evokes in *The Stranger* is the immense irrationality and potentiality for violence coiled at the heart of the most ordinary, everyday existence. It is crazily mirrored in Meursault's triple encounter with nature, with his own act, and with the institutions of society.

The use of force in human affairs is a factor whose nature and effects Simone Weil explores in her brilliant essay written at the very peak of Nazi triumph. It is indubitably one of the two or three main texts of the Occupation years, directly focused on a central issue: violence as pictured in Homer's *Iliad*, which she analyzes from that single point of view. What she discerns in the *Iliad* is the dangerous illusion of freedom that superior force gives men, allowing them to treat other men as objects, corpses, or slaves. But gaining momentum, violence boomerangs, destroying the agent of destruction in his turn. The *Iliad* describes war as an infernal cycle that has the implacable and purely mechanical inevitability of fate.

HENRI MICHAUX

THE LABYRINTH

Life is a labyrinth, a labyrinth death
An endless labyrinth, says the Master of Ho.

Plunging deeper, never freed
Suicide leads to further pain.

Prison opens into prison
Passages lead to other passages:

He who hopes to uncoil life's coil
Uncoils nothing whatever.

Nothing emerges anywhere
Even the centuries live underground, says the Master
   of Ho.

ALASTAIR HAMILTON

LABYRINTHE

Labyrinthe, la vie, labyrinthe, la mort
Labyrinthe sans fin, dit le Maître de Ho.

Tout enfonce, rien ne libère.
Le suicidé renaît à une nouvelle souffrance.

La prison ouvre sur une prison
Le couloir ouvre un autre couloir:

SOURCE NOTE: Henri Michaux, "Labyrinthe," *Épreuves, Exorcismes (1940–1945)* (Paris, Gallimard, 1945), pp. 66–67.

Celui qui croit dérouler le rouleau de sa vie
Ne déroule rien du tout.

Rien ne débouche nulle part
Les siècles aussi vivent sous terre, dit le maître de Ho.

JEAN GIRAUDOUX

1943

From SODOM AND GOMORRAH

The terrace of John's and Leah's villa above the plain; but though the setting is the same as in Act One, it no longer expresses security and happiness. The light is grey and threatening. Thin smoke rises from the Cities of the Plain in the distance. The house front, right, shows neglect. The awning sags; the birdcage on the wall is open and the bird has flown; the big white jar that held the bouquet of angels' feathers has fallen on its side and the feathers are scattered. RUTH *and* JOHN *enter from the left and lean over the balustrade.* RUTH's *attitude shows fear and terror,* JOHN's, *detachment.*

JOHN Lovely, isn't it, this spectacle of the world coming to an end!

RUTH For me, it is the end of the day spent with you. And it's horrible!

JOHN How curious! Something strange about the air today. In spite of the distance, you can see people running down there and hear their cries. What panic! Come nearer. Come and see human beings at their most harmonious—in fear—at their most exalted—in full flight . . .

SOURCE NOTE: Jean Giraudoux, *Sodome et Gomorrhe* (Paris, Grasset, 1947), Act II, Scene 2, pp. 96–105. First performed at the Théâtre Hébertot on October 11, 1943.

RUTH   No, no! I, too, am afraid!

JOHN   The end of the world. At least, that's what it's called.
I would say, rather, that God frees the world today of its
hypocrisies. This frenzy, this rumbling and roaring, these con-
flagrations—what are they but the world's naked truths? And
those stars breaking loose from their constellations and furrow-
ing the sky in their flight like runaway horses—what are they
but Heaven's naked truths? The end of the world is the moment when the world shows itself in its real light: explosive,
submersible, combustible. In the same way, war is the moment
when human nature reverts to its origins. We live in the midst
of fire that burns, water that drowns, gas that suffocates. We
live in the midst of hate and stupidity. Ruth, you're the one
that brought me here. You have got your way, so take advantage
of it . . .

RUTH   I brought you here to save us and to save myself . . .
and to bring Leah back to you.

JOHN   Leah will not come. You'll have plenty of time to see
the show. Come! Come nearer!

RUTH   She will come. Knowing James as I do, I can be sure
of it. Leah will come.

JOHN   To die at the end of the world and with the person one
loves. That's quite a privilege, isn't it?

RUTH   Save me!

JOHN   How? By forsaking you?

RUTH   No, John darling. But by not forsaking Leah. By returning to her. Oh, my dearest . . .

JOHN   All the tender words that women use to hold a lover,
you are using to drive me away.

RUTH   I'm only a living creature, John. I'm just one of those
ordinary creatures who need perfection in such simple things

as air and water. I need pure air to breathe, pure water to drink. Rather than die, I would do anything. I'm ready to disown you, lose you. Why do you force me to confess my cowardice? I love you more than anything in life; but ever since I heard that voice in the night declaring that only a perfect human couple, a happy man and wife, could save us from destruction, I have felt that God was still thinking of you and Leah. Since that voice crying in the darkness I have done everything to force you of your own accord to leave me. I counted upon this dawn and this awakening. I thought when you found me at your side, instead of Leah, that you would reckon up your losses with disgust. I turned my face to the wall. I thought perhaps God would mistake me for Leah. I pretended to be asleep. I had left the door half open. Oh, why didn't you run away? You stayed. But not because you preferred me. Admit it: you stayed because you preferred death!

JOHN   No. I stayed for a very simple reason. Leah guessed it. That's why she hasn't come and won't come. The fact is, I woke up this morning entirely happy to find myself there at your side.

RUTH   Don't say that. The Heavens are listening. You'll bring us all to destruction. You don't love me. You despise me.

JOHN   You needn't shout so loud. You'll not fool the Angel, if he's listening, for he knows that I liked to be there beside you.

RUTH   You called out Leah's name in your sleep.

JOHN   That's not true. I didn't have a dream. I didn't need to dream. Come here, Ruth. Stand near me, my sweet . . . Heaven has evidently ordained that at this world-shaking moment we should stand here, reciting the "Song of Songs" of the counterfeit married couple.

RUTH   I won't listen to you. It's sheer pride that's making you say such things.

JOHN   The "Song of Songs" of the false wife, the untruthful

wife. That's the idea. Put your arms around me. I will chant
it . . .

RUTH   Hush! You're bringing destruction upon all of us.

JOHN   Your soul is false: so false that the very word "false-
ness" sits lightly, like a caress upon you, becoming praise. Ah,
that makes you smile! Everything about you is suspect. But
with me you have been frankness incarnate. I was the first to
enjoy your candor. You have surrendered to me a virginity
which ceaselessly renews itself. You fed your husband upon lies
and infantilism. But everything you have given me has been
branded with truth. I have heard your true adventures, shared
your memories. Even the most trivial! That story you told me
about the lame nightingale and the crutch you made for it with
a tooth of your tortoise-shell comb—well, I believe it.

RUTH   It wasn't a nightingale—it was a sparrow. And my comb
wasn't genuine tortoise shell; it was imitation.

JOHN   James knew nothing of you but lies, lies, lies. You pretended to enjoy everything you loathed, everything that revolted
you. Your real joys you buried in silence. With me you have
been sincere. When you were sleepy you yawned. And in your
dreams you talked, you called my name.

RUTH   What are you getting at?

JOHN   I'll tell you. I left a woman whom, for five years as my
wife, I adored and esteemed and regarded with delight because
her loyalty to me seemed Divine, incredible. But at your side,
my beloved of one short day, I at last found reality in all its
peacefulness. There you have my balance sheet; that satisfies
me.

RUTH   Why do you say such things? Why do you pretend
you've not always known that the maximum of truth and tenderness and virtue can only be revealed to you by women who
are insincere, egotistic, and undisciplined? You've always
known, as all men know, that the best way to appreciate what

silence and submission can be is to live for a week or a day with a talkative and stubborn woman.

JOHN You have given me all the things that you withheld from your husband. For this, I thank you . . .

RUTH What have I to give? By comparison with you and Leah, James and I are very small indeed. That's why you two have made a very bad bargain. Leah is frank and generous; she could never conceal her real feelings, her contempt, from James. Just as you, who are naturally strong and gentle, have had to be weak and brutal in your dealings with me. Anyway, it's all over. I can't stand it any longer. Call Leah: save us, John. The city will be spared only through you and Leah! All the prophets have said so. All the echoes have repeated it. Oh! Don't you believe them?

JOHN I wish I could believe them. I know that God takes pleasure in tying up the destiny of the world and the destiny of each human being with small things, conditions, passwords, details. He forces us to employ, like token coins or counters, words and acts which seem irrelevant. Up to now I have always obeyed these sham orders. When I go downstairs, I always start off on the left foot; I don't walk on the cracks of the sidewalks; I break apples in two instead of cutting them, and so on. It is just possible, as you say, that our life today hangs in the balance because of some such formality. Perhaps Leah and I have only to take each other by the hand and call out, "Present!" and all the world would right itself again. But I cannot. I don't feel as though I were present in this world which is coming to an end. I feel more like shouting, "Absent!" with all my heart. And apparently Leah feels the same. For, as you see, she is still absent. I came up here to please God and to please Ruth, because men are always dutiful just as women are always right! Yes, Leah is right not to come. By staying away she is avoiding making a scene and a scandal. Since our quarrel—which she started yesterday—it would be impossible for us to meet as we formerly did. Our meeting would be more like a confrontation.

RUTH   She will come . . . Listen! She is coming . . . Call out
to her!

JOHN   No part of me calls out to her, except my voice.

RUTH   That is enough. Call her! Shout!

HERMA BRIFFAULT

ALBERT CAMUS

1942

From THE STRANGER

It is always interesting, even in the prisoner's dock, to hear
oneself being talked about. And certainly in the speeches of my
lawyer and the prosecuting counsel a great deal was said about
me; more, in fact, about me personally than about my crime.

Really there wasn't any very great difference between the two
speeches. Counsel for the defense raised his arms to heaven and
pleaded guilty, but with extenuating circumstances. The Prosecutor made similar gestures; he agreed that I was guilty, but
denied extenuating circumstances.

One thing about this phase of the trial was rather irksome.
Quite often, interested as I was in what they had to say, I was
tempted to put in a word, myself. But my lawyer had advised
me not to. "You won't do your case any good by talking," he
had warned me. In fact, there seemed to be a conspiracy to
exclude me from the proceedings; I wasn't to have any say and
my fate was to be decided out of hand.

It was quite an effort at times for me to refrain from cutting
them all short, and saying: "But, damn it all, who's on trial in

SOURCE NOTE: Albert Camus, *L'Étranger* (Paris, Gallimard, 1942), Part
II, Ch. 4.

this court, I'd like to know? It's a serious matter for a man, being accused of murder. And I've something really important to tell you."

However, on second thought, I found I had nothing to say. In any case, I must admit that hearing oneself talked about loses its interest very soon. The Prosecutor's speech, especially, began to bore me before he was halfway through it. The only things that really caught my attention were occasional phrases, his gestures, and some elaborate tirades—but these were isolated patches.

What he was aiming at, I gathered, was to show that my crime was premeditated. I remember his saying at one moment, "I can prove this, gentlemen of the jury, to the hilt. First, you have the facts of the crime, which are as clear as daylight. And then you have what I may call the night side of this case, the dark workings of a criminal mentality."

He began by summing up the facts, from my mother's death onward. He stressed my heartlessness, my inability to state Mother's age, my visit to the swimming pool where I met Marie, our matinee at the pictures where a Fernandel film was showing, and finally my return with Marie to my rooms. I didn't quite follow his remarks at first, as he kept on mentioning "the prisoner's mistress," whereas for me she was just "Marie." Then he came to the subject of Raymond. It seemed to me that his way of treating the facts showed a certain shrewdness. All he said sounded quite plausible. I'd written the letter in collusion with Raymond so as to entice his mistress to his room and subject her to ill-treatment by a man "of more than dubious reputation." Then, on the beach, I'd provoked a brawl with Raymond's enemies, in the course of which Raymond was wounded. I'd asked him for his revolver and gone back by myself with the intention of using it. Then I'd shot the Arab. After the first shot I waited. Then, "to be certain of making a good job of it," I fired four more shots deliberately, point-blank, and in cold blood, at my victim.

"That is my case," he said. "I have described to you the

series of events which led this man to kill the deceased, fully aware of what he was doing. I emphasize this point. We are not concerned with an act of homicide committed on a sudden impulse which might serve as extenuation. I ask you to note, gentlemen of the jury, that the prisoner is an educated man. You will have observed the way in which he answered my questions; he is intelligent and he knows the value of words. And I repeat that it is quite impossible to assume that, when he committed the crime, he was unaware what he was doing."

I noticed that he laid stress on my "intelligence." It puzzled me rather why what would count as a good point in an ordinary person should be used against an accused man as an overwhelming proof of his guilt. While thinking this over, I missed what he said next, until I heard him exclaim indignantly: "And has he uttered a word of regret for his most odious crime? Not one word, gentlemen. Not once in the course of these proceedings did this man show the least contrition."

Turning toward the dock, he pointed a finger at me, and went on in the same strain. I really couldn't understand why he harped on this point so much. Of course, I had to own that he was right; I didn't feel much regret for what I'd done. Still, to my mind he overdid it, and I'd have liked to have a chance of explaining to him, in a quite friendly, almost affectionate way, that I have never been able really to regret anything in all my life. I've always been far too much absorbed in the present moment, or the immediate future, to think back. Of course, in the position into which I had been forced, there was no question of my speaking to anyone in that tone. I hadn't the right to show any friendly feeling or possess good intentions. And I tried to follow what came next, as the Prosecutor was now considering what he called my "soul."

He said he'd studied it closely—and had found a blank, "literally nothing, gentlemen of the jury." Really, he said, I had no soul, there was nothing human about me, not one of those moral qualities which normal men possess had any place in my mentality. "No doubt," he added, "we should not reproach him with this. We cannot blame a man for lacking what it was never in his power to acquire. But in a criminal court the wholly passive ideal of tolerance must give place to a sterner, loftier ideal, that of justice. Especially when this lack of every decent instinct is such as that of the man before you, a menace to society." He proceeded to discuss my conduct toward my mother, repeating what he had said in the course of the hearing. But he spoke at much greater length of my crime— at such length, indeed, that I lost the thread and was conscious only of the steadily increasing heat.

A moment came when the Prosecutor paused and, after a short silence, said in a low, vibrant voice: "This same court, gentlemen, will be called on to try tomorrow that most odious of crimes, the murder of a father by his son." To his mind, such a crime was almost unimaginable. But, he ventured to hope, justice would be meted out without faltering. And yet, he made bold to say, the horror that even the crime of parricide inspired in him paled beside the loathing inspired by my callousness.

"This man, who is morally guilty of his mother's death, is no less unfit to have a place in the community than that other man who did to death the father that begat him. And, indeed, the one crime led on to the other; the first of these two criminals, the man in the dock, set a precedent, if I may put it so, and authorized the second crime. Yes, gentlemen, I am convinced" —here he raised his voice a tone—"that you will not find I am exaggerating the case against the prisoner when I say that he is also guilty of the murder to be tried tomorrow in this court. And I look to you for a verdict accordingly."

The Prosecutor paused again, to wipe the sweat off his face. He then explained that his duty was a painful one, but he would do it without flinching. "This man has, I repeat, no place in a community whose basic principles he flouts without compunction. Nor, heartless as he is, has he any claim to mercy. I ask you to impose the extreme penalty of the law; and I ask it without a qualm. In the course of a long career, in which it has often been my duty to ask for a capital sentence, never have I felt that painful duty weigh so little on my mind as in the present case. In demanding a verdict of murder without extenuating circumstances, I am following not only the dictates of my conscience and a sacred obligation, but also those of the natural and righteous indignation I feel at the sight of a criminal devoid of the least spark of human feeling."

When the Prosecutor sat down there was a longish silence. Personally I was quite overcome by the heat and my amazement at what I had been hearing. The presiding judge gave a short cough, and asked me in a very low tone if I had anything to say. I rose, and as I felt in the mood to speak, I said the first thing that crossed my mind: that I'd had no intention of killing the Arab. The Judge replied that this statement would be taken into consideration by the court. Meanwhile he would be glad to hear, before my counsel addressed the court, what were the motives of my crime. So far, he must admit, he hadn't fully understood the grounds of my defense.

I tried to explain that it was because of the sun, but I spoke too quickly and ran my words into each other. I was only too conscious that it sounded nonsensical, and, in fact, I heard people tittering.

My lawyer shrugged his shoulders. Then he was directed to address the court, in his turn. But all he did was to point out the lateness of the hour and to ask for an adjournment till the following afternoon. To this the judge agreed.

When I was brought back next day, the electric fans were still churning up the heavy air and the jurymen plying their gaudy little fans in a sort of steady rhythm. The speech for the defense seemed to me interminable. At one moment, however, I pricked up my ears; it was when I heard him saying: "It is true I killed a man." He went on in the same strain, saying "I" when he referred to me. It seemed so queer that I bent toward the policeman on my right and asked him to explain. He told me to shut up; then, after a moment, whispered: "They all do that." It seemed to me that the idea behind it was still further to exclude me from the case, to put me off the map, so to speak, by substituting the lawyer for myself. Anyway, it hardly mattered; I already felt worlds away from this courtroom and its tedious "proceedings."

My lawyer, in any case, struck me as feeble to the point of being ridiculous. He hurried through his plea of provocation, and then he, too, started in about my soul. But I had an impression that he had much less talent than the Prosecutor.

"I, too," he said, "have closely studied this man's soul; but, unlike my learned friend for the prosecution, I have found something there. Indeed, I may say that I have read the prisoner's mind like an open book." What he had read there was that I was an excellent young fellow, a steady, conscientious worker who did his best by his employer; that I was popular with everyone and sympathetic in others' troubles. According to him I was a dutiful son, who had supported his mother as long as he was able. After anxious consideration I had reached the conclusion that, by entering a home, the old lady would have comforts that my means didn't permit me to provide for her. "I am astounded, gentlemen," he added, "by the attitude taken up by my learned friend in referring to this Home. Surely if proof be needed of the excellence of such institutions, we need only remember that they are promoted and financed by a government department." I noticed that he made no reference to the funeral, and this seemed to me a serious omission. But, what with his long-windedness, the endless days and hours they had been discussing my "soul," and the rest of it, I found that my mind had gone blurred; everything was dissolving into a grayish, watery haze.

Only one incident stands out; toward the end, while my counsel rambled on, I heard the tin trumpet of an ice-cream vendor in the street, a small, shrill sound cutting across the flow of words. And then a rush of memories went through my mind—memories of a life which was mine no longer and had once provided me with the surest, humblest pleasures: warm smells of summer, my favorite streets, the sky at evening, Marie's dresses and her laugh. The futility of what was happening here seemed to take me by the throat, I felt like vomiting, and I had only one idea: to get it over, to go back to my cell, and sleep . . . and sleep.

Dimly I heard my counsel making his last appeal.

"Gentlemen of the jury, surely you will not send to his death a decent, hard-working young man, because for one tragic moment he lost his self-control? Is he not sufficiently punished by the lifelong remorse that is to be his lot? I confidently await your verdict, the only verdict possible—that of homicide with extenuating circumstances."

The court rose, and the lawyer sat down, looking thoroughly exhausted. Some of his colleagues came to him and shook his hand. "You put up a magnificent show, old man," I heard one of them say. Another lawyer even called me to witness: "Fine, wasn't it?" I agreed, but insincerely; I was far too tired to judge if it had been "fine" or otherwise.

Meanwhile the day was ending and the heat becoming less intense. By some vague sounds that reached me from the street I knew that the cool of the evening had set in. We all sat on, waiting. And what we all were waiting for really concerned nobody but me. I looked round the courtroom. It was exactly as it had been on the first day. I met the eyes of the journalist in gray and the robot woman. This reminded me that not once during the whole hearing had I tried to catch Marie's eye. It wasn't that I'd forgotten her; only I was too preoccupied. I saw her now, seated between Céleste and Raymond. She gave me a little wave of her hand, as if to say, "At last!" She was smiling, but I could tell that she was rather anxious. But my heart seemed turned to stone, and I couldn't even return her smile.

The judges came back to their seats. Someone read out to the jury, very rapidly, a string of questions. I caught a word here and there. "Murder of malice aforethought . . . Provocation . . . Extenuating circumstances." The jury went out, and I was taken to the little room where I had already waited. My lawyer came to see me; he was very talkative and showed more cordiality and confidence than ever before. He assured me that all would go well and I'd get off with a few years' imprisonment or transportation. I asked him what were the chances of getting the sentence quashed. He said there was no chance of that He had not raised any point of law, as this was apt to prejudice the jury. And it was difficult to get a judgment quashed except on technical grounds. I saw his point, and agreed. Looking at the matter dispassionately, I shared his view. Otherwise there would be no end to litigation. "In any case," the lawyer said, "you can appeal in the ordinary way. But I'm convinced the verdict will be favorable."

We waited for quite a while, a good three quarters of an hour, I should say. Then a bell rang. My lawyer left me, saying:

"The foreman of the jury will read out the answers. You will be called on after that to hear the judgment."

Some doors banged. I heard people hurrying down flights of steps, but couldn't tell whether they were nearby or distant. Then I heard a voice droning away in the courtroom.

When the bell rang again and I stepped back into the dock, the silence of the courtroom closed in round me, and with the silence came a queer sensation when I noticed that, for the first time, the young journalist kept his eyes averted. I didn't look in Marie's direction. In fact, I had no time to look, as the presiding judge had already started pronouncing a rigmarole to the effect that "in the name of the French people" I was to be decapitated in some public place.

It seemed to me then that I could interpret the look on the faces of those present; it was one of almost respectful sympathy. The policemen, too, handled me very gently. The lawyer placed his hand on my wrist. I had stopped thinking altogether. I heard the Judge's voice asking if I had anything more to say. After thinking for a moment, I answered, "No." Then the policemen led me out.

STUART GILBERT

THE ILIAD, POEM OF FORCE

The true hero, the true subject, the center of the *Iliad* is force. Force employed by man, force that enslaves man, force before which man's flesh shrinks away. In this work, at all times, the human spirit is shown as modified by its relations with force, as swept away, blinded by the very force it imagined it could handle, as deformed by the weight of the force it submits to. For those dreamers who considered that force, thanks to progress, would soon be a thing of the past, the *Iliad* could appear as a historical document; for others, whose powers of recognition are more acute and who perceive force, today as yesterday, at the very center of human history, the *Iliad* is the purest and the loveliest of mirrors.

To define force—it is that *x* that turns anybody who is subjected to it into a thing. Exercised to the limit, it turns man into a thing in the most literal sense: it makes a corpse out of him. Somebody was here, and the next minute there is nobody here at all; this is a spectacle the *Iliad* never wearies of showing us:

> . . . *the horses*
> *Rattled the empty chariots through the files of battle,*
> *Longing for their noble drivers. But they on the ground*
> *Lay, dearer to the vultures than to their wives.*

The hero becomes a *thing* dragged behind a chariot in the dust:

> *All around, his black hair*
> *Was spread; in the dust his whole head lay,*
> *That once-charming head; now Zeus had let his enemies*
> *Defile it on his native soil.*

SOURCE NOTE: Simone Weil (pseud. Émile Novis), "The Iliad, Poem of Force," *Chicago Review*, XVIII, No. 2 (1965), pp. 5–30. Originally appeared in the *Cahiers du Sud*, December 1940 and January 1941.

The bitterness of such a spectacle is offered us absolutely undiluted. No comforting fiction intervenes; no consoling prospect of immortality; and on the hero's head no washed-out halo of patriotism descends.

> His soul, fleeing his limbs, passed to Hades,
> Mourning its fate, forsaking its youth and its vigor.

Still more poignant—so painful is the contrast—is the sudden evocation, as quickly rubbed out, of another world: the far-away, precarious, touching world of peace, of the family, the world in which each man counts more than anything else to those about him.

> She ordered her bright-haired maids in the palace
> To place on the fire a large tripod, preparing
> A hot bath for Hector, returning from battle.
> Foolish woman! Already he lay, far from hot baths,
> Slain by gray-eyed Athena, who guided Achilles' arm.

Far from hot baths he was indeed, poor man. And not he alone. Nearly all the *Iliad* takes place far from hot baths. Nearly all of human life, then and now, takes place far from hot baths.

Here we see force in its grossest and most summary form—the force that kills. How much more varied in its processes, how much more surprising in its effects is the other force, the force that does *not* kill, i.e., that does not kill just yet. It will surely kill, it will possibly kill, or perhaps it merely hangs, poised and ready, over the head of the creature it *can* kill, at any moment, which is to say at every moment. In whatever aspect, its effect is the same: it turns a man into a stone. From its first property (the ability to turn a human being into a thing by the simple method of killing him) flows another, quite prodigious too in its own way, the ability to turn a human being into a thing while he is still alive. He is alive; he has a soul; and yet—he is a thing. An extraordinary entity this—a thing that has a soul. And as for the soul, what an extraordinary house it finds itself in! Who can say what it costs it, moment by moment, to accommodate itself to this residence, how much writhing and bending, folding and pleating are required of it? It was not made to live inside a thing; if it does so, under pressure of necessity, there is not a single element of its nature to which violence is not done.

A man stands disarmed and naked with a weapon pointing at him; this person becomes a corpse before anybody or anything touches him. Just a minute ago, he was thinking, acting, hoping:

> Motionless, he pondered. And the other drew near,
> Terrified, anxious to touch his knees, hoping in his heart
> To escape evil death and black destiny . . .
> With one hand he clasped, suppliant, his knees,
> While the other clung to the sharp spear, not letting go . . .

Soon, however, he grasps the fact that the weapon which is pointing at him will not be diverted; and now, still breathing, he is simply matter; still thinking, he can think no longer:

> Thus spoke the brilliant son of Priam
> In begging words. But he heard a harsh reply:
> He spoke. And the other's knees and heart failed him.
> Dropping his spear, he knelt down, holding out his arms.
> Achilles, drawing his sharp sword, struck
> Through the neck and breastbone. The two-edged sword
> Sunk home its full length. The other, face down,
> Lay still, and the black blood ran out, wetting the ground.

If a stranger, completely disabled, disarmed, strengthless, throws himself on the mercy of a warrior, he is not, by this very act, condemned to death; but a moment of impatience on the warrior's part will suffice to relieve him of his life. In any case, his flesh has lost that very important property which in the laboratory distinguishes living flesh from dead—the galvanic response. If you give a frog's leg an electric shock, it twitches. If you confront a human being with the touch or sight of something horrible or terrifying, this bundle of muscles, nerves, and flesh likewise twitches. Alone of all living things, the suppliant we have just described neither quivers nor trembles. He has lost the right to do so. As his lips advance to touch the object that is for him of all things most charged with horror, they do not draw back on his teeth—they cannot:

> No one saw great Priam enter. He stopped,
> Clasped the knees of Achilles, kissed his hands,
> Those terrible man-killing hands that had slaughtered so
>   many of his sons.

The sight of a human being pushed to such an extreme of suffering chills us like the sight of a dead body:

> As when harsh misfortune strikes a man if in his own
>   country
> He has killed a man, and arrives at last at someone else's
>   door,
> The door of a rich man; a shudder seizes those who see him.
> So Achilles shuddered to see divine Priam;
> The others shuddered too, looking one at the other.

But this feeling lasts only a moment. Soon the very presence of the suffering creature is forgotten:

> He spoke. The other, remembering his own father, longed
>   to weep;
> Taking the old man's arm, he pushed him away.
> Both were remembering. Thinking of Hector, killer of men,
> Priam wept, abased at the feet of Achilles.
> But Achilles wept, now for his father,
> Now for Patroclus. And their sobs resounded through the
>   house.

It was not insensibility that made Achilles with a single movement of his hand push away the old man who had been clinging to his knees; Priam's words, recalling his own old father, had moved him to tears. It was merely a question of his being as free in his attitudes and movements as if, clasping his knees, there were not a suppliant but an inert object. Anybody who is in our vicinity exercises a certain power over us by his very presence, and a power that belongs to him alone, that is, the power of halting, repressing, modifying each movement that our body sketches out. If we step aside for a passer-by on the road, it is not the same thing as stepping aside to avoid a billboard; alone in our rooms, we get up, walk about, sit down again quite differently from the way we do when we have a visitor. But this indefinable influence that the presence of another human being has on us is not exercised by men whom a moment of impatience can deprive of life, who can die before even thought has a chance to pass sentence on them. In their presence, people move about as if they were not there; they, on their side, running the risk of being reduced to nothing in a single instant, imitate nothingness in their own persons. Pushed, they fall. Fallen, they lie where they are, unless chance gives somebody the idea of raising them up again. But supposing that at long last they have been picked up, honored with cordial remarks, they still do not venture to take this resurrection seriously; they dare not express a wish lest an irritated voice return them forever to silence:

He spoke; the old man trembled and obeyed.

Force, in the hands of another, exercises over the soul the same tyranny that extreme hunger does; for it possesses, and *in perpetuo*, the power of life and death. Its rule, moreover, is as cold and hard as the rule of inert matter. The man who knows himself weaker than another is more alone in the heart of a city than a man lost in the desert.

> *Two casks are placed before Zeus's doorsill,*
> *Containing the gifts he gives, the bad in one, the good in*
>   *the other . . .*
> *The man to whom he gives baneful gifts, he exposes to*
>   *outrage;*
> *A frightful need drives across the divine earth;*
> *He is a wanderer, and gets no respect from gods or men.*

Force is as pitiless to the man who possesses it, or thinks he does, as it is to its victims; the second it crushes, the first it intoxicates. The truth is, nobody really possesses it. The human race is not divided up, in the *Iliad*, into conquered persons, slaves, suppliants on the one hand, and conquerors and chiefs on the other. In this poem there is not a single man who does

not at one time or another have to bow his neck to force.
Even to Achilles the moment comes; he too must shake and
stammer with fear, though it is a river that has this effect on
him, not a man. But, with the exception of Achilles, every man
in the *Iliad* tastes a moment of defeat in battle. Victory is less
a matter of valor than of blind destiny, which is symbolized
in the poem by Zeus's golden scales:

> Then Zeus the father took his golden scales,
> In them he put the two fates of death that cuts down all
> men,
> One for the Trojans, tamers of horses, one for the bronze-
> sheathed Greeks.
> He seized the scales by the middle; it was the fatal day of
> Greece that sank.

By its very blindness, destiny establishes a kind of justice. Blind
also is she who decrees to warriors punishment in kind. He
that takes the sword will perish by the sword. The *Iliad* formulated the principle long before the Gospels did, and in almost
the same terms:

> Ares is just, and kills those who kill.

Perhaps all men, by the very act of being born, are destined
to suffer violence; yet this is a truth to which circumstance shuts
men's eyes. The strong are, as a matter of fact, never absolutely
strong, nor are the weak absolutely weak, but neither is aware
of this. They have in common a refusal to believe that they
both belong to the same species: the weak see no relation
between themselves and the strong, and vice versa. The man
who is the possessor of force seems to walk through a non-
resistant element; in the human substance that surrounds him
nothing has the power to interpose, between the impulse and
the act, the tiny interval that is reflection. Where there is no
room for reflection, there is none either for justice or prudence.
Hence we see men in arms behaving harshly and madly. We
see their sword bury itself in the breast of a disarmed enemy
who is in the very act of pleading at their knees. We see them

triumph over a dying man by describing to him the outrages his corpse will endure. We see Achilles cut the throats of twelve Trojan boys on the funeral pyre of Patroclus as naturally as we cut flowers for a grave. These men, wielding power, have no suspicion of the fact that the consequences of their deeds will at length come home to them—they too will bow the neck in their turn. If you can make an old man fall silent, tremble, obey, with a single word of your own, why should it occur to you that the curses of this old man, who is after all a priest, will have their own importance in the gods' eyes? Why should you refrain from taking Achilles' girl away from him if you know that neither he nor she can do anything but obey you? Achilles rejoices over the sight of the Greeks fleeing in misery and confusion. What could possibly suggest to him that this rout, which will last exactly as long as he wants it to and end when his mood indicates it, that this very rout will be the cause of his friend's death, and, for that matter, of his own? Thus it happens that those who have force on loan from fate count on it too much and are destroyed.

But at the time their own destruction seems impossible to them. For they do not see that the force in their possession is only a limited quantity; nor do they see their relations with other human beings as a kind of balance between unequal amounts of force. Since other people do not impose on their movements that halt, that interval of hesitation, wherein lies all our consideration for our brothers in humanity, they conclude that destiny has given complete license to them and none at all to their inferiors. And at this point they exceed the measure of the force that is actually at their disposal. Inevitably they exceed it, since they are not aware that it is limited. And now we see them committed irretrievably to chance; suddenly things cease to obey them. Sometimes chance is kind to them, sometimes cruel. But in any case there they are, exposed, open to misfortune; gone is the armor of power that formerly protected their naked souls; nothing, no shield, stands between them and tears.

This retribution, which has a geometrical rigor, which oper-
ates automatically to penalize the abuse of force, was the main
subject of Greek thought. It is the soul of the epic. Under the
name of Nemesis, it functions as the mainspring of Aeschylus'
tragedies. To the Pythagoreans, to Socrates and Plato, it was
the jumping-off point of speculation upon the nature of man
and the universe. Wherever Hellenism has penetrated, we find
the idea of it familiar. In Oriental countries which are steeped
in Buddhism, it is perhaps this Greek idea that has lived on
under the name of Karma. The Occident, however, has lost it,
and no longer even has a word to express it in any of its
languages: conceptions of limit, measure, equilibrium, which
ought to determine the conduct of life, are in the West re-
stricted to a servile function in the vocabulary of technics. We
are only geometricians of matter; the Greeks were, first of all,
geometricians in their apprenticeship to virtue.

The progress of the war in the *Iliad* is simply a continual
game of seesaw. The victor of the moment feels himself
invincible, even though, only a few hours before, he may have
experienced defeat; he forgets to treat victory as a transitory
thing. At the end of the first day of combat described in the
Iliad, the victorious Greeks were in a position to obtain the
object of all their efforts, i.e., Helen and her riches—assuming
of course, as Homer did, that the Greeks had reason to believe
that Helen was in Troy. Actually, the Egyptian priests, who
ought to have known, affirmed later on to Herodotus that she
was in Egypt. In any case, that evening the Greeks are no longer
interested in her or her possessions:

> "For the present, let us not accept the riches of Paris;
> Nor Helen; everybody sees, even the most ignorant,
> That Troy stands on the verge of ruin."
> He spoke, and all the Achaeans acclaimed him.

What they want is, in fact, everything. For booty, all the riches
of Troy; for their bonfires, all the palaces, temples, houses; for
slaves, all the women and children; for corpses, all the men.
They forget one detail, that *everything* is not within their

power, for they are not in Troy. Perhaps they will be there
tomorrow; perhaps not. Hector, the same day, makes the same
mistake:

> For I know well in my entrails and in my heart,
> A day will come when Holy Troy will perish,
> And Priam, and the nation of Priam of the good lance.
> But I think less of the grief that is in store for the Trojans,
> And of Hecuba herself, and of Priam the king,
> And of my brothers, so numerous and so brave,
> Who will fall in the dust under the blows of the enemy,
> Than of you that day when a Greek in his bronze breastplate
> Will drag you away weeping and deprive you of your
>   liberty.
>
> But as for me, may I be dead, and may the earth have
>   covered me
> Before I hear you cry out or see you dragged away!

At this moment what would he not give to turn aside those
horrors which he believes to be inevitable? But at this moment
nothing he *could* give would be of any use. The next day but
one, however, the Greeks have run away miserably, and
Agamemnon himself is in favor of putting to sea again. And
now Hector, by making a very few concessions, could readily
secure the enemy's departure; yet now he is even unwilling to
let them go empty-handed:

> Set fires everywhere and let the brightness mount the skies
> Lest in the night the long-haired Greeks,
> Escaping, sail over the broad back of ocean . . .
> Let each of them take home a wound to heal
> . . . thus others will fear
> To bring dolorous war to the Trojans, tamers of horses.

His wish is granted; the Greeks stay; and the next day they
reduce Hector and his men to a pitiable condition:

> As for them—they fled across the plain like cattle
> Whom a lion hunts before him in the dark midnight . . .
> Thus the mighty Agamemnon, son of Atreus, pursued them,
> Steadily killing the hindmost; and still they fled.

In the course of the afternoon, Hector regains the ascendancy, withdraws again, then puts the Greeks to flight, then is repulsed by Patroclus, who has come in with his fresh troops. Patroclus, pressing his advantage, ends by finding himself exposed, wounded and without armor, to the sword of Hector. And finally that evening the victorious Hector hears the prudent counsel of Polydamas and repudiates it sharply:

> Now that wily Kronos' son has given me
> Glory at the ships; now that I have driven the Greeks to
>   the sea,
> Do not offer, fool, such counsels to the people.
> No Trojan will listen to you; nor would I permit it . . .
> So Hector spoke, and the Trojans acclaimed him . . .

The next day Hector is lost. Achilles has harried him across the field and is about to kill him. He has always been the stronger of the two in combat; how much the more so now, after several weeks of rest, ardent for vengeance and victory, against an exhausted enemy? And Hector stands alone, before the walls of Troy, absolutely alone, alone to wait for death and to steady his soul to face it:

> Alas, were I to slip through the gate, behind the rampart,
> Polydamas at once would heap dishonor on me . . .
> And now that through my recklessness I have destroyed my
>   people,
> I fear the Trojans and the long-robed Trojan women,
> I fear to hear from someone far less brave than I:
> "Hector, trusting his own strength too far, has ruined his
>   people" . . .
> Suppose I were to down my bossed shield,
> My massive helmet, and, leaning my spear against the wall,
> Should go to meet renowned Achilles? . . .
> But why spin out these fancies? Why such dreams?
> I would not reach him, nor would he pity me,
> Or respect me. He would kill me like a woman
> If I came naked thus . . .

Not a jot of the grief and ignominy that fall to the unfortunate is Hector spared. Alone, stripped of the prestige of force, he

discovers that the courage that kept him from taking to the
shelter of the walls is not enough to save him from flight:

> Seeing him, Hector began to tremble. He had not the heart
> To stay . . .
> . . . It is not for a ewe nor the skin of an ox,
> That they are striving, not these ordinary rewards of the
> race;
> It is for a life that they run, the life of Hector, tamer of
> horses.

Wounded to death, he enhances his conqueror's triumph by
vain supplications:

> I implore you, by your soul, by your knees,
>   by your parents . . .

But the auditors of the *Iliad* knew that the death of Hector
would be but a brief joy to Achilles, and the death of Achilles
but a brief joy to the Trojans, and the destruction of Troy but
a brief joy to the Achaeans.

Thus violence obliterates anybody who feels its touch. It
comes to seem just as external to its employer as to its victim.
And from this springs the idea of a destiny before which
executioner and victim stand equally innocent, before which
conquered and conqueror are brothers in the same distress. The
conquered brings misfortune to the conqueror, and vice versa:

> A single son, short-lived, was born to him.
> Neglected by me, he grows old—for far from home
> I camp before Troy, injuring you and your sons.

A moderate use of force, which alone would enable man to
escape being enmeshed in its machinery, would require super-
human virtue, which is as rare as dignity in weakness. Moreover,
moderation itself is not without its perils, since prestige, from
which force derives at least three quarters of its strength, rests
principally upon that marvelous indifference that the strong
feel toward the weak, an indifference so contagious that it
infects the very people who are the objects of it. Yet ordinarily
excess is not arrived at through prudence or politic considera-

tions. On the contrary, man dashes to it as to an irresistible temptation. The voice of reason is occasionally heard in the mouths of the characters in the *Iliad*. Thersites' speeches are reasonable to the highest degree; so are the speeches of the angry Achilles:

> *Nothing is worth my life, not all the goods*
> *They say the well-built city of Ilium contains . . .*
> *A man can capture steers and fatted sheep*
> *But, once gone, the soul cannot be captured back.*

But words of reason drop into the void. If they come from an inferior, he is punished and shuts up; if from a chief, his actions betray them. And failing everything else, there is always a god handy to advise him to be unreasonable. In the end, the very idea of wanting to escape the role fate has allotted one—the business of killing and dying—disappears from the mind:

> *We to whom Zeus*
> *Has assigned suffering, from the youth to old age,*
> *Suffering in grievous wars, till we perish to the last man.*

Already these warriors, like Craonne's so much later, felt themselves to be "condemned men."

It was the simplest trap that pitched them into this situation. At the outset, at the embarkation, their hearts are light, as hearts always are if you have a large force on your side and nothing but space to oppose you. Their weapons are in their hands; the enemy is absent. Unless your spirit has been conquered in advance by the reputation of the enemy, you always feel yourself to be much stronger than anybody who is not there. An absent man does not impose the yoke of necessity. To the spirits of those embarking no necessity yet presents itself; consequently they go off as though to a game, as though on holiday from the confinement of daily life.

> *Where have they gone, those braggadocio boasts*
> *We proudly flung upon the air at Lemnos,*
> *Stuffing ourselves with flesh of horned steers,*

Drinking from cups brimming over with wine?
As for Trojans—a hundred or two each man of us
Could handle in battle. And now one is too much for us.

But the first contact of war does not immediately destroy the
illusion that war is a game. War's necessity is terrible, altogether
different in kind from the necessity of peace. So terrible is it
that the human spirit will not submit to it so long as it can
possibly escape; and whenever it can escape it takes refuge in
long days empty of necessity, days of play, of revery, days
arbitrary and unreal. Danger then becomes an abstraction; the
lives you destroy are like toys broken by a child, and quite as
incapable of feeling; heroism is but a theatrical gesture and
smirched with boastfulness. This becomes doubly true if a
momentary access of vitality comes to reinforce the divine hand
that wards off defeat and death. Then war is easy and basely,
coarsely loved.

But with the majority of the combatants this state of mind
does not persist. Soon there comes a day when fear, or defeat,
or the death of beloved comrades touches the warrior's spirit,
and it crumbles in the hand of necessity. At that moment war
is no more a game or a dream; now at last the warrior cannot
doubt the reality of its existence. And this reality, which he
perceives, is hard, much too hard to be borne, for it enfolds
death. Once you acknowledge death to be a practical possibility,
the thought of it becomes unendurable, except in flashes. True
enough, all men are fated to die; true enough also, a soldier
may grow old in battles; yet for those whose spirits have bent
under the yoke of war, the relation between death and the
future is different than for other men. For other men death
appears as a limit set in advance on the future; for the soldier
death *is* the future, the future his profession assigns him. Yet
the idea of man's having death for a future is abhorrent to
nature. Once the experience of war makes visible the possibility
of death that lies locked up in each moment, our thoughts
cannot travel from one day to the next without meeting death's
face. The mind is then strung up to a pitch it can stand for

only a short time; but each new dawn reintroduces the same necessity; and days piled on days make years. On each one of these days the soul suffers violence. Regularly, every morning, the soul castrates itself of aspiration, for thought cannot journey through time without meeting death on the way. Thus war effaces all conceptions of purpose or goal, including even its own "war aims." It effaces the very notion of war's being brought to an end. To be outside a situation so violent as this is to find it inconceivable; to be inside it is to be unable to conceive its end. Consequently, nobody does anything to bring this end about. In the presence of an armed enemy, what hand can relinquish its weapon? The mind ought to find a way out, but the mind has lost all capacity to so much as look outward. The mind is completely absorbed in doing itself violence. Always in human life, whether war or slavery is in question, intolerable sufferings continue, as it were, by the force of their own specific gravity, and so look to the outsider as though they were easy to bear; actually, they continue because they have deprived the sufferer of the resources which might serve to extricate him.

Nevertheless, the soul that is enslaved to war cries out for deliverance, but deliverance itself appears to it in an extreme and tragic aspect, the aspect of destruction. Any other solution, more moderate, more reasonable in character, would expose the mind to suffering so naked, so violent that it could not be borne, even as memory. Terror, grief, exhaustion, slaughter, the annihilation of comrades—is it credible that these things should not continually tear at the soul, if the intoxication of force had not intervened to drown them? The idea that an unlimited effort should bring in only a limited profit or no profit at all is terribly painful.

> What? Will we let Priam and the Trojans boast
> Of Argive Helen, she for whom so many Greeks
> Died before Troy, far from their native land?
> What? Do you want us to leave the city, wide-streeted Troy,
> Standing, when we have suffered so much for it?

But actually what is Helen to Ulysses? What indeed is **Troy**, full of riches that will not compensate him for Ithaca's ruin? For the Greeks, Troy and Helen are in reality mere sources of blood and tears; to master them is to master frightful memories. If the existence of an enemy has made a soul destroy in itself the thing nature put there, then the only remedy the soul can imagine is the destruction of the enemy. At the same time the death of dearly loved comrades arouses a spirit of somber emulation, a rivalry in death:

> *May I die, then, at once! Since fate has not let me*
> *Protect my dead friend, who far from home*
> *Perished, longing for me to defend him from death.*
> *So now I go to seek the murderer of my friend,*
> *Hector. And death shall I find at the moment*
> *Zeus wills it—Zeus and the other immortals.*

It is the same despair that drives him on toward death, on the one hand, and slaughter on the other:

> *I know it well, my fate is to perish here,*
> *Far from father and dearly loved mother; but meanwhile*
> *I shall not stop till the Trojans have had their fill of war.*

The man possessed by this twofold need for death belongs, so long as he has not become something still different, to a different race from the race of the living.

What echo can the timid hopes of life strike in such a heart? How can it hear the defeated begging for another sight of the light of day? The threatened life has already been relieved of nearly all its consequence by a single, simple distinction: it is now unarmed; its adversary possesses a weapon. Furthermore, how can a man who has rooted out of himself the notion that the light of day is sweet to the eyes respect such a notion when it makes its appearance in some futile and humble lament?

> *I clasp tight your knees, Achilles. Have a thought, have*
> *pity for me.*
> *I stand here, O son of Zeus, a suppliant, to be respected.*
> *In your house it was I first tasted Demeter's bread,*
> *That day in my well-pruned vineyard you caught me*

> *And sold me, sending me far from father and friends,*
> *To holy Lemnos; a hundred oxen was my price.*
> *And now I will pay you three hundred for ransom.*
> *This dawn is for me my twelfth day in Troy,*
> *After so many sorrows. See me here, in your hands,*
> *Through some evil fate. Zeus surely must hate me*
> *Who again puts me into your hands. Alas, my poor mother*
>   *Laothoe,*
> *Daughter of the old man, Altes—a short-lived son you have*
>   *borne.*

What a reception this feeble hope gets!

> *Come, friend, you too must die. Why make a fuss about it?*
> *Patroclus, he too has died—a far better man than you are.*
> *Don't you see how handsome I am, how mighty?*
> *A noble father begat me, and I have a goddess for mother.*
> *Yet even I, like you, must some day encounter my fate,*
> *Whether the hour strikes at noon, or evening, or sunrise,*
> *The hour that comes when some arms-bearing warrior will*
>   *kill me.*

To respect life in somebody else when you have had to castrate
yourself of all yearning for it demands a truly heartbreaking
exertion of the powers of generosity. It is impossible to imagine
any of Homer's warriors being capable of such an exertion,
unless it is that warrior who dwells, in a peculiar way, at the
very center of the poem—I mean Patroclus, who "knew how
to be sweet to everybody," and who throughout the *Iliad* com-
mits no cruel or brutal act. But then how many men do we
know, in several thousand years of human history, who would
have displayed such godlike generosity? Two or three?—even
this is doubtful. Lacking this generosity, the conquering soldier
is like a scourge of nature. Possessed by war, he, like the slave,
becomes a thing, though his manner of doing so is different—
over him too, words are as powerless as over matter itself. And
both, at the touch of force, experience its inevitable effects:
they become deaf and dumb.

Such is the nature of force. Its power of converting a man
into a thing is a double one, and in its application double-edged.

To the same degree, though in different fashions, those who use it and those who endure it are turned to stone. This property of force achieves its maximum effectiveness during the clash of arms, in battle, when the tide of the day has turned, and everything is rushing toward a decision. It is not the planning man, the man of strategy, the man acting on the resolution taken, who wins or loses a battle; battles are fought and decided by men deprived of these faculties, men who have undergone a transformation, who have dropped either to the level of inert matter, which is pure passivity, or to the level of blind force, which is pure momentum. Herein lies the last secret of war, a secret revealed by the *Iliad* in its similes, which liken the warriors either to fire, flood, wind, wild beasts, or God knows what blind cause of disaster, or else to frightened animals, trees, water, sand, to anything in nature that is set into motion by the violence of external forces. Greeks and Trojans, from one day to the next, sometimes even from one hour to the next, experience, turn and turn about, one or the other of these transmutations:

> *As when a lion, murderous, springs among the cattle*
> *Which by thousands are grazing over some vast marshy*
> * field . . .*
> *And their flanks heave with terror; even so the Achaeans*
> *Scattered in panic before Hector and Zeus, the great father.*
>
> *As when a ravening fire breaks out deep in a bushy wood*
> *And the wheeling wind scatters sparks far and wide,*
> *And trees, root and branch, topple over in flames;*
> *So Atreus' son, Agamemnon, roared through the ranks*
> *Of the Trojans in flight . . .*

The art of war is simply the art of producing such transformations, and its equipment, its processes, even the casualties it inflicts on the enemy, are only means directed toward this end —its true object is the warrior's soul. Yet these transformations are always a mystery; the gods are their authors, the gods who kindle men's imagination. But however caused, this petrifactive quality of force, twofold always, is essential to its nature; and a soul which has entered the province of force will not escape this except by a miracle. Such miracles are rare and of brief duration.

The wantonness of the conqueror that knows no respect for any creature or thing that is at its mercy or is imagined to be so, the despair of the soldier that drives him on to destruction, the obliteration of the slave or the conquered man, the wholesale slaughter—all these elements combine in the *Iliad* to make a picture of uniform horror, of which force is the sole hero. A monotonous desolation would result were it not for those few luminous moments, scattered here and there throughout the poem, those brief, celestial moments in which man possesses his soul. The soul that awakes then, to live for an instant only and be lost almost at once in force's vast kingdom, awakes pure and whole; it contains no ambiguities, nothing complicated or turbid; it has no room for anything but courage and love. Sometimes it is in the course of inner deliberations that a man finds his soul: he meets it, like Hector before Troy, as he tries to face destiny on his own terms, without the help of gods or men. At other times, it is in a moment of love that men discover their souls—and there is hardly any form of pure love known to humanity of which the *Iliad* does not treat. The tradition of hospitality persists, even through several generations, to dispel the blindness of combat.

> *Thus I am for you a beloved guest in the breast of Argos . . .*
> *Let us turn our lances away from each other, even in battle.*

The love of the son for the parents, of father for son, of mother for son, is continually described, in a manner as touching as it is curt:

> *Thetis answered, shedding tears,*
> *"You were born to me for a short life, my child, as you*
> *   say . . ."*

Even brotherly love:

> *My three brothers whom the same mother bore for me,*
> *So dear . . .*

Conjugal love, condemned to sorrow, is of an astonishing purity. Imaging the humiliations of slavery which await a beloved wife, the husband passes over the one indignity which even in anticipation would stain their tenderness. What could be simpler than the words spoken by his wife to the man about to die?

> . . . Better for me
> Losing you, to go under the earth. No other comfort
> Will remain, when you have encountered your death-heavy
>   fate,
> Only grief, only sorrow . . .

Not less touching are the words expressed to a dead husband:

> Dear husband, you died young, and left me your widow
> Alone in the palace. Our child is still tiny,
> The child you and I, crossed by fate, had together.
> I think he will never grow up . . .
> For not in your bed did you die, holding my hand
> And speaking to me prudent words which forever
> Night and day, as I weep, might live in my memory.

The most beautiful friendship of all, the friendship between comrades-at-arms, is the final theme of The Epic:

> . . . But Achilles
> Wept, dreaming of the beloved comrade; sleep,
>   all-prevailing,
> Would not take him; he turned over again and again.

But the purest triumph of love, the crowning grace of war, is the friendship that floods the hearts of mortal enemies. Before it a murdered son or a murdered friend no longer cries out for vengeance. Before it—even more miraculous—the distance between benefactor and suppliant, between victor and vanquished, shrinks to nothing:

> But when thirst and hunger had been appeased,
> Then Dardanian Priam fell to admiring Achilles.
> How tall he was, and handsome; he had the face of a god;
> And in his turn Dardanian Priam was admired by Achilles,
> Who watched his handsome face and listened to his words.
> And when they were satisfied with contemplation of each
>   other . . .

These moments of grace are rare in the *Iliad*, but they are enough to make us feel with sharp regret what it is that violence has killed and will kill again.

However, such a heaping-up of violent deeds would have a frigid effect, were it not for the note of incurable bitterness that continually makes itself heard, though often only a single word marks its presence, often a mere stroke of the verse, or a run-on line. It is in this that the *Iliad* is absolutely unique, in this bitterness that proceeds from tenderness and that spreads over the whole human race, impartial as sunlight. Never does the tone lose its coloring of bitterness; yet never does the bitterness drop into lamentation. Justice and love, which have hardly any place in this study of extremes and of unjust acts of violence, nevertheless bathe the work in their light without ever becoming noticeable themselves, except as a kind of accent. Nothing precious is scorned, whether or not death is its destiny; everyone's unhappiness is laid bare without dissimulation or disdain; no man is set above or below the condition common to all men; whatever is destroyed is regretted. Victors and vanquished are brought equally near us; under the same head, both are seen as counterparts of the poet, and the listener as well. If there is any difference, it is that the enemy's misfortunes are possibly more sharply felt.

> *So he fell there, put to sleep in the sleep of bronze,*
> *Unhappy man, far from his wife, defending his own*
> *people . . .*

And what accents echo the fate of the lad Achilles sold at Lemnos!

> *Eleven days he rejoiced his heart among those he loved,*
> *Returning from Lemnos; the twelfth day, once more,*
> *God delivered him into the hands of Achilles,*
> *To him who had to send him, unwilling, to Hades.*

And the fate of Euphorbus, who saw only a single day of war,

> *Blood soaked his hair, the hair like to the Graces' . . .*

When Hector is lamented:

. . . guardian of chaste wives and little children . . .

In these few words, chastity appears, dirtied by force, and childhood, delivered to the sword. The fountain at the gates of Troy becomes an object of poignant nostalgia when Hector runs by, seeking to elude his doom:

> *Close by there stood the great stone tanks,*
> *Handsomely built, where silk-gleaming garments*
> *Were washed clean by Troy's lovely daughters and*
>   *housewives*
> *In the old days of peace, long ago, when the Greeks had*
>   *not come.*
> *Past these did they run their race, pursued and pursuer.*

The whole of the *Iliad* lies under the shadow of the greatest calamity the human race can experience—the destruction of a city. This calamity could not tear more at the heart had the poet been born in Troy. But the tone is not different when the Achaeans are dying, far from home.

Insofar as this other life, the life of the living, seems calm and full, the brief evocations of the world of peace are felt as pain:

> *With the break of dawn and the rising of the day,*
> *On both sides arrows flew, men fell.*
> *But at the very hour that the woodcutter goes home to fix*
>   *his meal*
> *In the mountain valleys when his arms have had enough*
> *Of hacking great trees, and disgust rises in his heart,*
> *And the desire for sweet food seizes his entrails,*
> *At that hour, by their valor, the Danaans broke the front.*

Whatever is not war, whatever war destroys or threatens, the *Iliad* wraps in poetry; the realities of war, never. No reticence veils the step from life to death:

> *Then his teeth flew out; from two sides,*
> *Blood came to his eyes; the blood that from lips and nostrils*
> *He was spilling, open-mouthed; death enveloped him in its*
>   *black cloud.*

The cold brutality of the deeds of war is left undisguised; neither victors nor vanquished are admired, scorned, or hated. Almost always, fate and the gods decide the changing lot of battle. Within the limits fixed by fate, the gods determine with sovereign authority victory and defeat. It is always they who provoke those fits of madness, those treacheries, which are forever blocking peace; war is their true business; their only motives, caprice and malice. As for the warriors, victors or vanquished, those comparisons which liken them to beasts or things can inspire neither admiration nor contempt, but only regret that men are capable of being so transformed.

There may be, unknown to us, other expressions of the extraordinary sense of equity which breathes through the *Iliad*; certainly it has not been imitated. One is barely aware that the poet is a Greek and not a Trojan. The tone of the poem furnishes a direct clue to the origin of its oldest portions; history perhaps will never be able to tell us more. If one believes with Thucydides that eighty years after the fall of Troy, the Achaeans in their turn were conquered, one may ask whether these songs, with their rare references to iron, are not the songs of a conquered people, of whom a few went into exile. Obliged to live and die, "very far from the homeland," like the Greeks who fell before Troy, having lost their cities like the Trojans, they saw their own image both in the conquerors, who had been their fathers, and in the conquered, whose misery was like their own. They could still see the Trojan war over that brief span of years in its true light, unglossed by pride or shame. They could look at it as conquered and as conquerors simultaneously, and so perceive what neither conqueror nor conquered ever saw, for both were blinded. Of course, this is mere fancy; one can see such distant times only in fancy's light.

In any case, this poem is a miracle. Its bitterness is the only justifiable bitterness, for it springs from the subjections of the human spirit to force, that is, in the last analysis, to matter. This subjection is the common lot, although each spirit will bear it differently, in proportion to its own virtue. No one in

the *Iliad* is spared by it, as no one on earth is. No one who
succumbs to it is by virtue of this fact regarded with contempt. Whoever, within his own soul and in human relations,
escapes the dominion of force is loved but loved sorrowfully
because of the threat of destruction that constantly hangs over
him.

Such is the spirit of the only true epic the Occident possesses. . . .

The relations between destiny and the human soul, the
extent to which each soul creates its own destiny, the question
of what elements in the soul are transformed by merciless
necessity as it tailors the soul to fit the requirement of shifting
fate, and of what elements can on the other hand be preserved,
through the exercise of virtue and through grace—this whole
question is fraught with temptations to falsehood, temptations
that are positively enhanced by pride, by shame, by hatred, contempt, indifference, by the will to oblivion or to ignorance.
Moreover, nothing is so rare as to see misfortune fairly por-
trayed; the tendency is either to treat the unfortunate person as
though catastrophe were his natural vocation, or to ignore the
effects of misfortune on the soul, to assume, that is, that the
soul can suffer and remain unmarked by it, can fail, in fact, to
be recast in misfortune's image. The Greeks, generally speaking,
were endowed with spiritual force that allowed them to avoid
self-deception. The rewards of this were great; they discovered
how to achieve in all their acts the greatest lucidity, purity,
and simplicity. But the spirit that was transmitted from the
Iliad to the Gospels by way of the tragic poets never jumped
the borders of Greek civilization; once Greece was destroyed,
nothing remained of this spirit but pale reflections. . . .

REVOLT AND FREEDOM

FOR SIMONE WEIL only that flicker of the mind, awareness, can stay the hand, leaving room for man's free decision consciously to halt the "absurd" mechanism of his own destruction. Likewise Meursault's awakening to the same absurd mechanism establishes the movement that leads him from awareness to a revolt and contestation which, in Camus's view, is the ground of any fruitful human engagement in life, of man's subsequent freedom, within the limits of his condition, to choose in what manner he will live his life and bear the weight of his own freedom. But the very fact that man's freedom is grounded in an instinctive surge of revolt against the irrationality, injustice, and incoherence of the world leads Camus to further examine what constitutes a fruitful as opposed to a futile revolt. Caligula is the proponent and victim of a fruitless and costly revolt. In search of an absolute, symbolized by the moon, Caligula aspires to establish a coherent pattern of action in keeping with his understanding of the world. Nature follows its own patterns, in which human aspirations have no place. Caligula acts with the arbitrary cruelty and senseless disregard for human emotions and values characteristic of the natural world. In the last scene, he reaps the harvest he has so abundantly sown. Conceived and in great part written before World War II, Camus's *Caligula* could to some degree be understood as a parable for the whole Nazi adventure and its eventual disastrous ending.

Sartre's play *The Flies* turns the Orestes myth into an assertion of man's freedom as first truth and fundamental human reality. In Sartrian terms, this freedom is an awesome fact that men try to mask in order to evade their own responsibility. For men, as Sartre sees them, have no master other than themselves and are totally responsible for the man-made order they impose and accept. This is the discovery Sartre's Orestes and presumably Sartre's audience make, in flagrant contradiction to the Greek myth. Sartre developed the play as a series of confrontations between the various characters and Zeus. In Act II, Scene 2, Aegisthus, the ruler of Argos and murderer of Agamemnon, weary of his own treachery and deceit, confronts the god whose image he has created; and Zeus confronts the image whereby he exists. In Act III, Scene 2, Orestes and Electra, pursued by the Furies after the murder of Clytemnestra and Aegisthus, have sought refuge at the feet of the statue of Apollo: the final confrontation takes place between man and god.

Aragon's transparently allegorical poem in the form of a ballad speaks of a reality discovered on the far side of dream and disaster. Symbolized in the person of Eleanor of Aquitaine—the French queen repudiated and exiled by her royal spouse and reinstated to her royal dignity by the King of England—is the dream of courtly love and chivalry of which Eleanor was one of the initiators. The crusade itself is symbolized by the ascetic figure of Peter the Hermit, who launched the first, disastrous expedition to Jerusalem. So the hard reality of combat and the dream cannot be disentangled. But in their confrontation with death the crusaders discover their real allegiance: not to a dream or a cause but to the freedom to move, to think, to decide to commit their lives to a cause—freedoms denied to the French people but now alive in England. The present and the past fuse in dream and aspiration. The dream figure that emerges is the symbol of freedom.

Saint-Exupéry's meditation on his experience of combat and defeat as one of France's airmen intertwines the themes of freedom, fraternity, and solidarity. What he has rediscovered is an essential humanism, characteristic of Western civilization. The "absurd" vision of life is transcended. Saint-Exupéry sees each individual life as drawing its meaning from participation in a common task: to create and faithfully maintain a high image of man reflecting men's highest potentialities.

HENRI MICHAUX

ENORMOUS VOICE

Enormous voice
that drinks
that drinks

Enormous voices drinking
drinking
drinking

I laugh, I laugh alone in another
in another
in another beard

I laugh, my cannon laughs
the cannoned body
I, I've, I'm

elsewhere!
elsewhere!
elsewhere!

A gap, what difference does it make?
a rat, what difference does that make?
a spider?

Being a bad farmer I ruined my father
no, don't bring a light
well I ruined him

SOURCE NOTE: Henri Michaux, "Immense Voix," *Épreuves, Exorcismes* *(1940–1945)* (Paris, Gallimard, 1945), pp. 11–14.

The word of command guttered
no more voice. At least more deadened.
Twenty years later, once more, what do I hear?

Enormous voice that drinks our voices
enormous father rebuilt gigantic
by the care, the carelessness of events

Enormous Roof that covers our woods
our joys
that covers cats and rats

Enormous cross that curses our rafts
that undoes our wits
that prepares our graves

Enormous voice for nothing
for the shroud
for crumbling our columns

Enormous "debit" "duty"
duty duty duty
Enormous imperious starch

With a feigned grandeur
enormous business
that freezes us

Were we born for the ore-seam?
Were we born, broken-fingered, to give
a lifetime to a bad problem?

to who knows what for who knows whom
to a who knows whom for a who knows what.
forever towards more cold

Enough! no singing here
You shall not have my voice, great voice
You shall not have my voice, great voice

You'll go without great voice
You too will go
You'll go, great voice

ÉMILE CAPOUYA

IMMENSE VOIX

Immense voix
qui boit
qui boit

Immenses voix qui boivent
qui boivent
qui boivent

Je ris, je ris tout seul dans une autre
dans une autre
dans une autre barbe

Je ris, j'ai le canon qui rit
le corps canonné
je, j'ai, j'suis

ailleurs!
ailleurs!
ailleurs!

Une brèche, qu'est-ce que ça fait?
un rat qu'est-ce que que ça fait?
une araignée?

Étant mauvais cultivateur je perdis mon père
non, n'apportez pas de lumière
donc je le perdis

Le commandement s'éteignit
plus de voix. Plus étouffée du moins
Après vingt ans, à nouveau, qu'est-ce que j'entends?

Immense voix qui boit nos voix
immense père reconstruit géant
par le soin, par l'incurie des événements

Immense Toit qui couvre nos bois
nos joies
qui couvre chats et rats

Immense croix qui maudit nos radeaux
qui défait nos esprits
qui prépare nos tombeaux

Immense voix pour rien
pour le linceul
pour s'écrouler nos colonnes

Immense « doit » « devoir »
devoir devoir devoir
Immense impérieux empois.

Avec une grandeur feinte
immense affaire
qui nous gèle

Étions-nous nés pour la gangue?
Étions-nous nés, doigts cassés, pour donner
toute une vie à un mauvais problème?

à je ne sais quoi pour je ne sais qui
à un je ne sais qui pour un je ne sais quoi.
toujours vers plus de froid

Suffit! ici on ne chante pas
Tu n'auras pas ma voix, grande voix
Tu n'auras pas ma voix, grande voix

Tu t'en passeras grande voix
Toi aussi tu passeras
Tu passeras, grande voix

ALBERT CAMUS

1938

From *CALIGULA*

He turns around wildly, goes toward the mirror.
CALIGULA Caligula! You too, you too are guilty. So, after all,
a little more, a little less! But who would dare condemn me in
a world without a judge, where nobody is innocent! (*He
presses himself up against the mirror. In despair.*) You see that
Helicon hasn't come. I won't have the moon. But it's bitter to
be right, and to have to go to the end. Because I'm scared of
the end. I hear arms! It's innocence preparing its triumphal
entry. Would I were in their position! I'm scared. How foul to
feel one's own cowardice after despising others for it. But that
doesn't matter. Fear doesn't last either. I'll find that void where
the heart meets peace. (*He recoils a little, returns to the mirror.*

SOURCE NOTE: Albert Camus, *Caligula*, in *Le Malentendu suivi de Caligula* (Paris, Gallimard, 1958), Act IV, Scene 14, pp. 225–27.

He seems calmer. He starts talking again, but in a lower, more intense voice.) Everything looks so complicated. And yet it's all so simple. If I had the moon, if love were enough, it would all be different. But where can I quench this thirst? What heart, what god, would be as deep as a lake for me? (*He kneels down and weeps.*) Nothing suits me, in this world or the other. But I know, and so do you (*he stretches his hands toward the mirror, weeping*), that it would be enough for the impossible to be. The impossible! I've looked for it at the edges of the world, at the boundaries of myself. I've stretched out my hands (*weeping*), I stretch out my hands and it's you whom I find, always you in front of me, and I'm full of hatred for you. I haven't taken the path I should have taken; I haven't come out on anything. My liberty isn't the right one. Helicon! Helicon! Nothing! Nothing yet! Oh, this night is so heavy! Helicon won't come! We'll be guilty forever! This night is as heavy as human pain.

A sound of arms and whispering is heard in the wings.

HELICON (*appearing from the back of the stage*) Look out, Caius! Look out! *An invisible hand stabs* HELICON. CALIGULA *stands up, takes a chair in his hands, and goes up to the mirror, panting. He looks at himself, pretends to plunge forward, and confronted by the symmetrical leap of his mirror image, throws his chair at the mirror as hard as he can, shouting.*

CALIGULA To history, Caligula, to history. (*The mirror breaks and at the same time armed conspirators rush in:* CALIGULA *faces them, laughing helplessly. The* OLD PATRICIAN *stabs him in the back,* CHEREA *in the face.* CALIGULA's *laugh turns into sobs. All stab him. In a last sob, laughing and gasping,* CALIGULA *shouts*) I'm still alive!

Curtain.

ALASTAIR HAMILTON

JEAN-PAUL SARTRE

1943

From *THE FLIES*

ZEUS That's right. Complain away! You're only a king, like every other king.

AEGISTHUS Who are you? What are you doing here?

ZEUS So you don't recognize me?

AEGISTHUS Begone, stranger, or I shall have you thrown out by my guards.

ZEUS You don't recognize me? Still, you have seen me often enough, in dreams. It's true I looked more awe-inspiring. (*Flashes of lightning, a peal of thunder.* ZEUS *assumes an awe-inspiring air.*) And now do you know me?

AEGISTHUS Zeus!

ZEUS Good! (*Affable again, he goes up to the statue.*) So that's meant to be I? It's thus the Argives picture me at their prayers? Well, well, it isn't often that a god can study his likeness, face to face. (*A short silence.*) How hideous I am! They cannot like me much.

AEGISTHUS They fear you.

ZEUS Excellent! I've no use for love. Do you, Aegisthus, love me?

AEGISTHUS What do you want of me? Have I not paid heavily enough?

SOURCE NOTE: Jean-Paul Sartre, *Les Mouches*, in *Théâtre I* (Paris, Gallimard, 1943), Act II, Tableau II, Scene 5, pp. 72–79; Act III, Scene 2, pp. 93–103. First performed at the Théâtre de la Cité, June 3, 1943, with Charles Dullin directing.

ZEUS Never enough.

AEGISTHUS But it's killing me, the task I have undertaken.

ZEUS Come now! Don't exaggerate! Your health is none too bad; you're fat. Mind, I'm not reproaching you. It's good, royal fat, yellow as tallow—just as it should be. You're built to live another twenty years.

AEGISTHUS Another twenty years!

ZEUS Would you rather die?

AEGISTHUS Yes.

ZEUS So, if anyone came here now, with a drawn sword, would you bare your breast to him?

AEGISTHUS I—I cannot say.

ZEUS Now mark my words. If you let yourself be slaughtered like a dumb ox, your doom will be exemplary. You shall be King in Hell for all eternity. That's what I came here to tell you.

AEGISTHUS Is someone planning to kill me?

ZEUS So it seems.

AEGISTHUS Electra?

ZEUS Not only Electra.

AEGISTHUS Who?

ZEUS Orestes.

AEGISTHUS Oh! . . . Well, that's in the natural order of things, no doubt. What can I do against it?

ZEUS (*mimicking his tone*) What can I do? (*Imperiously*) Bid your men arrest a young stranger going under the name of Philebus. Have him and Electra thrown into a dungeon—and if you leave them there to rot, I'll think no worse of you. Well? What are you waiting for? Call your men.

AEGISTHUS   No.

ZEUS   Be good enough to tell me why that "No."

AEGISTHUS   I am tired.

ZEUS   Don't stare at the ground. Raise your big, bloodshot eyes and look at me. That's better. Yes, you're majestically stupid, like a horse; a kingly fool. But yours is not the stubbornness that vexes me; rather, it will add a spice to your surrender. For I know you will obey me in the end.

AEGISTHUS   I tell you I refuse to fall in with your plans. I have done so far too often.

ZEUS   That's right. Show your mettle! Resist! Resist! Ah, how I cherish souls like yours! Your eyes flash, you clench your fists, you fling refusal in the teeth of Zeus. None the less, my little rebel, my restive little horse, no sooner had I warned you than your heart said "Yes." Of course you'll obey. Do you think I leave Olympus without good reason? I wished to warn you of this crime because it is my will to avert it.

AEGISTHUS   To warn me! How strange!

ZEUS   Why "strange"? Surely it's natural enough. Your life's in danger and I want to save it.

AEGISTHUS   Who asked you to save it? What about Agamemnon? Did you warn *him*? And yet *he* wished to live.

ZEUS   Oh miserable man, what base ingratitude! You are dearer to me than Agamemnon, and when I prove this, you complain!

AEGISTHUS   Dearer than Agamemnon? I? No, it's Orestes whom you cherish. You allowed me to work my doom, you let me rush in, axe in hand, to King Agamemnon's bath—and no doubt you watched from high Olympus, licking your lips at the thought of another damned soul to gloat over. But today you are protecting young Orestes against himself; and I, whom you egged on to kill his father—you have chosen me to restrain the young man's hand. I was a poor creature, just qualified for murder; but Orestes, it seems, you have higher destinies in view.

ZEUS What strange jealousy is this! But have no fear; I love him no more than I love you. I love nobody.

AEGISTHUS Then see what you have made of me, unjust God that you are. And tell me this. If today you hinder the crime Orestes has in mind, why did you permit mine of fifteen years ago?

ZEUS All crimes do not displease me equally. And now, Aegisthus, I shall speak to you frankly, as one king to another. The first crime was mine; I committed it when I made man mortal. Once I had done that, what was left for you, poor human murderers, to do? To kill your victims? But they already had the seed of death in them; all you could do was to hasten its fruition by a year or two. Do you know what would have befallen Agamemnon, if you had not killed him? Three months later he'd have died of apoplexy in a pretty slave-girl's arms. But your crime served my ends.

AEGISTHUS What ends? For fifteen years I have been atoning for it—and you say it served your ends!

ZEUS Exactly. It's because you are atoning for it that it served my ends. I like crimes that *pay*. I like yours because it was a clumsy, boorish murder, a crime that did not know itself, a crime in the antique mode, more like a cataclysm than an act of man. Not for one moment did you defy me. You struck in a frenzy of fear and rage. And then, when your frenzy had died down, you looked back on the deed with loathing, and disowned it. Yet what a profit I have made on it! For one dead man, twenty thousand living men wallowing in penitence. Yes, it was a good bargain I struck that day.

AEGISTHUS I see what lies behind your words. Orestes will have no remorse.

ZEUS Not a trace of it. At this moment he is thinking out his plan, coolly, methodically, cheerfully. What good to me is a carefree murder, a shameless, sedate crime, that lies light as thistledown on the murderer's conscience? No, I won't allow it. Ah, how I loathe the crimes of this new generation; thankless and sterile as the wind! Yes, that nice-minded young man will kill you as he'd kill a chicken; he'll go away with red hands and a clean heart. In your place I should feel humiliated. So—call your men!

AEGISTHUS Again I tell you, I will *not*. The crime that is being hatched displeases you enough for me to welcome it.

ZEUS Aegisthus, you are a king, and it's to your sense of kingship I appeal; for you enjoy wielding the scepter.

AEGISTHUS Continue.

ZEUS You may hate me, but we are akin; I made you in my image. A king is a god on earth, glorious and terrifying as a god.

AEGISTHUS You, terrifying?

ZEUS Look at me. (*A long silence.*) I told you you were made in my image. Each keeps order; you in Argos, I in heaven and on earth—and you and I harbor the same dark secret in our hearts.

AEGISTHUS I have no secret.

ZEUS You have. The same as mine. The bane of gods and kings. The bitterness of knowing men are free. Yes, Aegisthus, they are free. But your subjects do not know it, and you do.

AEGISTHUS Why, yes. If they knew it, they'd send my palace up in flames. For fifteen years I've been playing a part to mask their power from them.

ZEUS So you see we are alike.

AEGISTHUS Alike? A god likening himself to me—what freak of irony is this? Since I came to the throne, all I said, all my acts, have been aimed at building up an image of myself. I wish each of my subjects to keep that image in the foreground of his mind, and to feel, even when alone, that my eyes are on him, severely judging his most private thoughts. But I have been trapped in my own net. I have come to see myself only as they see me. I peer into the dark pit of their souls and there, deep down, I see the image that I have built up. I shudder, but I cannot take my eyes off it. Almighty Zeus, who am I? Am I anything more than the dread that others have of me?

ZEUS   And I—who do you think *I* am? (*Points to the statue.*) I, too, have my image, and do you suppose it doesn't fill me with confusion? For a hundred thousand years I have been dancing a slow, dark ritual dance before men's eyes. Their eyes are so intent on me that they forget to look into themselves. If I forgot myself for a single moment, if I let their eyes turn away . . .

AEGISTHUS   Yes?

ZEUS   Enough. That is *my* business. Aegisthus, I know that you are weary of it all; but why complain? You'll die one day—but I shall not. So long as there are men on earth, I am doomed to go on dancing before them.

AEGISTHUS   Alas! But who has doomed us?

ZEUS   No one but ourselves. For we have the same passion. You, Aegisthus, have, like me, a passion for order.

AEGISTHUS   For order? That is so. It was for the sake of order that I wooed Clytemnestra, for order that I killed my king; I wished that order should prevail, and that it should prevail through me. I have lived without love, without hope, even without lust. But I have kept order. Yes, I have kept good order in my kingdom. That has been my ruling passion; a godlike passion, but how terrible!

ZEUS   We could have no other, you and I; I am God, and you were born to be a king.

AEGISTHUS   Aye, more's the pity!

ZEUS   Aegisthus, my creature and my mortal brother, in the name of this good order that we serve, both you and I, I ask you—nay, I command you—to lay hands on Orestes and his sister.

AEGISTHUS   Are they so dangerous?

ZEUS   Orestes knows that he is free.

AEGISTHUS   (*Eagerly*)   He knows he's free? Then, to lay hands on him, to put him in irons, is not enough. A free man in a city acts like a plague-spot. He will infect my whole kingdom and bring my work to nothing. Almighty Zeus, why stay your hand? Why not fell him with a thunderbolt?

ZEUS   (*Slowly*)   Fell him with a thunderbolt? (*A pause. Then, in a muffled voice*) Aegisthus, the gods have another secret . . .

AEGISTHUS   Yes?

ZEUS   Once freedom lights its beacon in a man's heart, the gods are powerless against him. It's a matter between man and man, and it is for other men, and for them only, to let him go his gait, or to throttle him.

AEGISTHUS   (*Observing him closely*)   To throttle him? Be it so. Well, I shall do your will, no doubt. But say no more, and stay here no longer—I could not bear it.

         *   *   *   *   *

[After the murder: Electra and Orestes are at the feet of the statue of Apollo.]

ZEUS   Poor children. (*He goes up to* ELECTRA.) So to this you've come, unhappy pair? My heart is torn between anger and compassion. Get up, Electra. So long as I am here, my Furies[1] will not hurt you. (*He helps her to rise, and gazes at her face.*) Ah, what a cruel change! In a night, a single night, all the wild-rose bloom has left your cheeks. In one night your body has gone to ruin, lungs, gall, and liver all burnt out. The pride of headstrong youth—see what it has brought you to, poor child.

ORESTES Stop talking in that tone, fellow. It is unbecoming for the King of the Gods.

ZEUS And you, my lad, drop that haughty tone. It's unbecoming for a criminal atoning for his crime.

ORESTES I am no criminal, and you have no power to make me atone for an act I don't regard as a crime.

ZEUS So you may think, but wait awhile. I shall cure you of that error before long.

ORESTES Torture me to your heart's content; I regret nothing.

ZEUS Not even the doom you have brought upon your sister?

ORESTES Not even that.

ZEUS Do you hear, Electra? And this man professed to love you!

ORESTES She is dearer to me than life. But her suffering comes from within, and only she can rid herself of it. For she is free.

ZEUS And you? You, too, are free, no doubt?

ORESTES Yes, and well you know it.

ZEUS A pity you can't see yourself as you are now, you fool, for all your boasting! What an heroic figure you cut there, cowering between the legs of a protecting god, with a pack of hungry vixens keeping guard on you! If you can brag of freedom, why not praise the freedom of a prisoner languishing in fetters, or a slave nailed to the cross?

ORESTES Certainly. Why not?

ZEUS Take care. You play the braggart now because Apollo is protecting you. But Apollo is my most obedient servant. I have but to lift a finger and he will abandon you.

ORESTES   Then do so. Lift a finger, lift your whole hand, while you are about it.

ZEUS   No, that is not my way. Haven't I told you that I take no pleasure in punishment? I have come to save you both.

ELECTRA   To save us? No, it is too cruel to make sport of us. You are the lord of vengeance and of death but, god though you are, you have no right to delude your victims with false hopes.

ZEUS   Within a quarter of an hour, you can be outside that door.

ELECTRA   Safe and sound?

ZEUS   You have my word for it.

ELECTRA   And what do you want from me in return?

ZEUS   Nothing, my child. Nothing.

ELECTRA   Nothing? Did I hear right? Then you are a kind god, a lovable god.

ZEUS   Or next to nothing. A mere trifle. What you can give most easily—a little penitence.

ORESTES   Take care, Electra. That trifle will weigh like a mill-stone on your soul.

ZEUS (To ELECTRA)   Don't listen to him. Answer me, instead. Why hesitate to disavow that crime? It was committed by someone else; one could hardly say even that you were his accomplice.

ORESTES   Electra! Are you going to go back on fifteen years of hope and hatred?

ZEUS   What has she to go back on? Never did she really wish that impious deed to be accomplished.

ELECTRA   If only that were true!

ZEUS   Come now! Surely you can trust my word. Do I not read in men's hearts?

ELECTRA   (*Incredulously*)   And you read in mine that I never really desired that crime? Though for fifteen years I dreamt of murder and revenge?

ZEUS   Bah! I know you nursed bloodthirsty dreams—but there was a sort of innocence about them. They made you forget your servitude, they healed your wounded pride. But you never really thought of making them come true. Well, am I mistaken?

ELECTRA   Ah Zeus, dear Zeus, how I long to think you are not mistaken!

ZEUS   You're a little girl, Electra. A mere child. Most little girls dream of becoming the richest or the loveliest woman on earth. But you were haunted by the cruel destiny of your race, you dreamt of becoming the saddest, most criminal of women. You never willed to do evil; you willed your own misfortune. At an age when most children are playing hopscotch or with their dolls, you, poor child, who had no friends or toys, you toyed with dreams of murder, because that's a game to play alone.

ELECTRA   Yes, yes! I'm beginning to understand.

ORESTES   Listen, Electra! It's *now* you are bringing guilt upon you. For who except yourself can know what you really wanted? Will you let another decide that for you? Why distort a past that can no longer stand up for itself? And why disown the firebrand that you were, that glorious young goddess, vivid with hatred, that I loved so much? Can't you see this cruel god is fooling you?

ZEUS   No, Electra, I'm not fooling you. And now hear what I offer. If you repudiate your crime, I'll see that you two occupy the throne of Argos.

ORESTES   Taking the places of our victims?

ZEUS   How else?

ORESTES   And I shall put on the royal robe, still warm from the dead king's wearing?

ZEUS   That or another. What can it matter?

ORESTES   Nothing of course—provided that it's black.

ZEUS   Are you not in mourning?

ORESTES   Yes, I was forgetting: in mourning for my mother. And my subjects—must I have them, too, wear black?

ZEUS   They wear it already.

ORESTES   True. We can give them time to wear out their old clothes. . . . Well, Electra, have you understood? If you shed some tears, you'll be given Clytemnestra's shifts and petticoats —those dirty, stinking ones you had to wash for fifteen years. And the part she played is yours for the asking. Now that you have come to look so much like her, you will play the part superbly; everyone will take you for your mother. But I—I fear I am more squeamish—I refuse to wear the breeches of the clown I killed.

ZEUS   You talk big, my boy. You butchered a defenseless man and an old woman who begged for mercy. But, to hear you speak, one would think you'd bravely fought, one against a crowd, and were the savior of your city.

ORESTES   Perhaps I was.

ZEUS   You, a savior! Do you know what's afoot behind that door? All the good folk of Argos are waiting there. Waiting to greet you with stones and pikes and pitchforks. Oh, they are very grateful to their savior! . . . You are lonely as a leper.

ORESTES   Yes.

ZEUS   So you take pride in being an outcast, do you? But the solitude you're doomed to, most cowardly of murderers, is the solitude of scorn and loathing.

ORESTES The most cowardly of murderers is he who feels remorse.

ZEUS Orestes, I created you, and I created all things. Now see! (*The walls of the temple draw apart, revealing the firmament, spangled with wheeling stars.* ZEUS *is standing in the background. His voice becomes huge—amplified by loudspeakers—but his form is shadowy.*) See those planets wheeling on their appointed ways, never swerving, never clashing. It was I who ordained their courses, according to the law of Justice. Hear the music of the spheres, that vast, mineral hymn of praise, sounding and resounding to the limits of the firmament. (*Sounds of music.*) It is my work that living things increase and multiply, each according to his kind. I have ordained that man shall always beget man, and dog give birth to dog. It is my work that the tides with their innumerable tongues creep up to lap the sand and draw back at the appointed hour. I make the plants grow, and my breath fans round the earth the yellow clouds of pollen. You are not in your own home, intruder; you are a foreign body in the world, like a splinter in flesh, or a poacher in his lordship's forest. For the world is good; I made it according to my will, and I am Goodness. But you, Orestes, you have done evil, the very rocks and stones cry out against you. The Good is everywhere, it is the coolness of the wellspring, the pith of the reed, the grain of flint, the weight of stone. Yes, you will find it even in the heart of fire and light; even your own body plays you false, for it abides perforce by my Law. Good is everywhere, in you and about you; sweeping through you like a scythe, crushing you like a mountain. Like an ocean it buoys you up and rocks you to and fro, and it enabled the success of your evil plan, for it was in the brightness of the torches, the temper of your blade, the strength of your right arm. And that of which you are so vain, the Evil that you think is your creation, what is it but a reflection in a mocking mirror, a phantom thing that would have no being but for Goodness. No, Orestes, return to your saner self; the universe refutes you, you are a mite in the scheme of things. Return to Nature, Nature's thankless son. Know your sin, abhor it, and tear it from you as one tears out a rotten, noisome tooth. Or else—beware lest the very seas shrink back at your approach, springs dry up when you pass by, stones and rocks roll from your path, and the earth crumble under your feet.

ORESTES Let it crumble! Let the rocks revile me, and flowers wilt at my coming. Your whole universe is not enough to prove me wrong. You are the king of gods, king of stones and stars, king of the waves of the sea. But you are not the king of man.

The walls draw together. ZEUS *comes into view, tired and dejected, and he now speaks in his normal voice.*

ZEUS Impudent spawn! So I am not your king? Who, then, made you?

ORESTES You. But you blundered; you should not have made me free.

ZEUS I gave you freedom so that you might serve me.

ORESTES Perhaps. But now it has turned against its giver. And neither you nor I can undo what has been done.

ZEUS Ah, at last! So this is your excuse?

ORESTES I am not excusing myself.

ZEUS No? Let me tell you it sounds much like an excuse, this freedom whose slave you claim to be.

ORESTES Neither slave nor master. I *am* my freedom. No sooner had you created me than I ceased to be yours.

ELECTRA Oh, Orestes! By all you hold most holy, by our father's memory, I beg you do not add blasphemy to your crime!

ZEUS Mark her words, young man. And hope no more to win

her back by arguments like these. Such language is somewhat new to her ears—and somewhat shocking.

ORESTES To my ears, too. And to my lungs which breathe the words, and to my tongue, which shapes them. In fact I can hardly understand myself. Only yesterday you were still a veil on my eyes, a clot of wax in my ears; yesterday, indeed, I had an excuse. You were my excuse for being alive, for you had put me in the world to fulfill your purpose, and the world was an old pander prating to me about your goodness, day in, day out. And then you forsook me.

ZEUS I forsook you? How?

ORESTES Yesterday, when I was with Electra, I felt at one with Nature, this Nature of your making. It sang the praises of the Good—*your* Good—in siren tones, and lavished intimations. To lull me into gentleness, the fierce light mellowed and grew tender as a lover's eyes. And, to teach me the forgiveness of offenses, the sky grew bland as a pardoner's face. Obedient to your will, my youth rose up before me and pleaded with me like a girl who fears her lover will forsake her. That was the last time, the last, I saw my youth. Suddenly, out of the blue, freedom crashed down on me, and swept me off my feet. Nature sprang back, my youth went with the wind, and I knew myself alone, utterly alone in the midst of this well-meaning little universe of yours. I was like a man who's lost his shadow. And there was nothing left in heaven, no Right or Wrong, nor anyone to give me orders.

ZEUS What of it? Do you want me to admire a scabby sheep that has to be kept apart; or the leper mewed in a lazar house? Remember, Orestes, you once were of my flock, you fed in my pastures amongst my sheep. Your vaunted freedom isolates you from the fold; it means exile.

ORESTES Yes, exile.

ZEUS But the disease can't be deeply rooted yet; it began only yesterday. Come back to the fold. Think of your loneliness; even your sister is forsaking you. Your eyes are big with anguish, your face is pale and drawn. The disease you're suffering from is inhuman, foreign to my nature, foreign to yourself. Come back. I am forgetfulness, I am peace.

ORESTES Foreign to myself—I know it. Outside nature, against nature, without excuse, beyond remedy, except what remedy I find within myself. But I shall not return under your Law; I am doomed to have no other law but mine. Nor shall I come back to Nature, the Nature you found good; in it are a thousand beaten paths all leading up to you—but I must blaze my own trail. For I, Zeus, am a man, and every man must find out his own way. Nature abhors man, and you too, god of gods, abhor mankind.

ZEUS That is true; men like you I hold in abhorrence.

ORESTES Take care; those words were a confession of your weakness. As for me, I do not hate you. What have I to do with you, or you with me? We shall glide past each other, like ships in a river, without touching. You are God and I am free; each of us is alone, and our anguish is akin. How can you know I did not try to feel remorse in the long night that has gone by? And to sleep? But no longer can I feel remorse, and I can sleep no more.

A short silence.

ZEUS What do you propose to do?

ORESTES The folk of Argos are my folk. I must open their eyes.

ZEUS Poor people! Your gift to them will be a sad one, of loneliness and shame. You will tear from their eyes the veils I had laid on them, and they will see their lives as they are, foul and futile, a barren boon.

ORESTES Why, since it is their lot, should I deny them the despair I have in me?

ZEUS What will they make of it?

ORESTES What they choose. They're free; and human life begins on the far side of despair.

A short silence.

ZEUS Well, Orestes, all this was foreknown. In the fullness of time a man was to come, to announce my decline. And you're that man, it seems. But seeing you yesterday—you with your girlish face—who'd have believed it?

ORESTES Could I myself have believed it? . . . The words I speak are too big for my mouth, they tear it; the load of destiny I bear is too heavy for my youth, and has shattered it.

ZEUS I have little love for you, yet I am sorry for you.

ORESTES And I, too, am sorry for *you.*

ZEUS Goodbye, Orestes. (*He takes some steps forward.*) As for you, Electra, bear this in mind. My reign is not yet over— far from it—and I shall not give up the struggle. So choose if you are with me or against me. Farewell.

STUART GILBERT

NOTE

1. Furies: Greek goddesses, called Furies by the Romans, who were supposed to punish the crimes of men. They were often depicted as having serpents in lieu of hair and as carrying in one hand a flaming torch and in the other a sword. In Sartre's play they are symbolized by the flies that give the play its name.

LOUIS ARAGON

THE CRUSADERS

Queen of the Courts of Love, O dubious princess
It was you they dreamed about when they died in
    the desert
The fine and desperate youths who joined the crusades
    for you
Eleanor Eleanor of Aquitaine!

She had invented for the wild hearts of the wise
All the crucifixions of a ceremony
It was for no such trivial offense that she was
    excommunicated
Pale among her evasive pages

But her lovers Barons and Troubadours
Remembered they had once followed Peter the Hermit
Ruined Knights of the cursèd Queen
With her greyhounds her lions and her bears

They recalled their exaltation under the great oaks
In the Romanesque town where Peter spoke to them
Vézelay Vézelay Vézelay Vézelay
And her sleeves seemed heavy with the weight of chains

SOURCE NOTE: Louis Aragon, "Les Croisés," *Le Crève-coeur* (Paris, Galli-mard, 1941), pp. 56–58.

The Holy Sepulcher was nothing to them then
Listening to the words on those transparent lips
Corrupted with a dalliance hideously profane
Lovers Lovers Lovers Lovers

And when they heard the words Holy Land
How they joined their cries to the fanatical shouts
And at the purest words only kisses rained down
And even her absence was painted upon the silence

The shadows checkered her gown
The blaspheming echo repeated I love you
When the preacher spoke of Jerusalem
And her eyes sparkled like a flock of flying doves

Later later after the lunatic venture
I loathe to speak of even as you
For my heart is full of another defeat
Which can never be effaced

Later when the banished Queen
Had left behind her palace and France and her loves
The memory of those days returned to them
And the impassioned words of their litanies

Awakened the opposing rhyme of the words
Of the black-and-white preacher they had flouted
For them the Cross had assumed a meaning unavowed
With impunity they might call the sweet mushrooms
    Christ's-Blood

But at last it was only in some unknown Syria
That they truly understood the sounding syllables
And wounded to the death they knew that Eleanor
Was your name Freedom beloved Freedom

LES CROISÉS

Reine des cours d'amour o princesse incertaine
C'est à toi que rêvaient les mourants au désert
Beaux fils désespérés qui pour toi se croisèrent
Éléonore Éléonore d'Aquitaine[1]

Elle avait inventé pour le coeur fou des sages
Tous les crucifiements d'un cérémonial
Ce n'est pas pour si peu qu'on l'excommunia
Livide au milieu de la fuite des pages

Mais ses adorateurs barons et troubadours
Se souvinrent d'avoir suivi Pierre l'Ermite[2]
Chevaliers perdus de la reine maudite
Avec ses lévriers ses lions et ses ours

Ils se souvinrent du frisson sous les grands chênes
Dans la ville romane où Pierre leur parlait
Vézelay Vézelay Vézelay Vézelay
Et ses manches semblaient lourdes du poids des chaînes

Le Saint Sépulcre[3] alors ce n'était rien pour eux
Écoutaient-ils les mots des lèvres diaphanes
Qu'ils y mêlaient un jeu terriblement profane
Amoureux amoureux amoureux amoureux

Ah quand ils entendaient dire La Terre Sainte
S'ils joignaient leurs clameurs aux cris fanatisés
C'est qu'aux mots les plus purs il pleuvait des baisers
Et son absence encore au silence était peinte

Le clair obscur jetait sur sa robe un damier
L'écho blasphémateur répétait je vous aime
Quand le prédicateur disait Jérusalem
Et ses yeux s'éclairaient comme un vol de ramiers

Plus tard plus tard après la démente aventure
Dont j'aime autant ne pas parler comme vous faites
Parce que j'ai le coeur plein d'une autre défaite
A laquelle il n'y a pas de deleatur

Plus tard quand la souveraine bannie
Eut quitté son palais la France et ses amours
Ils retrouvèrent la mémoire de ces jours
Et les mots passionnés de leurs litanies

Éveillèrent la rime inverse des paroles
Du prêcheur noir et blanc qu'ils avaient bafoué
La croix a pris pour eux un sens inavoué
Sans crime on peut nommer Sang-du-Christ les girolles

Mais ce ne fut enfin que dans quelque Syrie
Qu'ils comprirent vraiment les vocables sonores
Et blessés à mourir surent qu'Éléonore
C'était ton nom Liberté Liberté chérie

NOTES

1. *Eleanore of Aquitaine*: Eleanor of Aquitaine (1122–1204), Duchess of Aquitaine and Countess of Poitou; repudiated by Louis VII, King of France, she married Henry II, a Plantagenet and King of England. She favored the arts and her court was one of the centers that developed the courtly tradition in love and literature. She lived at the time of the Second, Third, and Fourth Crusades.
2. *Peter the Hermit*: Peter the Hermit (1050–1115), a monk and chief preacher of the First Crusade, in which he later participated. The Second Crusade was launched by Saint Bernard from the church at Vézelay. Aragon seems to have confused the two.
3. *The Holy Sepulcher*: the Holy Sepulcher, the tomb of Christ.

ANTOINE DE SAINT-EXUPÉRY

1941

THE AWAKENING

And now I seem to have come to the end of a long pilgrimage. I have made no discovery. Like a man waking out of sleep, I am once again looking at that to which I had for so long been blind. I see now that in my civilization it is Man who holds the power to bind into unity all the individual diversities. There is in Man, as in all beings, something more than the mere sum of the materials that went to his making. A cathedral is a good deal more than the sum of its stones. It is geometry and architecture. The cathedral is not to be defined by its stones, since those stones have no meaning apart from the cathedral, receive from it their sole significance. And how diverse the stones that have entered into this unity! The most grimacing of the gargoyles are easily absorbed into the canticle of the cathedral.

But the significance of Man, in whom my civilization is summed up, is not self-evident: it is a thing to be taught. There is in mankind no natural predisposition to acknowledge the existence of Man, for Man is not made evident by the mere existence of men. It is because Man exists that we are men, not the other way round. My civilization is founded upon the reverence for Man present in all men, in each individual. My civilization has sought through the ages to reveal Man to men, as it might have taught us to perceive the cathedral in a mere heap of stones. This has been the text of its sermon—that Man is higher than the individual.

SOURCE NOTE: Antoine de Saint-Exupéry, *Pilote de guerre* (New York, Éditions de la Maison française, 1942), pp. 225–34; 238–43. Written in New York, an edition was printed by Gallimard in 1942, then suppressed in 1943 by the Vichy government. A clandestine edition was printed by the Imprimerie Nouvelle Lyonnaise in December 1943.

And this, the true significance of my civilization, is what I had little by little forgotten. I had thought that it stood for a sum of men as stone stands for a sum of stones. I had mistaken the sum of stones for the cathedral, wherefore little by little my heritage, my civilization, had vanished. It is Man who must be restored to his place among men. It is Man that is the essence of our culture. Man, the keystone in the arch of the community. Man, the seed whence springs our victory.

It is easy to establish a society upon the foundation of rigid rules. It is easy to shape the kind of man who submits blindly and without protest to a master, to the precepts of a Koran. The real task is to succeed in setting man free by making him master of himself.

But what do we mean by setting man free? You cannot free a man who dwells in a desert and is an unfeeling brute. There is no liberty except the liberty of someone making his way towards something. Such a man can be set free if you will teach him the meaning of thirst, and how to trace a path to a well. Only then will he embark upon a course of action that will not be without significance. You could not liberate a stone if there were no law of gravity—for where will the stone go, once it is quarried?

My civilization sought to found human relations upon the belief in Man above and beyond the individual, in order that the attitude of each person towards himself and towards others should not be one of blind conformity to the habits of the anthill, but the free expression of love. The invisible path of gravity liberates the stone. The invisible slope of love liberates man. My civilization sought to make every man the ambassador of their common prince. It looked upon the individual as the path or the message of a thing greater than himself. It pointed the human compass towards magnetized directions in which man would ascend to attain his freedom.

I know how this field of energy came to be. For centuries my civilization contemplated God in the person of man. Man was created in the image of God. God was revered in Man. Men were brothers in God. It was this reflection of God that conferred an inalienable dignity upon every man. The duties of each towards himself and towards his kind were evident from the fact of the relations between God and man. My civilization was the inheritor of Christian values.

It was the contemplation of God that created men who were equal, for it was in God that they were equal. This equality possessed an unmistakable significance. For we cannot be equal except we be equal *in* something. The private and the captain are equal in the Nation. Equality is a word devoid of meaning if nothing exists in which it can be expressed.

This equality in the rights of God—rights that are inherent in the individual—forbade the putting of obstacles in the way of the ascension of the individual; and I understand why. God had chosen to adopt the individual as His path. But as this choice also implied the equality of the rights of God "over" the individual, it was clear that individuals were themselves subjected to common duties and to a common respect for law. As the manifestation of God, they were equal in their rights. As the servants of God, they were also equal in their duties.

I understand why an equality that was founded upon God involved neither contradiction nor disorder. Demagogy enters at the moment when, for want of a common denominator, the principle of equality degenerates into a principle of identity. At that moment the private refuses to salute the captain, for by saluting the captain he is no longer doing honor to the Nation, but to the individual.

As the inheritor of God, my civilization made men equal in Man.

I understand the origin of the respect of men for one another. The scientist owed respect to the stoker, for what he respected in the stoker was God; and the stoker, no less than the scientist, was an ambassador of God. However great one man may be, however insignificant another, no man may claim the power to enslave another. One does not humble an ambassador. And yet this respect for man involved no degrading prostration before the insignificance of the individual, before brutishness or ignorance—since what was honored was not the individual himself but his status as ambassador of God. Thus the love of God founded relations of dignity between men, relations between ambassadors and not between mere individuals.

As the inheritor of God, my civilization founded the respect for Man present in every individual.

I understand the origin of brotherhood among men. Men were brothers in God. One can be a brother only *in* something. Where there is no tie that binds men, men are not united but merely lined up. One cannot be a brother to nobody. The pilots of Group 2-33 are brothers in the Group. Frenchmen are brothers in France.

As the inheritor of God, my civilization made men to be brothers in Man.

I understand the meaning of the duties of charity which were preached to me. Charity was the service of God performed through the individual. It was a thing owed to God, however insignificant the individual who was its recipient. Charity never humiliated him who profited from it, nor ever bound him by the chains of gratitude, since it was not to him but to God that the gift was made. And the practice of charity, meanwhile, was never at any time a kind of homage rendered to insignificance, to brutishness, or to ignorance. The physician owed it to himself to risk his life in the care of a plague-infested nobody. He was serving God thereby. He was never a lesser man for having spent a sleepless night at the bedside of a thief.

As the inheritor of God, my civilization made charity to be a gift to Man present in the individual.

I understand the profound meaning of the humility exacted

from the individual. Humility did not cast down the individual, it raised him up. It made clear to him his role as ambassador. As it obliged him to respect the presence of God in others, so it obliged him to respect the presence of God in himself, to make himself the messenger of God or the path taken by God. It forced him to forget himself in order that he might wax and grow; for if the individual exults in his own importance, the path is transformed into a sea.

As the inheritor of God, my civilization preached self-respect, which is to say respect for Man present in oneself.

I understand, finally, why the love of God created men responsible for one another and gave them hope as a virtue. Since it made of each of them the ambassador of the same God, in the hands of each rested the salvation of all. No man had the right to despair, since each was the messenger of a thing greater than himself. Despair was the rejection of God within oneself. The duty of hope was translatable thus: "And dost thou think thyself important? But thy despair is self-conceit!"

As the inheritor of God, my civilization made each responsible for all, and all responsible for each. The individual was to sacrifice himself in order that by his sacrifice the community be saved; but this was no matter of idiotic arithmetic. It was a matter of the respect for Man present in the individual. What made my civilization grand was that a hundred miners were called upon to risk their lives in the rescue of a single miner entombed. And what they rescued in rescuing that miner was Man.

I understand by this bright light the meaning of liberty. It is liberty to grow as the tree grows in the field of energy of its seed. It is the climate permitting the ascension of Man. It is like a favorable wind. Only by the grace of the wind is the bark free on the waters.

A man built in this wise disposes of the power of the tree.

What space may his roots not cover! What human pulp may
he not absorb to grow and blossom in the sun!

But I had ruined everything. I had dissipated the inheritance.
I had allowed the notion of Man to rot.

And yet my civilization had expended a good share of its
genius and its energy to preserve the cult of a Prince revealed
in the existence of individual men, and the high quality of
human relations established by that cult. All the efforts of
Humanism tended towards this end in the age of the Renaissance and after. Humanism assigned to itself the exclusive
mission of brightening and perpetuating the ideal of the
primacy of Man over the individual. What Humanism preached
was Man.

But as soon as we seek to speak of Man, our language displays
itself insufficient. Man is not the same as men. We say nothing
essential about the cathedral when we speak of its stones. We
say nothing essential about Man when we seek to define him
by the qualities of men. Humanism strove in a direction
blocked in advance when it sought to seize the notion of Man
in terms of logic and ethics, and by these terms communicate
that notion to the human consciousness. Unity of being is not
communicable in words. If I knew men to whom the notion of
the love of country or of home was strange, and I sought to
teach them the meaning of these words, I could not summon
a single argument that would waken the sense of country or
home in them. I may, if I like, speak of a farm by referring to
its fields, its streams, its pastures, its cattle. Each of these by
itself, and all of them together, contribute to the existence of
the farm. Yet in that farm there must be something which
escapes material analysis, since there are farmers who are
ready to ruin themselves for their farms. And it is that "something else" which is the essence of the farm and enhances the
particles of which the farm is composed. The cattle, by that
something else, become the cattle of a farm, the meadows the
meadows of a farm, the fields the fields of a farm.

Thus man becomes the man of a country, of a group, of a

craft, of a civilization, of a religion. But if we are to clothe ourselves in these higher beings we must begin by creating them within ourselves. The being of which we claim to form part is created within us not by words but only by acts. A being is not subject to the empire of language, but only to the empire of acts. Our Humanism neglected acts. Therefore it failed in its attempt.

The essential act possesses a name. Its name is sacrifice.

Sacrifice signifies neither amputation nor repentance. It is in essence an act. It is the gift of oneself to the being of which one forms part. Only he can understand what a farm is, what a country is, who shall have sacrificed part of himself to his farm or country, fought to save it, struggled to make it beautiful. Only then will the love of farm or country fill his heart. A country—or a farm—is not the sum of its parts. It is the sum of its gifts.

So long as my civilization leaned upon God it was able to preserve the notion of sacrifice whereby God is created in the hearts of men. Humanism neglected the essential role of sacrifice. It thought itself able to communicate the notion of Man by words and not by acts. In order to save the vision of Man present in all men, it could do no more than capitalize the word. And mankind was meanwhile moving down a dangerous slope—for we were in danger of mistaking the average of mankind or the arithmetical sum of mankind for Man. We were in danger of mistaking the sum of the stones for the cathedral. Wherefore little by little we lost our heritage.

Instead of affirming the rights of Man present in the individual we had begun to talk about the rights of the collectivity. We had bit by bit introduced a code for the collectivity which neglected the existence of Man. That code explains clearly why the individual should sacrifice himself for the community. It does not explain clearly and without ambiguity why the community should sacrifice itself for a single member. Why it is equitable that a thousand die to deliver a single man from unjust imprisonment. We still remember vaguely that this should be, but progressively we forget it more and more. And yet it is this principle alone which differentiates us from the anthill and which is the source of the grandeur of mankind. For want of an effective concept of humanity—which can rest only upon Man—we have been slipping gradually towards the anthill, whose definition is the mere sum of the individuals it contains.

What did we possess that we could set up against the religions of the State and of the Party? What had become of our great ideal of Man born of God? That ideal is scarcely recognizable now beneath the vocabulary of windy words that covers it.

Little by little forgetting Man, we limited our code to the problems of the individual. We have gone on preaching the equality of men. But having forgotten Man, we no longer knew what it was we were preaching. Having forgotten in what men were equal, we enunciated a vague affirmation that was of no use to us. How can there be any material equality between individuals as such—the sage and the brute, the imbecile and the genius? On the material plane, equality implies that all men are identical and occupy the same place in the community; which is absurd. Wherefore the principle of equality degenerates and becomes the principle of identity.

We have gone on preaching the liberty of men. But having forgotten Man, we have defined our liberty as a sort of vague license limited only at the point where one man does injury to another. This seeming ideal is devoid of meaning, for in fact no man can act without involving other men. If I, being a soldier, mutilate myself, I am shot. An isolated individual does not exist. He who is sad, saddens others.

And even liberty of this sort had to be subjected to a thousand subterfuges before we could make use of it. We found it impossible to say when this right was valid and when it was not valid, and as we wanted very much to preserve the vague principle of the thing from the innumerable assaults which every society necessarily makes upon the liberty of the individual, we turned hypocrite and shut our eyes.

As for charity, we have not even dared go on preaching it. There was a time when the sacrifice which created beings took the name of charity each time that it honored God in His image upon earth. By our charity to the individual we made our gift to God, and later to Man. But having forgotten both God and Man, we found ourselves giving only to the individual. And from that moment charity became an unacceptable course. It is society and not the mood of the individual that should ensure equity in the sharing of the goods of this world. The dignity of the individual demands that he be not reduced to vassalage by the largesse of others. What a paradox—that men who possessed wealth should claim the right, over and above their possessions, to the gratitude of those who were without possessions!

But above all our miscomprehended charity turned against its own goal. It was founded exclusively upon feelings of pity with regard to individuals—wherefore it forbade us all educative chastisement. But true charity, being the practice of the rites rendered to Man over and above the individual, taught that the individual must be fought in order that Man grow great.

And thus Man became lost to us. And losing Man we emptied all warmth out of that very fraternity which our civilization had preached to us—since we are brothers *in* something, and not brothers in isolation. It is not by contributions to a pool that fraternity is ensured. Fraternity is the creation of sacrifice alone. It is the creation of the gift made to a thing greater than ourselves. But we, mistaking the very root of all true existence, seeing in it a sterile diminution of our goods, reduced our fraternity to no more than a mutual tolerance of one another.

We ceased to give. Obviously, if I insist upon giving only to myself, I shall receive nothing. I shall be building nothing of which I am to form part, and therefore I shall be nothing. And when, afterwards, you come to me and ask me to die for certain interests, I shall refuse to die. My own interest will command me to live. Where will I find that rush of love that will compensate my death? Men die for a home, not for walls and tables. Men die for a cathedral, not for stones. Men die for a people, not for a mob. Men die for love of Man—provided that Man is the keystone in the arch of their community. Men die only for that by which they live.

The sole reason why our society still seemed a fortunate one, and man seemed still to be distinguishable from the collectivity, was that our true civilization, which we were betraying in our ignorance, still sent forth its dying rays and still, despite ourselves, continued to preserve us.

LEWIS GALANTIERE

NOSTALGIA: THE PAST
AND THE FUTURE

THE UNIVERSE OF OCCUPATION, conceptualized and idealized, is projected in Sartre's nostalgic farewell to the past at the time of liberation. He projects an image of the reality experienced which is both familiar and alien to the ordinary man, both true and distorted. Oppression, solitude, mortality: for Sartre the Occupation years imposed on the French an awareness of man's metaphysical condition. Concomitantly each individual also discovered his freedom to refuse that condition, his responsibility to revolt against submission in the name of all other men. Sartre had mentally modeled his experience so that it coincided with his own existentialist view of human reality, as he had spelled it out in *Being and Nothingness*. He had thus operated a curious reversal of values that was to haunt his later work. The nostalgia for violence, contestation, martyrdom in an absolutely just cause is a romantic heritage he was to carry through into the aftermath of war.

JEAN-PAUL SARTRE

THE REPUBLIC OF SILENCE

We have never been so free as under German occupation. We had lost every right, and above all the right of speech: we were insulted every day and we had to remain silent; we were deported as laborers, as Jews, as political prisoners; everywhere, on the walls, in the newspapers, and on the screen, we saw the foul and listless face which our oppressors wanted to give us. Because of all this we were free. Since the Nazi venom penetrated our very thoughts, every true thought was a victory. Since an all-powerful police tried to force us to be silent, each word became as precious as a declaration of principle. Since we were hounded, every one of our movements had the importance of commitment. The often atrocious circumstances of our struggle had at last put us in a position to live our life without pretenses—to live in this torn, unbearable condition which we call the human condition. Exile, captivity, and above all death, which is ably disguised in periods of happiness, became the perpetual object of our concern; we discovered that they were not evitable accidents or even constant but external threats: they had become our *lot*, our destiny, the source of our reality as men. Each second we fully realized the meaning of the trite little phrase "All men are mortal." And the choice which each man made on his own was genuine, since he made it in the presence of death, since he would always have been able to express it in terms of "better death than . . ." And I'm not talking of the elite formed by the true resistants, but of every Frenchman who, at every hour of the day and night, for four years, said no. The cruelty of the enemy pushed us to

SOURCE NOTE: Jean-Paul Sartre, "La République du silence," *Situations III* (Paris, Gallimard, 1949), pp. 11–14.

the extremes of our condition by forcing us to ask these questions which we avoid in peacetime: each of us—and what
Frenchman did not at one point find himself in this position?
—who knew certain details concerning the Resistance wondered
anxiously: "If I were tortured, would I hold out?" Thus the
question of liberty was raised and we were on the brink of the
deepest knowledge that man can have of himself. Because man's
secret is not his Oedipus complex or his inferiority complex, it
is the limit of his freedom, it is his power to resist torture and
death. To those who were active in the underground, the
circumstances of this struggle were a new experience: they did
not fight in the open, like soldiers; they were hunted in solitude,
arrested in solitude, and it was all alone that they resisted
torture: alone and naked before well-shaved, well-fed, well-
dressed executioners who laughed at their wretched flesh, who,
with clean consciences and unlimited power, looked as though
they were in the right. And yet at the depths of this solitude it
was the others, all the others, all the comrades of the Resistance
whom they defended. One word was enough to cause ten, a
hundred arrests. Is not total responsibility in total solitude the
revelation of our liberty? The need, the solitude, the enormous
risk were the same for everybody, for the leaders and the men.
For those who carried messages and did not know what they
contained as for those who organized the whole Resistance,
there was only one sentence: imprisonment, deportation, death.
There is no army in the world with such equal risks for the
soldiers and the general. And that is why the Resistance was a
real democracy: for the soldier and for the leader there was the
same danger, the same responsibility, the same absolute liberty
in discipline. Thus, in darkness and in blood, the strongest
republic was formed. Each of its citizens knew that he owed
himself to everyone and could only count on himself; each one
performed his historic part in total solitude. Each one, in
defiance of the oppressor, undertook to be himself; irremediably
and by freely choosing himself, he chose freedom for everybody.
This republic without institutions, without army or police, had

to be conquered by each Frenchman and established at every
moment against Nazism. We are now on the brink of another
Republic: can't we preserve by day the austere virtues of the
Republic of Silence and Night?

ALASTAIR HAMILTON

"ADMITTEDLY OR NOT," writes Henry Miller, "the
artist is obsessed with the thought of re-creating the world
in order to restore man's innocence. He knows, moreover,
that man can only recover his innocence by regaining his
freedom. Freedom here meaning the death of the automa-
ton."* Whether or not this is always true is a matter for
debate. But during the Occupation years it was indeed a
central obsession. Perhaps because of the circumstances and
the intense emotional ambience they generated, because the
actual world, it seemed, would have to be remade and
freedom in every dimension of living regained, the artistic
and the political endeavor fused, the realms of vision and
fact, of literature and reality.

In her meditation on the *Iliad*, Simone Weil had distinguished as the source of its greatness the poet's uncom-
promising refusal of a Manichaean vision of life embodied
in the clash of force against force. She had pointed to the
visionary realism and power of disengagement and compassion with which the poet had depicted the universal
mechanism of violence, rejecting any ambivalence in
thought and judgment. This, in her eyes, gave the poem its
humanizing power. In contrast, a most striking feature of
the literary creations of the Occupation is their increasingly
messianic trend and their unconscious emotional ambivalence. There is still a power of self-scrutiny and impartiality
in the point of view of a Giraudoux or an Anouilh that no
longer prevails in the lyricism of Orestes' revolt against the
order favored by Zeus and the secular authority of Aegis-

* Henry Miller, *Evergreen Review*, No. 17, p. 22.

thus, the "hollow" king, its counterpart: both are clearly branded as spurious, and the issue is thus simplified. And Orestes' anarchistic self-assertion is itself a far cry from the highly idealized community of "just men" projected in the "Republic of Silence." It is with this idealized community that Sartre identifies and for whom he speaks, although he did not suffer from the martyrdom he evokes. That community is depicted as united in purity of conscience, exemplary in thought and act. Sartre's ideal model of the Resistance, in which the French community is incarnated, is polarized, structured in terms of innocence and guilt, virtue and vice. So incontrovertible in his eyes is the inner evidence on which it is founded that he has no doubts as to its objectivity. Moral truth speaks authoritatively through Sartre's voice, as Man speaks through Saint-Exupéry's. There are no questions and no compromises. The same Manichaean vision and human ambivalence are apparent in Camus's fourth letter to his German friend, included in the last section of our book. There the polarization has taken place: all that Camus so fiercely hates in life—cruelty, injustice, wanton destruction of human lives—is embodied in the German, in contrast to his French opponent. Yet Camus is not at ease within this frame, which is contested in his play *Caligula*. There the emperor's yearning to create a coherent world—an echo of the artist's—proves disastrous when applied to human society.

There is a Nietzschean undertow in the single-minded emphasis of these works upon the individual's capacity morally to counter apparently insuperable odds. They tend to assert the absolute validity of some system of value founded on an intensely subjective emotional reaction to harsh circumstances. These values are then embodied in exemplary fictional actions, projected as norms. But all other considerations are set aside, and insofar as a literary creation does reveal something of the sensibility of the moment, it does seem that the French Resistance drew its strength from an idealized, quasi-mythical view of reality that could also temporarily feed the partisan passions and the surge of irrational violence which characterized the post-Liberation "purge" of the "collaborationists." That same Manichaean view had had its counterpart in the political myths of the collaborationists. The subsequent post-Liberation clash of the myth with the hard realities of political fact and necessity, its deflation yet its underground persistence, were factors in the uneasy course of the postwar years, literary, intellectual, and political. For though the words used were the same: revolt, freedom, justice, commitment, revolution, the visions polarized by the emotional climate were in fact mutually exclusive.

PART FOUR

THE SWING OF THE PENDULUM

THE BALANCE SHIFTS

FOR MEN LIKE Brasillach and Drieu La Rochelle, committed to a National Socialist revolution, the defeat of 1940 had been real but ambivalent. It had corroborated their ideas. Upon this corroboration, in behalf of the future of their country, they had based their attitudes and their actions, and thereto committed their lives. Though fully aware of the risks involved, they had not, in 1940, doubted the outcome. The defeat of Germany destroyed the very ground on which they stood, canceling out their efforts. It is difficult—indeed, almost impossible—for us today, reversing established perspectives, to see the events of 1943–1945 in a collaborationist view, as a French defeat. Yet that is how Brasillach saw it. Between April and September 1943 he confronted the growing gap between events and the future he had forecast for France. He slowly relinquished the myth, though never entirely. It is to a "fraternal adversary" that he addresses his remarks in the passage given below, borrowing from an otherwise unsigned letter in which a French prisoner of war had questioned his positions. There is no animosity in his tone, but a singular mixture of untenable, simplistic prejudice, partial truth, and genuine passion and insight. The cliché to which Brasillach clings is the view of Marxism as the

enemy of Western civilization both within France and
without, and of Germany as the strategic bulwark upon
which the survival of an non-Marxian Western European
civilization depends.

Camus's fourth letter to his German friend, written
barely a year later, is couched in the language of meta-
physics and morality. He envisages no meeting ground
between the two men. Though he eschews the notion of
hatred, resentment, or revenge, his letter is not addressed
to a "fraternal adversary." To be sure Camus is not, like
Brasillach, addressing a Frenchman, but a German whom
he accuses of betrayal: Nazi Germany has betrayed mankind, aligned itself with the irrational universe against
humanity. The passion that drives Camus on the eve of
victory is deep and, one feels, implacable.

ROBERT BRASILLACH

1943

THE TURNING POINT OF THE WAR
April 2, 1943

Dissidence cannot simply be dismissed as communism, for the French do not know what communism is. They have only bookish and indirect visions of it, which they do not always believe—and they are wrong. But the French know the Popular Front,[1] they saw it. . . .

. . . The Popular Front was also the greatest betrayal of the workers. It was bread, peace, liberty, promised by men who four years later would give our country its defeat and its consequences. It was certain substantial material advantages, a few promises, some of which were justified, but made in such a climate of lies that they could only give rise to what happened . . .

. . . The French worker, who has retained the bitter recollection of the Popular Front and the lost illusions, must know that that is exactly what Giraud[2] and Roosevelt want to give him. . . .

. . . The Popular Front is both the main cause of our misfortunes and America's cherished child. Nostalgia for the Popular Front is the basis of Mr. Roosevelt's European policy. He does not hate Pierre Laval[3] for any high-minded reason of foreign policy; he hates him because he considers him the adversary of the Popular Front. He does not want the defeat of the Germans for love of us, but to bring back Blum,[4] of whom he spoke so tenderly and nostalgically in June 1940. Before he could judge the new French government and when he only knew the Marshal as a former soldier, ambassador to

SOURCE NOTE: Robert Brasillach, "Le Tournant de la guerre," *Journal d'un homme occupé* (Paris, Les Sept Couleurs, 1955), pp. 242–46; 248–50.

Franco, and the author of certain speeches and writings, he exclaimed with hatred: "Pétain is a Nazi!" This was because Roosevelt saw him as a man detested by the Popular Front, and nothing else.

On whichever side they stand, the main traitors are those who want to lead us back to the period of the French catastrophe, the origin of our misfortunes, to the bloody and base infamy of those months when our defeat was consummated. And whoever is taken in by them, as certain people seem to have been in Algiers,[5] is a fool unworthy of consideration.

Behind the mask of dissidence, or behind any other mask, the Popular Front remains the archenemy of France.

                                                    May 1943
. . . There are no valid dreams in politics, but there are aims. Distant aims, aims hard to attain, but real aims. Peace is an aim. Understanding between nations is an aim. Mutual defense against Marxist and Jewish poisons is an aim. It may be quite possible for different ideologies to live on the same planet, just as there can be different races and different zones of influence. But these ideologies or races must be limited and kept in check, and not allowed to destroy the very sense of our communal life. All that provides a barrier against destruction must be assisted, sustained, and, let us not be afraid to say, understood. Defeat is hard for a nationalist, but there is something worse than defeat: the end of one's country and the end of the West. We are lucky enough never to have to be neighbors of the Russian Empire, whatever its future forms; we will always have the German rampart between us. It is better not to attack the rampart. The English always understand too late.

The world can change shape, my brotherly adversaries, but the changes will not modify our way of seeing things, inscribed not in history, which is not always a good teacher, but in geography, which I prefer. And our inner duties are also inscribed in another form of reality which no change can really modify. Neither defeat nor victory can mean that the law of a Western nation is justifiably based on a parliamentary democracy incubated in a hundred and fifty years of folly. We would be wrong ever to neglect the effects of social justice, public order, racial defense, honor due to work, and peace to be protected. Whether it be after the victory of 1918 as it was after the defeat of 1940, whether it be under an army of occupation or an interallied bankers' control, whoever neglects these essential factors in the life of a nation has neglected the very life of the nation. These are basic truths which I am almost ashamed to repeat, and someone among my adversaries occasionally agrees with all these points. What worries him is his present form of existence; it simply obstructs his whole horizon. His horizon is so obstructed that he cannot even perceive the worst evil which could befall him.

One day, as after every civil war, we will have to proceed to French reconciliation. Henry IV[6] did so, Napoleon[7] tried to do so, and Louis XVIII[8] wanted to do so. We have no illusions: there will be numerous converts clamoring to bear the banner. What am I saying? They are already there! We shall shrug our shoulders and remember. But above all we shall know that a reconciliation is only possible in accordance with our principles and no others. We proclaimed these principles yesterday as we will proclaim them tomorrow. We are pleased to make this known.

* * * * *

May 14, 1943

. . . Some old fogeys think the war is over because Tunis has fallen and because the losers of Pearl Harbor and Singapore now stand before the vast trench of the Mediterranean. They do not even want to see the material and physical dangers which can befall France and the French (English shells do not distinguish between Gaullists and anti-Gaullists). They do not see that none of the reasons for supporting a truly Western

policy have changed, and that even if Germany were to lose—
a hypothesis which we must include for the sake of argument—
it would be precisely she to whom we would have to cling in
our effort to be saved. Without an indestructible France and
Germany peace can never be established in Europe. If we try
to annihilate one or the other the germs of war will ceaselessly
return. Not only is Germany the only power in the world which
can block the road to the Marxist revolution, whether we like
it or not, but she is also the center of Europe and will always
remain there; without her strength, nothing is possible.

*   *   *   *   *

August 14, 1943

I do not want to be romantic. We have nothing to repudiate.
But what now is the government's duty? *To prepare, whatever
may happen, for a future Franco-German alliance. To prepare,
if necessary, for a losers' alliance.* But not to let itself be dragged
to disaster without having tried everything. Let us be logical:
in 1938 we yelled that we were not going to embark on the
boat which sank with the Czechs;[9] in 1939 Déat laughed at the
people who wanted to die for Danzig.[10] Should we die today
so that Danzig can remain German? I say no. I am against
Bolshevism because it is total death. Otherwise *I am a German-
ophile and a Frenchman,* more French than National Socialist,
to be exact. In case of danger one must stick to one's country.
She alone never deceives you. Because if Germany recovers, as
she may, so much the better for her and for us. But we must
know how to act, and never say *never* in politics. We cannot
always write all that, but we do not need to write the opposite.
In any case I will have nothing to do with any denationaliza-
tion. Admittedly some of our friends tend to do this, consciously
or unconsciously. Even our opponents once considered our
paper the "best French weekly" and now there is an attempt to
turn it into "fascism and nothing but fascism." This is
Maurrassianism reversed.

I am against mumbling, "We should have done this or that . . ." because Maurras has done nothing but conjugate "we should have done" for forty years. That is not politics.

There is talk of a meeting between Hitler and Laval. A whole lot of members of the Cathala and Bichelonne cabinets[11] have been arrested for no clear reason. Katyn[12] is a joke compared to the bombing raids. . . .

September 1943

After Italy's defeat it is clear that Germany can no longer win the war. What remains of the collaborationist policy? The memory of a friendship which cannot be effaced either by the dramatic present or by a certain future.

Of course the reasons for a Franco-German reconciliation remain. No vague military communiqué—always misinterpreted —can affect what has become a basic truth: before a power as terrifying and dynamic as Russian sovietism, I cannot imagine anyone in his right mind who desires Germany's collapse. We no longer have the right to reproach Clemenceau[13] for having partitioned Austria-Hungary rather than Germany, for what barrier could a hotchpotch of divided nationalities present to the East? That is a selfish point of view, but one must talk to each man according to his interests. Apart from the war, the necessity of Franco-German coexistence, of a Franco-German appeasement, is the golden rule for future peace. To say that "conquered France must come to terms with her conqueror" is not enough from the mere point of view of national salvation. We are of the opinion that defeated France should first come to terms with Germany; if the worst comes to the worst they should form a losers' alliance, otherwise they should form a union of the powerful West. The laws for future peace on the Continent remain unchanged, and unchangeable.

ALASTAIR HAMILTON

NOTES

1. *Popular Front*: see page 57, note 20.
2. *Giraud*: Henri Honoré Giraud (1879–1949), head of French forces in Allied-occupied North Africa from 1942 on. De Gaulle took over the leadership of all Free French forces in 1943.
3. *Laval*: *see* Chronology, pages 370 ff.
4. *Blum*: Léon Blum, see page 57, note 19.
5. *Algiers*: reference to Darlan's defection to the Allied cause and the subsequent Allied invasion of North Africa on November 8, 1942.
6. *Henry IV*: (1553–1610), King of France; he united his kingdom after the wars of religion in the sixteenth century.
7. *Napoleon*: (1769–1821), Emperor of France; after the French Revolution he attempted a reconciliation with the Church and tried to win over the aristocracy to his regime.
8. *Louis XVIII*: (1755–1824), Restoration monarch after Napoleon's defeat; he made an attempt at conciliating the aristocracy and the new bourgeoisie.
9. *Czechs*: reference to their yielding to the German demand for annexation of Czechoslovakian Sudetenland as a measure of appeasement.
10. *Déat*: a journalist and politician with neosocialist leanings, he was opposed to France's participation in World War II and, after the defeat of France, became one of the more articulate advocates of collaboration and a rival of Jacques Doriot, a supporter of Laval. One of the leaders of the collaborationist Rassemblement National Populaire, then of the Front Révolutionnaire National. Sought refuge in Italy at the time of the Liberation, where he died in 1955. The slogan "Why die for Danzig?" first brought him into the limelight. *Danzig*: free city in Polish Corridor; invaded by Germans on September 1, 1939, marking the beginning of World War II.
11. *Cathala and Bichelonne cabinets*: cabinets participating in the Vichy government.
12. *Katyn*: Russian village; Russian forces killed some 4,500 Polish officers near here early in the war; the mass grave was discovered by the Germans in 1943.
13. *Clémenceau*: reference to terms of Treaty of Versailles, 1919.

ALBERT CAMUS

July 1944

FOURTH LETTER

*Man is mortal. That may be; but let us die
resisting; and if our lot is complete annihilation,
let us not behave in such a way that it seems
justice!*   OBERMANN, Letter 90

Now the moment of your defeat is approaching. I am
writing to you from a city known throughout the world which
is preparing against you a future of freedom. Our city knows
this is not easy and that first it will have to live through an
even darker night than the one which began, four years ago,
with your coming. I am writing to you from a city deprived
of everything, devoid of light and devoid of heat, starved, and
still not crushed. Soon something you cannot even imagine
will inflame the city. If we were lucky, you and I should then
stand face to face. Then we could fight each other knowing
what is at stake. I have a fair idea of your motives and you can
imagine mine.

These July nights are both light and heavy. Light along the
Seine and in the trees, but heavy in the hearts of those who
are awaiting the only dawn they now long for. I am waiting
and I think of you: I still have one more thing to tell you—and
it will be the last. I want to tell you how it is possible that,
though so similar, we should be enemies today, how I might
have stood beside you and why all is over between us now.

For a long time we both thought that this world had no
ultimate meaning and that consequently we were cheated. I
still think so in a way. But I came to different conclusions from
the ones you used to talk about, which, for so many years now,

SOURCE NOTE: Albert Camus, "Lettre IV," *Lettres à un ami allemand*
(Paris, Gallimard, 1948), pp. 71–87.

you have been trying to introduce into History. I tell myself
now that if I had really followed your reasoning, I ought to
approve what you are doing. And this is so serious that I must
stop and consider it, during this summer night so full of
promises for us and of threats for you.

You never believed in the meaning of this world, and you
therefore deduced the idea that everything was equivalent and
that good and evil could be defined according to one's wishes.
You supposed that in the absence of any human or divine code
the only values were those of the animal world—in other words,
violence and cunning. Hence you concluded that man was
negligible and that his soul could be killed, that in the maddest
of histories the only pursuit for the individual was the adventure of power and his only morality, the realism of conquests.
And to tell the truth, I, believing I thought as you did, saw
no argument to answer you except a fierce love of justice which,
after all, seemed to me as unreasonable as the most sudden
passion.

Where lay the difference? Simply that you readily accepted
despair and I never yielded to it. Simply that you saw the
injustice of our condition to the point of being willing to add
to it, whereas it seemed to me that man must exalt justice in
order to fight against eternal injustice, create happiness in order
to protest against the universe of unhappiness. Because you
turned your despair into intoxication, because you freed yourself from it by making a principle of it, you were willing to
destroy man's works and to fight him in order to add to his
basic misery. Meanwhile, refusing to accept that despair and
that tortured world, I merely wanted men to rediscover their
solidarity in order to wage war against their revolting fate.

As you see, from the same principle we derived quite different
codes, because along the way you gave up the lucid view and
considered it more convenient (you would have said a matter
of indifference) for another to do your thinking for you and
for the millions of Germans. Because you were tired of fighting
heaven, you relaxed in that exhausting adventure in which you

had to mutilate souls and destroy the world. In short, you chose injustice and sided with the gods. Your logic was merely apparent.

I, on the contrary, chose justice in order to remain faithful to the world. I continue to believe that this world has no ultimate meaning. But I know that something in it has meaning and that is man, because he is the only creature to insist on having one. This world has at least the truth of man and our task is to provide its justifications against fate itself. And it has no justification but man; hence he must be saved if we want to save the idea we have of life. With your scornful smile you will ask me: What do you mean by saving man? And with all my being I shout to you that I mean not mutilating him and yet giving a chance to the justice which man alone can conceive.

This is why we are fighting. This is why we first had to follow you on a path we did not want and why at the end of that path we met defeat. For your despair constituted your strength. The moment despair is alone, pure, sure of itself, pitiless in its consequences, it has a merciless power. That is what crushed us while we were hesitating with our eyes still fixed on happy images. We thought that happiness is the greatest of conquests, a victory over the fate imposed upon us. Even in defeat this longing did not leave us.

But you did what was necessary, and we went down in history. And for five years it was no longer possible to enjoy the call of birds in the cool of the evening. We were forced to despair. We were cut off from the world because to each moment of the world clung a whole mass of mortal images. For five years the earth has not seen a single morning without death agonies, a single evening without prisons, a single noon without slaughters. Yes, we had to follow you. But our difficult achievement consisted in following you into war without forgetting happiness. And despite the clamor and the violence, we tried to preserve in our hearts the memory of a happy sea, of a remembered hill, the smile of a beloved face. For that matter, this was our best weapon, the one we shall never put away. For as soon as we lost it we should be as dead as you are. But we know now that the weapons of happiness cannot be forged without considerable time and too much blood.

We had to enter into your philosophy and be willing to resemble you somewhat. You chose a vague heroism, because it is the only value left in a world that has lost its meaning. And, having chosen it for yourselves, you chose it for everybody else and for us. We were forced to imitate you in order not to die. But we became aware then that our superiority over you consisted in our having a direction. Now that it is all about to end, we can tell you what we have learned—that heroism is not much and that happiness is more difficult.

At present everything must be obvious to you; you know that we are enemies. You are the man of injustice and there is nothing in the world that my heart loathes so much. But now I know the reasons for what was once merely a passion. I am fighting you because your logic is as criminal as your heart. And in the horror you have lavished upon us for four years, your reason plays as large a part as your instinct. This is why my condemnation will be sweeping; you are already dead as far as I am concerned. But at the very moment when I am judging your horrible behavior, I shall remember that you and we started out from the same solitude, that you and we, with all Europe, are caught in the same tragedy of the intelligence. And, despite yourselves, I shall still apply to you the name of man. In order to keep faith with ourselves, we are obliged to respect in you what you do not respect in others. For a long time that was your great advantage since you kill more easily than we do. And to the very end of time that will be the advantage of those who resemble you. But to the very end of time, we, who do not resemble you, shall have to bear witness so that mankind, despite its worst errors, may have its justification and its proof of innocence.

This is why, at the end of this combat, from the heart of this city that has come to resemble hell, despite all the tortures inflicted on our people, despite our disfigured dead and our villages peopled with orphans, I can tell you that at the very moment when we are going to destroy you without pity, we still feel no hatred for you. And even if tomorrow, like so many others, we had to die, we should still be without hatred. We cannot guarantee that we shall not be afraid; we shall simply try to be reasonable. But we can guarantee that we shall not hate anything. And we have come to terms with the only thing in the world I could loathe today, I assure you, and we want to destroy you in your power without mutilating you in your soul.

As for the advantage you had over us, you see that you continue to have it. But it likewise constitutes our superiority. And it is what makes this night easy for me. Our strength lies in thinking as you do about the essence of the world, in rejecting no aspect of the drama that is ours. But at the same time we have saved the idea of man at the end of this disaster of the intelligence, and that idea gives us the undying courage to believe in a rebirth. To be sure, the accusation we make against the world is not mitigated by this. We paid so dear for this new knowledge that our condition continues to seem desperate to us. Hundreds of thousands of men assassinated at dawn, the terrible walls of prisons, the soil of Europe reeking with millions of corpses of its sons—it took all that to pay for the acquisition of two or three slight distinctions which may have no other value than to help some among us to die more nobly. Yes, that is heartbreaking. But we have to prove that we do not deserve so much injustice. This is the task we have set ourselves; it will begin tomorrow. In this night of Europe filled with the breath of summer, millions of men, armed or unarmed, are getting ready for the fight. The dawn about to break will mark your final defeat. I know that heaven that was indifferent to your horrible victories will be equally indifferent to your just defeat. Even now I expect nothing from heaven. But we shall at least have helped to save man from the solitude to which you wanted to relegate him. Because you scorned such faith in mankind, you are the men who, by thousands, are going to die solitary. Now, I can say farewell to you.

JUSTIN O'BRIEN

THE LAST
CONFRONTATIONS

ON AUGUST 18–19, 1944, with the Allied forces
rapidly approaching Paris, the French Forces of the Interior
staged an uprising in order to liberate the capital themselves, a political-psychological rather than a military event.
On August 25 the German command capitulated. The war
was to continue for several more months until May 7, 1945,
the day of the unconditional surrender of Germany. But
for the French, the essential confrontation truly took place
after the liberation of most of the territory of the country,
the confrontation of collaborationist and resistant.

Of the selections given below, two were written in prison.
Brasillach had gone into hiding at the start of the insurrection; he gave himself up on September 14, was tried on
January 19, 1945, and executed on February 6. Drieu La
Rochelle, after a first early attempt at suicide to which he
alludes, committed suicide on March 15. The mechanism
of force described by Simone Weil was working with
rigorous precision. For at a time when even the most lucid
among the French, a Guéhenno or a Camus, found it
difficult not to give way to hate, the thirst for vengeance
among the less lucid was violent and not discriminating.
In this context, as Brasillach discovered, an adverse political
opinion became high treason. Brasillach's account of those

days reveals the genuine limitations of his own intellectual world, as he discovered a reality hidden from collaborationist view, the extent of Nazi brutality that rebounded in the brutality of the French purge.

In Drieu's "secret account" of his last confrontation with history there is an eerie withdrawal, accentuated in the entry we have selected by his use of English. In his own eyes his commitments take on the inconsistency of dreams, torn apart by an incongruous reality. In the final disengagement that precedes suicide, he sees a future from which he is excluded. What he foresees is a confrontation between the Anglo-Saxon democracies and the Marxist countries, not the leap into freedom the French were meanwhile so wholeheartedly celebrating. Instead of the new departure enthusiastically planned by the Liberation forces, he anticipates only a monotonous repetition of iniquities in the name of justice, peace, and humanity.

Exhilaration at the moment and concern for the future are clearly differentiated in Paul Valéry's confrontation with himself and his countrymen in the first days of liberation. For him the freedom regained was real, an emotion coloring all the perceptions of the senses and the mind. But it was an emotion, and emotions are not, he points out, adequate counselors for the mind. The real confrontation France faced, as he saw it, was no longer between resistants and collaborationists; Fascists, democrats, and Marxists; Russia and the United States. The real confrontation was between emotional involvement in France's past and the capacity to build the future rationally on a hard core of fact and circumstance, lucidly assessed. The greatest challenge to be met then would be to leave behind the mythical thinking and Manichaean world of the past.

ROBERT BRASILLACH

1944

THE LIBERATION AS SEEN FROM AN ATTIC

I had another appointment with Maurice[1] at the restaurant of the Gare Montparnasse where we had lunched together the day before. Around the station they were selling red-white-and-blue rosettes and ribbons. They were saying that Versailles had been taken, that a curfew was scheduled for half past two in the afternoon, and that the Germans had mined all the Paris bridges. Everywhere posters pasted up by the Resistance committees or the Communist Party called for revolt and for submission to the new authorities. In the morning there had been shooting on the Champs-Elysées and the Boulevard Saint-Germain, but in the course of my long walk I had seen nothing.

From the conversation of the people sitting at the table next to ours we learned that the Resistance had already made arrests, in particular that of Bernard Faÿ. We should have to separate. The hour had come. Henri Poulain had not ventured into Paris for three days and must be lying low in his obscure suburb, under a false name; and Well Allot too had disappeared, somewhere, along with Lucien Gambelle,[2] after our lunch together. The young friends with whom I had camped and held discussions had all gone mysteriously under cover. I took leave of Maurice around two o'clock, at which hour no curfew had been officially announced, in spite of the rumors. We embraced under the blazing sun, and without the concierge of my refuge even noticing, I went back up to my attic room. Five minutes later there was fairly heavy gunfire nearby. The Police Headquarters, so they said, had given the signal for

SOURCE NOTE: Robert Brasillach, "La Libération vue d'une mansarde," *Journal d'un homme occupé* (Paris, Les Sept Couleurs, 1955), pp. 287–95.

insurrection. On this glorious August 19, as Well Allot later wrote, for the first time in the history of Paris, police and insurgents were to fight on the same side of the barricades. "Never had we fallen so low."

For a whole month I was to lead a strange existence, completely alone and, for the first few days, with no news whatsoever of what was going on. No friend had chosen the solution which chance had imposed upon me: a lonely hideout from which I could not emerge. The day-to-day problems were not easy to resolve. It was best that my presence be undetected, for my continuous stay in one small room, where nobody knew that I had a trunkful of provisions, would have seemed surprising and indeed suspicious. But in spite of all its advantages my refuge had no running water;[3] the nearest tap was almost a hundred feet away, on the other side of the stairs. And to top it all, during these days of scarce electricity, water didn't get up to the top floors before evening, just at the hour when the chambermaids came up to their rooms, near mine. I had to be as stealthy as a Sioux Indian and keep watch for some time before creeping out to fill my pitchers with water that, to my despair, barely trickled from the tap. But I was caught at it only once, near the end of my stay, when it didn't so much matter. The gas, too, was almost entirely cut off for a whole week. I had only a quart of alcohol and a paper stove, of the kind made by prisoners in Germany, which I had recently bought as a matter of precaution. My provisions consisted mostly of noodles, which can hardly be eaten uncooked. There was no question, of course, of putting on the light at night or of opening the window by day, because across the street there was an apartment on the same level whose tenant never stirred from home during the week of maximum agitation. The only good point was that the room opposite mine in the hall was empty. My own room was charmingly decorated and there were books. It was livable enough, if I had the patience. . . .

For two or three days I knew literally nothing of the world

outside. The house was exceedingly quiet; in the two hours
when there was sufficient electric current no one even listened
to the radio. I heard sounds of shooting from an uncertain
direction. Occasionally a tenant would lean out of a window
giving onto the courtyard. Monday, as I remember, there was
a truce, negotiated by the Swedish consul[4] with right-wing
members of the Resistance. I heard a woman say that cars,
flying white flags, were going up the street, and indeed there
was no more shooting. In the evening the same voice said that
the truce had been broken on the initiative of the Communists,
who wanted to have "their days" of glory. I spent most of the
day with my ear glued to the window in a passionate attempt
to snatch bits of news and reconstruct what was going on. In
between two outbursts of gunfire a cautious householder called
out to his maid (these were his exact words, I swear it):

"They've stopped shooting, Marie. You can go get some
bread."

Of course he didn't dream of going himself; you never can
tell! . . .

I caught only a few scattered phrases on which to feed my
thoughts, from chance adult conversations or from children
limited to playing in the courtyard all day long. It was hot,
but my window had to stay closed on account of the man
across the street. Fortunately I was dead sleepy and spent a
lot of my time in bed. Wednesday, if I remember correctly,
I had a visit from M.D., who brought me tomatoes and bits
of late news, including that of the appearance of new newspapers, which he didn't bring with him because the Germans
were still around. Underway already was the fabulous series of
arrests, which were to throw three hundred thousand Frenchmen into jails and prison camps, to "skim off the cream of the
country," as the English press was to put it, to try to put over
the idea that the biggest businessmen, the greatest writers and
artists, were a bunch of traitors. Old Maillol,[5] the most famous
scuptor of the present day, was said to have sinned against his
country, and there was a three-line account of his death in an

automobile accident. Was this a credible story? The First Republic had forever on its head the blood of André Chénier[6] and Lavoisier,[7] but apparently the Fourth Republic intended to outdo it.

In the night between August 24 and 25 there was much noise and conversation, and I heard people in my house going down into the cellar. Of course, having so long kept my secret, I didn't budge. I heard church bells ring mysteriously and saw the red glow from a small fire at the Grand-Palais. There was shooting all day on the twenty-fifth, the feast of Saint Louis, when during my childhood I used to go to dance in the square on Mont-Louis in Cerdagne.[8] Even in my isolated hideout I could feel that this was the end. Toward the end of the afternoon the gunfire ceased and a woman announced to the courtyard that French officers were approaching the nearest German barricade with white flags in their hands, as if to strike a truce. After about an hour had gone by I heard the strains of the *Marseillaise*. The last strongholds of German resistance had fallen.

I had few illusions about the military valor of the "week of glory"; I knew that only a few thousand Germans were left in the city and that, without the American advance, the "French Forces of the Interior"[9] could never have dislodged them. I never put much stock in the myth which may have served propaganda purposes, of the heroic uprising of Paris. Nevertheless, I must set down that, all alone in my room, I had a very strange feeling. I was cut off from my fellow men, their joy seemed to me naive and founded on a lie, and I did not yet know with what crimes "Liberation" was besmirched. Plain people, I said to myself, so happy to see the German troops out of the way, would be disillusioned when they saw that the war wasn't over, that cold, hunger, and bloodshed were still in store. But naive as they were, these happy people were mine. I didn't share their joy as I should have, and I felt dispossessed, heretical, and alienated. What stopped me from going down onto the street and waving my flag? I should have been as happy as any passer-by embracing an American-uniformed soldier of Leclerc's[10] army, or welcoming the first tanks . . . And here I was alone and unjustly punished.

The next afternoon I had the most emotional experience of my life as a recluse. To my surprise there was sudden gunfire outside. I started to peer cautiously through the barely open window and saw, without being seen, a man with a big revolver at one of the windows of the hall. Soon other men appeared on the rooftops. They were Republican Guards,[11] who proceeded to ask the first fellow whether he had seen anyone. Later I learned that this was the famous day of the "rooftop sharpshooters," when "militiamen"[12] (at no other time were there so many of these "militiamen" in the city) were accused of having shot into the crowd below. It was also the day when there was a mysterious attempt to take the life of General de Gaulle[13] while he was entering Notre-Dame for a *Te Deum* which was never sung, and from which the Archbishop of Paris[14] was conspicuously absent. Never was a chief of state crowned under auspices more somber.

The guards, in any case, thought they were on the trail of a "rooftop sharpshooter," probably a product of their imagination, and they began to search the house. They appeared, in the company of an old man with a mustache, probably the house manager, in the apartment across from mine. And what was more serious, they were already in my hall and starting to break through the entrance to the room next door. Now no one, I felt reasonably sure, knew that I was there. I should have to give a highly embarrassing explanation of my presence. Fortunately they didn't come in. It seems that the concierge— a saintly woman if ever there was one—said to them:

"Here there's only a nice young man; you wouldn't want to bother him."

"We're only after rascals," was their high-minded reply.

But I was very perturbed. It occurred to me that the newspapers would be calling (and so they were) for the installation of soviets or watchdog committees in apartment buildings. This was probably the reason for the campaign against the real or imaginary "rooftop sharpshooters." If at least I hadn't been all alone in the room . . . In any case, the place was becoming unhealthy and I was tempted to go spend the night somewhere else. At about six o'clock I went out, unobserved.

I found myself walking through an amazing Paris, filled with French flags, interspersed with occasional flags of the Allies and a very few of the Soviet Union. Every now and then broken paving stones bore witness to the street fighting which, I must admit, did not seem to have been very violent. There was an enormous crowd on the streets, an atmosphere like that of a county fair and undoubtedly free, and at intervals an overturned barricade or a gutted German blockhouse.[15] I walked along, without my glasses, a somewhat ridiculous stratagem with which to protect myself from recognition, toward the Observatory and the Avenue d'Orléans. The weather was mild, this was the first day of the famous Liberation, and I stopped in front of the shop windows to look at the photographs which had replaced those of Marshal Pétain, the "English Spoken" signs where "German Spoken" had been posted before, and all other evidence of turncoat tradesmen's wiles.

The friends to whose house I had decided to go were, unforunately not there, and after I had waited until eight thirty on the landing they had still not come home. I decided to go see if Maurice Bardèche was still with the people with whom he was momentarily residing. He was there, and his friends received me with somewhat terrified surprise, stuffing into my pockets the new papers that said I must have gone off to Germany, and gave news of the "rooftop sharpshooters" and the attempted assassination of De Gaulle. Maurice told me that his brother Henri had been arrested August 23, after having for twenty-four hours possessed a pass issued by the armed Resistance, the famous "FFI," the French Forces of the Interior, or "Fifis," as everyone was beginning to call them. His arrest was highly dramatic, accompanied by cries of "Kill him" and abominable brutality. We wondered how it would all turn out. Maurice had already engaged a lawyer, who had assured him that the Communists were ruling the roost. I couldn't hang around too long, and so I decided that rather than go to the hotel to which Maurice had moved, I would return to my own hideout. I embraced Maurice and went down into the unlighted streets. When would I see Maurice again? The air was heavy with threats.

When I got back another adventure awaited me. The Germans suddenly sent planes to bomb Paris. Was it out of rage over their forced departure or in revenge for the violence and murder which German prisoners and even women had suffered during the day? I had no way of knowing. In any case, dull thuds of the kind we had almost forgotten echoed in the sky and crude air-raid warning sirens began to whistle. All the people in my house were rushing down to the cellar. I lingered for a moment, ill at ease, in the courtyard, while the sky turned red. The manager rushed up to me and asked if I was a passer-by. I didn't dare say yes, for fear I should be seen, later on, going up to my room, and so I said that I was staying, temporarily, in a room lent to me by a woman tenant. He showed surprise and complained about not having been told. In order to cut short his lament I said that I would drop in to see him the next day.

This I did, armed with my false papers. I told him, with the greatest of ease, that I was from the north and couldn't get home, that I was staying with friends in the outskirts but had come into Paris in order to see the glorious victory parade. He took me at my word, and while showing him my papers, I began to make up a long story about my youth. We became very friendly, and he told me:

"We've had all sorts of surprises. Another tenant handed his apartment over to friends, whom we saw for the first time during an air-raid alarm . . . very common people, not at all up to the tone of the house . . . They'd been prisoners together . . . What can I say?"

I shook my head, understandingly. He went on to tell me

about the sharpshooters and the search that had taken place in the afternoon, of which I pretended to know nothing. He took down my name and said that now that he knew my face he could answer for me. Upon reflection I realized that my misadventure was a piece of luck, because my presence in the house was now accounted for. And I took up my residence again more philosophically than before.

My two friends, Jacques and M.D., started to call on me again, alternately, every three or four days, bringing biscuits, bread, fruit, and newspapers. I began to find my way around in the amazing press born of the Liberation. I read smug accounts of German atrocities and the tortures inflicted by the "French Gestapo." At the same time, among the hundreds of books in my room, I read a report by Andrée Viollis on Indochina, with a preface by André Malraux,[16] where there was an account of French police atrocities in 1931, at the time of the disturbances at Yenbay.[17] The two series of events seemed to be modeled one on the other, with tortures by electric current, village massacres, and sexual excesses. They inspired me with disgust for the police, whatever its nationality. Certainly we were becoming aware of real abominations. On June 9, when the whole countryside was in open revolt, an SS brigade had set fire to the village of Oradour-sur-Glane, shot all the men, and burned the women and children in the church. No law of retaliation can justify such crimes, although, as I realized from reading Andrée Viollis's book, no single country can be said to have a monopoly of them. I read, also, some books of Aragon, including one in which he said "shit to the whole French Army," and at the same time his recent patriotic poems. In short, I added extra hours to my course in philosophy . . . The papers told me that the liberation of Paris was a feat of arms glorious above all others, but they kept under cover the murders, the acts of personal vengeance, and the abominable crimes of the weeks whose seamy political side was not easy, at first, to analyze.

FRANCES FRENAYE

NOTES

1. *Maurice Bardèche*: French critic, brother-in-law to Brasillach.
2. *Bernard Fay, Henri Poulain, Well Allot, Lucien Gambelle*: fascist friends of Brasillach.
3. *my refuge had no running water*: Paris bourgeois apartments were built at the beginning of the century with a sixth floor for maids' rooms devoid of electricity and with a single faucet of cold running water for the entire floor.
4. *Swedish consul*: Raoul Nordberg, whose tireless action in favor of war victims is described in *Paris Brennt*.
5. *Maillol*: the sculptor Aristide Maillol (1861–1944), in his eighties at the time of the Liberation, was accused of collaboration, and a year later his works were put on the index list drawn up by the Front National des Arts.
6. *André Chénier*: French poet (1762–1794) who took part in the French Revolution and was later guillotined for protesting the excesses of the Reign of Terror.
7. *Lavoisier*: Antoine Lavoisier (1743–1794), French chemist, also executed during the Reign of Terror.
8. *Cerdagne*: region of the French Pyrenees. Brasillach had spent many summers there in the past.
9. *"French Forces of the Interior"*: Resistance counterpart of the Free French Forces under de Gaulle.
10. *Leclerc*: Jacques-Philippe Leclerc (1902–1947). One of the first officers to join de Gaulle, he rapidly rose to the rank of general, fought in Chad, Libya, and Tunisia, and as general commanding the 2nd Armored Division, took part in the invasion of Normandy and spearheaded the Allied advance into Paris. He was posthumously made a marshal.
11. *Republican Guards*: French Parisian national guard.
12. *"militiamen"*: members of the Milice, the French counterpart of the German SS.
13. *attempt . . . life of General de Gaulle*: as De Gaulle entered Notre-Dame and advanced up the aisle, shots were fired three times, somewhat at random.
14. *Archbishop of Paris*: Cardinal Suhard, Archbishop of Paris, considered a collaborationist by the resistants; assassinated June 28, 1944, because he had received Marshal Pétain at Notre-Dame just four months before the Liberation and officiated at the funeral ceremony for Philippe Henriot, minister in the Pétain government. He had been requested not to take part in the Liberation ceremony at Notre-Dame.
15. *blockhouse*: small cement fortifications of the Germans.
16. *André Malraux*: (1901–   ), French novelist and art historian, an anticolonialist who took part in the anti-French under-

ground activities in Indochina. He later fought against Franco in Spain, and under the pseudonym of Colonel Berger, fought in the *maquis* and later on the Rhine.

17. *Yenbay, 1931:* town in North Vietnam, on the Red River, under French colonial rule. Andrée Viollis, a left-wing reporter, revealed to the French public the methods of repression used by the Army against the Viet Minh.

PIERRE DRIEU LA ROCHELLE
1944

From JOURNAL (1944-45)

December 31, 1944

« Well, what a year: I regret nothing; no, I regret one thing: not to have succeeded on the 12th August.[1] But now, I am again in life, and much more than the first months of this year. It seems, it seems!—that things are turning good; there are no more arrests, they are fed up with arrests; 30,000 people in jail, said the Minister of the Interior. That is perhaps enough. It is no less than Vichy had in its camps. It will be perhaps like that always in Europe now: it was like that in a part of Europe since a long time, since 1914.

« What will become of me? I don't know and don't care. Between democracy and communism there is no more interest for me, I suppose. I was for Europe, and Europe has been spoilt by Hitler in 1940; I was for European socialism, and it does not exist any more, Europe beeing torn between the Saxons and the Russians. Shall I write? I wrote because it has become an habit, late, too late. But it does not mean much: the time of literature and art is closed. The trouble is I am too old to enter a new trade, and, I am not enough a mystic to get out really of life. Well, I shall be a wanderer as I have been always in fact. But, if I can't travel, I think I shan't have patience to wait for death. »

NOTE

1. *12th August*: date of Drieu La Rochelle's first attempt at suicide.

SOURCE NOTE: Pierre Drieu La Rochelle, "31 décembre 1944," *Récit secret suivi de Journal (1944–1945) et d'Exorde* (Paris, Gallimard, 1951), pp. 72–73.

PAUL VALÉRY

September 1944

TO BREATHE

Liberty is a sensation. It is something you breathe. The idea that we are free swells the future of every moment. It opens deep inside us inner unknown wings with the power to make us soar dizzily aloft. We take a fresh, deep breath at the universal well where we draw the substance of life, and our being is pervaded by a renewal of its genuine wishes. It enters into possession of itself. It arouses every hope and plan in itself. It recovers the integrity of speech. It can talk to everyone as it talks to itself. It becomes aware of the full value of its steps, which meet with no more barriers or obstacles, and it smiles at the good women who hastily try with their small saws to turn a hideous forest of defense scaffolding into simple logs. All the broken, crushed, empty defense mechanisms, the ruined casemates, dislocated tanks, destroyed and now being reduced to scrap, the buildings riddled with bullets, wounded

SOURCE NOTE: Paul Valéry, "Respirer," *Vues* (Paris, La Table Ronde, 1948), pp. 397-99. Reprinted from *le Figaro*, September 2, 1944.

by explosions, disfigured by fire, convey the sense of some
extraordinary power, arising from life itself and against which
the most carefully devised obstacles, the most fearful weapons
in the hands of the most determined men, concrete, machines,
subterranean armies, and all that the toughest will can imagine
and create to master a revolt cannot prevail. We have seen
and experienced what a large and illustrious city can do when
it wants to breathe. And at last the vague term, the soul, has
an admirable meaning.

But, by regaining possession of itself, the mind recovers the
prerogatives and exercises them against the very instant in
which it regained them. It cannot be shackled by the delight
of living, of living anew. It must reanimate its own superior
code, which is not to yield to the moment or give way to its
joy. It must guard against the shock of euphoria which great
events can produce on the mind. Events are but the froth of
things. The ideas we have about them are wrong, and what
we learn from these blatant facts is arbitrary and dangerous.
We know what the "lessons" of preceding wars cost us in 1914
and 1940. It is enough to think of the infinite quantity of coin-
cidences which compose every "event" to realize that we cannot reason about them. Those who reason about them can
only do so through vulgar simplifications and the verbal, super-
ficial analogies which they entail. But today the mind must
retain its full lucidity. If the French mind possesses in fact its
proverbial virtue of clarity, it never was offered a more urgent
occasion to put it to use. We must try to conceive a new era.
Here we stand before a universal chaos of images and questions.
A quantity of unprecedented situations and problems will confront us in regard to which almost all that the past may teach
us is more to be feared than to be studied. We must start by a
thorough analysis of the present, not in order to foresee events
about which or about the consequences of which one is always
wrong, but to prepare, plan, or create what is needed to guard
against events, to resist them, and to use them. The instinctive
resources which organisms master in order to defend them-

selves against sudden unforeseen variations in their environment contain a great lesson.

This is no time to enlarge on these brief considerations. I shall only repeat what I have often said already: let us beware of entering the future backward . . . That's why I don't much like to hear people speak of rebuilding France: what I should like people to want is to build France.

ALASTAIR HAMILTON

Historians have looked to the chain of circumstances that led to the catastrophe of World War II, and to the complex network of problems that brought a nation like France to disaster. Historians and literary critics alike have also examined the background and prewar options of the writers who clashed so bitterly and irremediably during the Occupation years. Certainly the main lines of the ideological conflicts had long been developing, and had been stridently voiced in the political confrontations of the thirties. But in 1940 the "theatrical" or "circus" aspects of such involvement brusquely receded. Nazi domination, in a climate of unprecedented violence, created a situation that for the people living within it was political only secondarily. It had to be lived at a personal level in a day-by-day struggle with hard facts that tore through the edifice of assumptions upon which each man's view of the legitimacy of these ideologies rested. Prewar ideological convictions, indifference, or skepticism gave way before the reality of fundamental options, involving the whole fabric of a personality. The intellectuals' drive to take an active part in the struggle on whatever side reflected an often desperate belief in the power of the individual to determine the course of history, to shape the future of the French nation, and, beyond it, of world history, and a fierce desire to wrest meaning from the terror of events. Put to the test of events, their convictions were tragically overshadowed by a sense of the power and savagery of the forces set in

motion by war. This was true even of the convinced
Marxists, who could view the long-term future with a
measure of confidence but were fully aware of the toll
taken in terms of individual lives.

It is clear that men like Drieu La Rochelle, Brasillach,
Céline, and Montherlant all shared essentially not so much
an ideology as an acute sense of what they called the
decadence of France, a symptom in their eyes of a crisis in
Western civilization. Underlying the options of men like
Drieu and Brasillach were two basic attitudes, not ideological in kind nor consciously formulated: a nostalgic
image of a "happy" human order and the sense that, as
intellectuals, they could lead the masses toward its
immediate establishment, on the other side of an apoca-
lypse—the fascist revolution. The short-term realities of
World War II were too immediate to sustain the myth.
Those realities, in contrast—all ideology aside—brought the
resistant writer increasingly close to the practical problems
and immediate feelings of the mass of the French people,
however reluctant many were to take a heroic stance. The
"right" and "wrong" were simply and absolutely defined
in ethical, national, ideological cultural terms that meshed
for each individual in a single assertion and a fierce drama-
tization in human terms of the French reality. Though
many people remained neutral, "attentiste," the emotional
climate nonetheless was present and shared through the
twists and turns of events. The collaborationist myth was
not viable.

Yet the outcome, brought about by outside forces, remained blurred. The collective dilemmas of the French
nation—new institutions, changing civilization and future
—remained unsolved. If a certain capacity for self-deception allowed men as sensitively concerned for the future
of their country as a Brasillach or a Drieu La Rochelle to
overlook the Nazi reality in favor of the myth and so bear
the burden of complicity, the same holds true today for

many intellectuals who engaged them in combat over a myth just as gigantic: the myth of the moral and just society evolved in Stalin's Russia, some of whose less admirable aspects surfaced in the post-Liberation purge.

In fact, it is less the political content of the French situation than a grasp of its human implications that sorted out the men of moral stature from the others, reaching far into the conscience and awareness of the writers. The whole event raised old questions in a new perspective and provided only ambiguous answers: problems of art and reality; of the value of social action as compared to artistic creation; of the validity and nature of the writer's activity in the context of modern warfare and mass extermination; of his participation in violence and its legitimacy. Throughout, one senses the writers' concern for the course taken by Western civilization. A momentous event for the French, the years of occupation are merely an interlude in what was a complex historical event. In the last analysis, as the rhetoric fades, what judges the pieces we have assembled is each man's effort, against great odds, to maintain his integrity in thought, action, and word, and in the uncertainty of action, to confront his vulnerability and truths.

Chronology

1939 September 3   Great Britain and France declare war on Germany; period of the "phony war" as troops face each other on the Maginot and Siegfried lines.

1940 March 20   Daladier's regime collapses from public disfavor when, after a stubborn resistance, the Finns capitulate under Russian attack; Daladier succeeded by his Finance Minister, Reynaud.

May 13, 14   French front broken on the Meuse; the exodus (flight of refugees) begins.

May 19   General Gamelin replaced by Weygand as commander in chief of the French; Pétain enters the government as Vice-Premier and chief military advisor to Reynaud.

May 27–June 4   Evacuation of British troops from Dunkirk.

June 10   Italy joins the attack on France; French government abandons Paris for the region of Tours.

June 12, 13   French government collapses; Weygand and Pétain ask for an armistice with Germany.

June 14   German Army enters Paris.

June 16   Resignation of Premier Reynaud, succeeded by Pétain.

June 18   Military resistance ends; De Gaulle's first appeal to resist via a broadcast from London.

June 22	Signing of the Franco-German Armistice; De Gaulle's second appeal.
June 23	Laval, who advocates collaboration with Germany, becomes Vice-Premier.
June 24	Armistice with Italy.
July 1	French government set up in Unoccupied Zone at Vichy.
July 3	English attack French fleet at Mers-el-Kebir near Oran to prevent the French Navy from falling into the hands of the Germans.
July 10	National Assembly votes Pétain full power.
July 11	Vote of constitutional laws; ministry of Laval.
Summer	First formation of small, scattered Resistance groups: Henri Frenay groups military resistants in southern zone creating Libertés; also initiated: Libération, France-Libre (Franc-Tireur), etc.
September 23	Unsuccessful attack on the French forces at Dakar, Senegal, by English and Gaullists.
October 22	First meeting at Montoire, between Hitler and Laval.
October 24	Second meeting at Montoire, between Hitler and Pétain.
October 27	Laval, ardently pro-Nazi, made Foreign Minister.
December 13	After plotting to do away with Pétain in order to set up a more pro-Nazi government at Versailles, Laval is dismissed, indicating a shift away from a commitment to total collaboration.
1941 January	Founding of Le Rassemblement National Populaire, a Paris-centered organization of extreme pro-Nazi Orientation, to promote fuller cooperation with the Nazis.
May 27	Signing of the May Protocols, giving the Germans military facilities in Syria and North Africa for the Axis campaign there.
June 22	Russia invaded by Germany; active participation of French Communist Party in the Resistance movement begins, ending the

	Communists' passive attitude toward the Nazis dating back to the signing of the German-Soviet Pact.
July 26	Beginning of assassination attempts against Vichy.
August 12	Message by Pétain indicating a tightening of authority due to the increase in Resistance activities.
October	Initiation of the "Procès de Riom": trial of government officials of the Third Republic in an attempt to discredit the Republic. Daladier, Blum, etc., skillfully turned the debate into a discussion of the responsibilities for the French defeat, thus unearthing much evidence embarrassing to the Pétain government. The trial was never completed.
December 7	Japanese attack the U.S. fleet at Pearl Harbor; entrance of the United States into the war.
1942 January	First French *maquis* set up near Grenoble: armed bands grouping together in the French countryside to avoid compulsory transfer to work in Germany. Jean Moulin is sent by De Gaulle to coordinate the Resistance groups inside France and to establish secret intelligence liaison with them.
June	Germans demand that France turn in the Jewish refugees in the Unoccupied Zone and that the number of French sent to work in Germany be increased.
April	Return to power of Laval, representing a more pro-Nazi orientation at Vichy.
November 8	Anglo-American invasion of North Africa, aided by Darlan, who cunningly switches sides. Inauguration of a more rigid attitude on the part of the Germans toward Vichy.
November 11	Germans move into the Unoccupied Zone of France.
November 27	French fleet scuttled by the French at Toulon to avoid a German takeover; Pétain's government increasingly loses its influence with the Germans.

December 24	Assassination of Darlan; Giraud named head of French forces in the now Ally-occupied North Africa.
1943 February 1	Creation of the French Milice on the pattern of the German SS to aid the Germans in the hunt for Jews and Resistants.
February 2	Russians defeat the Germans at Stalingrad.
June	Committee of National Liberation formed at Algiers (De Gaulle and Giraud).
September	Liberation of Corsica, first triumph of the Resistance movement.
1944 January	Extremist proponents of collaboration from Paris enter the government at demand of Germans for Laval to reform the Pétain regime.
June 6	Allied landing in Normandy.
August 20	Pétain and Laval forcibly transferred to Belfort by the Germans; later to Sigmaringen in Germany.
August 26	De Gaulle enters Paris.

Biographical Glossary

ANOUILH, JEAN (1910–   ). French playwright, who won popular acclaim between the wars. Some of his better-known plays are *Le Bal des voleurs, Le Voyageur sans bagages, Antigone, La Répétition,* and *L'Alouette.*

ARAGON, LOUIS (1897–   ). French poet and novelist, once, with André Breton, outstanding personality of the surrealist movement. An ardent member of the French Communist Party. During the Occupation, Aragon helped found, in the southern zone, the National Committee of Writers (Comité National des Ecrivains) and contributed to the clandestine *Bibliothèque française* and the *Lettres françaises.* At the Editions de Minuit he published, under the pseudonym "François la Colère," a collection of poems, *Le Musée Grévin,* and under the pseudonym "Le Témoin des Martyrs," *Le Crime contre l'esprit.*

AURY, DOMINIQUE (1907–   ). French journalist, associate editor of *L'Arche.* With Jean Paulhan, she founded *Les Lettres françaises,* one of the earliest clandestine literary sheets.

AVELINE, CLAUDE (1901–   ). French novelist, essayist, and music critic. In 1940 Aveline founded with Jean Cassou the small group "Français libres de France." He also helped edit *Résistance.* After the affair of the Musée de l'Homme, he took refuge in the southern zone in 1941 but returned clandestinely in 1942. He contributed to *Liberté* and *Combat,* and helped found the *Cahiers de Libération.*

AYMÉ, MARCEL (1902–   ). French novelist, writer of short stories, and playwright. His works often combine satire with fantasy. His best-known works are *La Jument verte* (novel) and *Lucienne et le boucher* and *La Tête des autres* (plays).

BEAUVOIR, SIMONE DE (1908–   ). French essayist, novelist, playwright, and author of memoirs, who has long associated herself
with Jean-Paul Sartre and the existentialist movement. Author of
L'Invitée, Le Sang des autres, Les Mandarins (novels), *Mémoire
d'une jeune fille rangée, La Force de l'âge, La Force des choses*
(autobiographical writings), *Pour une morale de l'ambiguité, Le
Deuxième Sexe* (essays).

BRASILLACH, ROBERT (1909–1945). French novelist, essayist, and
journalist. During the Occupation he wrote for *L'Action française* and *Je suis partout,* the most adamant collaborationist
newspapers, as well as for *Révolution nationale, L'Echo de la
France,* and *La Gerbe.* After his imprisonment at Fresnes in
1944, many prominent Resistance and collaborationist writers
appealed to De Gaulle to spare his life. Nevertheless, he was
executed February 6, 1945.

CAMUS, ALBERT (1913–1960). French novelist, essayist, playwright,
and journalist who achieved fame after World War II. During
the Occupation, he wrote for the clandestine newspapers *Combat*
and *Cahiers de Libération.* His most famous works are *L'Etranger*
and *La Peste* (novels) and *Caligula* and *Les Justes* (plays). His
two essays *Le Mythe de Sisyphe* and *L'Homme révolt* are also
widely read.

CÉLINE, LOUIS-FERDINAND (1894–1961; pseudonym of Louis-
Ferdinand Destouches). French novelist and doctor who fought
in World War I and received injuries which were to cause him
suffering the rest of his life. Traveled to Africa, England, and
the United States. Achieved immediate success with *Voyage au
bout de la nuit* and *Mort à crédit,* which he wrote while practic-
ing at a clinic in Paris. During the Occupation he wrote violent
polemics attacking French political attitudes, Jews, politicians,
and the Resistance, and eventually was forced into exile in
Denmark from 1945 to 1951. He returned to France and continued his writing and medical practice, living in poverty and
seclusion.

DRIEU LA ROCHELLE, PIERRE (1893–1945). French novelist, essayist, and playwright. During the Occupation he supported the
Vichy government by his writings, although often with certain
hesitations. On March 15, 1945, having learned that an arrest
warrant had been filled out in his name, he committed suicide.

ÉLUARD, PAUL (1895–1952). French poet, once a member of the
surrealist movement. Certainly one of the principal Resistance
writers, he wrote for the *Lettres françaises,* the Éditions de
Minuit under the name "Jean du Haut" (*L'Honneur des Poètes*).
He founded the *Éternelle Revue* and the *Bibliothèque française.*

He was at that time a member of the French Communist Party. In 1942 he published a collection of poetry, *Poésie et vérité*, under his own name.

GIDE, ANDRÉ (1869–1951). French novelist, essayist, critic, and playwright. His principal works are *Les Nourritures terrestres*, *L'Immoraliste*, *La Porte étroite*, *Les Caves du Vatican*, *La Symphonie pastorale*, and *Les Faux-Monnayeurs*. Gide, quite old at this time, spent the years of the Occupation in the southern zone, in Tunisia, and in Algeria.

GIONO, JEAN (1895–   ). French novelist and essayist, born in the village of Manosque in Upper Provence, where he has lived most of his life. Independent and an anarchist in his political attitudes, Giono created in his novels a world of men and women living in close harmony with nature and free of the debasing influence of the mechanical civilization he hated.

GIRAUDOUX, JEAN (1882–1944). French novelist and playwright. Minister of Information in 1939. During the Occupation he acted as a liaison man for De Gaulle, furnishing information on the clandestine activities of the French intellectuals. Giraudoux's best known plays are *Amphitryon 38*, *Intermezzo*, *La Guerre de Troie n'aura pas lieu*, *Electre*, and *Ondine*.

GUÉHENNO, JEAN (1890–   ). French scholar and essayist of working-class origin, an ardent socialist and very active in left-wing activities during the *"entre deux guerres."* During the Occupation, he was a member of the Comité National des Ecrivains and wrote for the Editions de Minuit and the *Lettres françaises*. He published *Dans la prison* under the pseudonym "Cévennes."

LESCURE, PIERRE DE (1891–   ). French novelist. Founded the Éditions de Minuit with Jean Bruller (Vercors) and Yvonne Desvignes.

MAURIAC, FRANÇOIS (1885–   ). French Catholic novelist and playwright. During the Occupation, he published articles outside of France in the neutral countries and in France the *Cahier noir* under the pseudonym "Forez." His best-known novels are *Thérèse Desqueyroux* and *Le Noeud de Vipères*.

MAURRAS, CHARLES (1868–1952). French essayist and journalist, founder and editor of the royalist *Action française*. Dogmatic supporter of Pétain and the Vichy government. One of the spiritual leaders of the young French fascist movement. Imprisoned in 1944, he was finally released in 1952 shortly before his death.

MICHAUX, HENRI (1899–   ). Born in Belgium, naturalized French; a painter and poet whose best-known works are *Voyage en Grande-Garabagne*, *L'Espace du dedans*, and *Ailleurs*.

MONTHERLANT, HENRY DE (1896–   ). French novelist, essayist, and playwright. During the Occupation Montherlant neither collaborated nor resisted. As his *Solstice de juin* shows, his cult of virility and force put him in sympathy with certain aspects of the fascist spirit. His best-known plays are *La Reine morte* and *Port-Royal.*

SAINT-EXUPÉRY, ANTOINE DE (1900–1944). French novelist and aviator. Saint-Exupéry disappeared while flying a mission for the Liberation forces in 1944. He is best known for *Vol de nuit, Terre des hommes, Pilote de guerre,* and *Le Petit Prince.*

SARTRE, JEAN-PAUL (1905–   ). French philosopher, playwright, essayist, and novelist. Leader of the existentialist movement in France. During the Occupation, Sartre contributed to *Combat* and the *Eternelle Revue.* Well-known among his works are: *L'Etre et le Néant, Critique de la raison dialectique* (philosophy); *Les Mouches, Huis-clos, Le Diable et le Bon Dieu, Les Séquestrés d'Altona* (plays); *La Nausée* and *Les Chemins de la liberté* (novels). *Les Temps modernes,* an independent socialist-orientated publication which Sartre founded immediately after the war, has steadily taken positions on all political issues, national and international, since 1945.

THOMAS, EDITH (1909–   ). French novelist and journalist. During the Occupation she helped Claude Morgan reconstitute the Comité National des Ecrivains after the execution of its founder, the Communist deputy Jacques Decour. Edith Thomas also contributed to *Lettres françaises,* the *Eternelle Revue,* and published a collection of short stories, *Contes,* under the pseudonym "Auxois," and some poems under the name "Anne."

VALÉRY, PAUL (1871–1945). French poet, essayist, and critic. Though much opposed to the Vichy government and fascism, Valéry probably did not participate actively in the Resistance movement due to his advanced age and poor health. His best-known poetic works are *La Jeune Parque, Le Cimetière marin,* and *Charmes.*

WEIL, SIMONE (1909–1943). French philosophy professor and essayist of a mystical bent. She spent part of her life sharing the work and hardships of the working class. In 1942 she left France to join her parents in New York. In spite of poor health she was intent on joining the Resistance movement and joined the Gaullist forces in England, where she died in 1943 of self-imposed deprivation. The only works she published during her lifetime were articles in periodicals. After her death appeared *La Pesanteur et la grâce, La Connaissance surnaturelle, La Source grecque, La Condition ouvrière,* and *Ecrits historiques et politiques.*

Bibliography

I. *Bibliographical Works*

Catalogue des périodiques clandestins diffusés en France de 1939 à 1945, suivi d'un catalogue des périodiques clandestins diffusés à l'étranger. Paris, Bibliothèque nationale, 1954.

Debû-Bridel, Jacques, *Les Éditions de Minuit, historique et bibliographie.* Paris, Éditions de Minuit, 1945.

Jong, Dirk de, *Bibliographie des éditions françaises clandestines imprimées aux Pays-Bas pendant l'occupation allemande, 1940–1945.* The Hague, Stols, 1947.

Michel, Henri, *Bibliographie critique de la Résistance.* Paris, Institut Pédagogique National, 1964.

II. *General Historical Works About This Period*

Amoureux, Henri, *La Vie des Français sous l'occupation.* Paris, Fayard, 1961.

Aron, Robert, *Histoire de la libération de la France, juin 1944–mai 1945.* Paris, Fayard, 1959.

———, *Histoire de Vichy, 1940–1944.* Paris, Fayard, 1954.

Audiat, Pierre, *Paris pendant la guerre, juin 1940–août 1944.* Paris, Hachette, 1946.

Baudot, Marcel, *L'Opinion publique sous l'occupation; l'exemple d'un département français, 1939–1945.* Paris, Presses Universitaires de France, 1960.

Dussane, Béatrice, *Notes de Théâtre, 1940–1950.* Lyons, Lardanchet, 1951.

Ehrlich, Blake, *Resistance: France 1940–1945.* Boston, Little, Brown, 1965.

Freiberg, Reinhard, *Die Presse der französischen Resistance (Technik und Positionen einer untergrund Presse) 1940–1944.* Berlin, Ernst-Renter Gesellschaft, 1962.

Jamet, Claude, *Images mêlées de la littérature, et du théâtre pendant l'Occupation.* Paris, Editions de l'Élan, 1948.

———, *Le Rendez-vous manqué de 1944; vingt ans après, seize anciens résistants, Vichystes et collaborationnistes confrontent leurs points de vue dans un débat organisé, animé et présenté par Claude Jamet*. Paris, Éditions Empire, 1964.

Martin du Gard, Maurice, *La Chronique de Vichy, 1940–1944*. Paris, Flammarion, 1948.

Michel, Henri, *Les Courants de pensée de la Résistance*. Paris, Presses Universitaires de France, 1962.

———, *Histoire de la Résistance (1940–1944)*. "Que sais-je"; Paris, Presses Universitaires de France, 1950.

———, *Les Idées politiques et sociales de la résistance (documents clandestins 1940–1944)*. Paris, Presses Universitaires de France, 1954.

Parrot, Louis, *L'Intelligence en guerre, panorama de la pensée française dans la clandestinité*. Paris, La Jeune Parque, 1945.

Peyre, Henri, "French Literature Between 1940–1944," Franco-American Pamphlets, 3rd series, No. 4, American Society of the Legion of Honor, 1945.

Toynbee, Philip, "The Literary Situation in France," *Horizon* (November, 1944).

III. *Texts Written During the Occupation and Shortly After*

Adam, George (pseud. Hainaut), *À l'Appel de la liberté*. Paris, Éditions de Minuit, 1944.

Anouilh, Jean, *Antigone*. Paris, La Table Ronde, 1946.

———, *Eurydice*, in *Pièces noires*. Paris, Calmann-Lévy, 1942.

Aragon, Louis, *Le Crève-coeur*. Paris, Gallimard, 1941.

——— (pseud. Le Témoin des Martyrs), *Le Crime contre l'esprit*. Paris, Éditions de Minuit, 1944.

———, *La Diane française*. Paris, Seghers, 1946.

——— (pseud. François la Colère), *Le Musée. Grévin*. Paris, Éditions de Minuit, 1943.

Association des écrivains combattants, *Anthologie des écrivains morts à la guerre, 1939–1945*. Paris, Albin Michel, 1960.

Aymé, Marcel, *Le Passe-muraille*. Paris, Gallimard, 1943.

Beauvoir, Simone de, "Journal de guerre," in *La Force de l'âge*. Paris, Gallimard, 1960. Pp. 459–72.

Benda, Julien, *Exercice d'un enterré vif (juin 1940–août 1944)*, Geneva and Paris, Éditions des Trois Collines, 1945.

——— (pseud. Comminges), *Le Rapport d'Uriel*, in *Chroniques interdites*. Paris, Éditions de Minuit, 1943. Pp. 43–56.

Béraud, Henri, *Qu'as-tu fait de ta jeunesse?* Paris, Les Éditions de France, 1943.

Bernanos, Georges, *Lettre aux Anglais*. Rio de Janeiro, Atlantica editoria, 1942.

Bieber, Konrad, *L'Allemagne vue par les écrivains de la résistance française*. Preface by Albert Camus. Geneva, Droz, 1954.

Bloch, Marc, *L'Étrange défaite; témoignage écrit en 1940*. Paris, Albin Michel, new edition 1957.

Borwiz, Michel, *Écrits des condamnés à mort sous l'occupation allemande (1939–1945)*. Paris, Presses Universitaires de France, 1954.

Bost, Pierre (pseud. Vivarais), *La Haute Fourche*. Paris, Éditions de Minuit, 1944.

Brasillach, Robert, *Journal d'un homme occupé*. Paris, Les Sept Couleurs, 1955.

——, *Lettre à un soldat de la classe soixante; suivie de textes écrits en prison*. Paris, Les Sept Couleurs, 1960.

——, *Notre Avant-guerre*. Paris, Plont, 1941.

——, *Poèmes de Fresnes*. Paris, Les Sept Couleurs, 1949.

Bruller, Jean (pseud. Santerre), *Désespoir est mort*, in *Chroniques interdites*. Paris, Éditions de Minuit, 1943. Pp. 75–91.

—— (pseud. Vercors), *La Marche à l'étoile*. Paris, Éditions de Minuit, 1943.

——, *Le Silence de la mer*. Paris, Éditions de Minuit, 1942.

Camus, Albert, *Caligula*. Paris, Gallimard, 1944.

——, *L'Étranger*. Paris, Gallimard, 1942.

——, *Lettres à un ami allemand*. Paris, Gallimard, 1948.

——, *Le Malentendu*. Paris, Gallimard, 1944.

——, *Le Mythe de Sisyphe*. Paris, Gallimard, 1942.

Cassou, Jean (pseud. Jean Noir), *Trente-trois Sonnets composés en secret*. Paris, Éditions de Minuit, 1944.

Céline, Louis Ferdinand (real name Louis-Ferdinand Destouches), *Bagatelles pour un massacre*. Paris, Denoël, 1941.

——, *Les Beaux Draps*. Paris, Nouvelles Éditions Françaises, 1941.

——, *Guignol's Band I*. Paris, Denoël, 1944.

Chamson, André, *Fragments d'un Liber Veritatis (1941–1942)*. Paris, Gallimard, 1946.

——, (pseud. Lauter), *Le Puits des Miracles*, in *Nouvelles Chroniques interdites*. Paris, Éditions de Minuit, 1944. Pp. 75–92.

Chardonne, Jacques (pseud. Jacques Boutelleau), *Attachements (chronique privée)*. Paris, Stock, 1943.

——, *Chronique privée. Autour de Barbezieux*. Paris, Stock, 1940.

——, *Chronique privée de l'an 1940*. Paris, Stock, 1941.

——, *Voir la figure*. Paris, Grasset, 1941.

Chateaubriant, Alphonse de, *Cahiers 1906–1955*. Paris, Grasset, 1955.

——, *Chef et son peuple*. Éditions des Trois Épis, 1942.

——, *Les Pas ont chanté*. Paris, Livre moderne illustré, 1941; Grasset, 1943.

Chroniques interdites. Paris, Éditions de Minuit, 1943.

Claudel, Paul, *Poèmes et paroles durant la Guerre de Trente Ans*. Paris, Gallimard, 1945.

Debû-Bridel, Jacques (pseud. Argonne), *Angleterre*. Paris, Éditions de Minuit, 1943.

——, *Pages de Journal*, in *Chroniques interdites*. Paris, Éditions de Minuit, 1943. Pp. 63–74.

Decour, Jacques (pseud. Daniel Decourdemanche; member of the underground killed by the Gestapo). *Comme je vous en donne l'exemple*. Edited by Louis Aragon. Paris, Editions Sociales, 1945.

——, "Lettre d'adieu," in Jean Paulhan and Dominique Aury, eds., *La Patrie se fait tous les jours*. Paris, Éditions de Minuit, 1947.

——, *Pages choisies avec une bibliographie des oeuvres de Jacques Decour*. Paris, Éditions de Minuit, secret edition.

De Gaulle, Charles, *La France n'a pas perdu la guerre (Discours et Messages)*. New York, Didier, 1944.

Desvignes, Yvonne (pseud. Queyras), *L'Indignation*, in *Chroniques interdites*. Paris, Éditions de Minuit, 1943. Pp. 35–41.

Drieu La Rochelle, Pierre, *Notes pour comprendre le siècle*. Paris, Gallimard, 1941.

——, *Récit secret, suivi de Journal (1944–1945) et d'Exorde*. Paris, Gallimard, 1961.

Éluard, Paul, (pseuds. Jean du Haut, Maurice Hervent), *Au Rendez-vous allemand, suivi de Poésie et vérité 1942*. Paris, Éditions de Minuit, 1945.

—— (pseud. L'Honneur des Poètes), *Europe*. Paris, Éditions de Minuit, 1944.

Emmanuel, Pierre, *Combats avec tes défenseurs*. Paris, Seghers, 1943.

Fabre-Luce, Alfred (pseud. Sapiens), *Journal de la France, mars 1939–juillet 1940*. Paris, Trévoux, 1940.

Gide, André, *Attendu que*. Algiers, Charlot, 1943.

——, *Fragments d'un journal, 1942–1943*, in *Nouvelles Chroniques interdites*. Paris, Éditions de Minuit, 1943. Pp. 23–39.

——, *Journal 1939–1942*. Paris, Gallimard, 1946.

——, *Journal 1942–1949*. Paris, Gallimard, 1950.

Giono, Jean, *Ides et calendes*. Paris, Grasset, 1942.

Giraudoux, Jean, *Littérature*. Paris, Grasset, 1941.

——, *Sodome et Gomorrhe*. Paris, Grasset, 1947.

Green, Julien, *Journal*. Paris, Plon, 1961.

Guéhenno, Jean (pseud. Cévennes), *Dans la prison*. Paris, Éditions de Minuit, 1944.

——, *Journal des années noires 1940–1944*. Paris, Gallimard, 1947.

Jouve, Pierre-Jean, *A une soie*. Paris, Egloff, 1945.

Lannes, Roger, *La Peine capitale*. Paris, Denoël, 1943.

Lanza Del Vasto, *Le Vitrail*. Algiers, Fontaine, 1941.

Malraux, André, *La Lutte avec l'ange. 1. Les Noyers de l'Altenburg*. Geneva, Éditions du Haut Pays, 1943.

Maritain, Jacques, *À Travers le désastre*. New York, Éditions de la Maison française, 1941.

——, *Le Crépuscule de la civilisation*. Montreal, Éditions de l'Arbre, 1941.

——, *De la justice politique; notes sur la présente guerre*. Paris, Plon, 1940.

——, *Messages (1941–1944)*. New York, Éditions de la Maison française, 1945.

Massis, Henri, *Les Idées restent*. Lyons, Lardanchet, 1941.

Masson, Loÿs, *Délivrez-nous du mal*. Montreal, Éditions L. Parizeau, 1946.

Mauriac, François (pseud. Forez), *Le Cahier noir*. Paris, Éditions de Minuit, 1943.

——, *Les Mals Aimés*. Paris, Grasset, 1945.

Maurois, André, *Espoirs et Souvenirs*. New York, Éditions de la Maison française, 1943.

——, *Tragédie en France*. New York, Éditions de la Maison française, 1940.

Maurras, Charles, *De la Colère à la justice; réflexions sur un désastre*. Geneva, Éditions du Milieu du Monde, 1942.

————, *La Seule France, chronique des jours d'épreuve*. Lyons, Lardan-chet, 1941.

Michaux, Henri, *Épreuves, exorcismes 1940–1944*. Paris, Gallimard, 1945.

Montherlant, Henry de, *Fils de Personne*. Paris, Laffont, 1943.

————, *La Reine morte*. Paris, Gallimard, 1942.

————, *Le Solstice de juin*. Paris, Grasset, 1941.

————, *Textes sous l'occupation 1940–1944*. Paris, Gallimard, 1953.

Monzie, Anatole de, *Ci-devant*. Paris, Flammarion, 1941.

————, *La Saison des juges*. Paris, Flammarion, 1943.

Morgan, Claude (pseud. Montagne), *La Marque de l'homme*. Paris, Éditions de Minuit, 1944.

Nouvelles Chroniques interdites. Paris, Éditions de Minuit, 1944.

Paulhan, Jean (pseud. Lomagne), *Jacques Decour*, in *Chroniques interdites*. Paris, Éditions de Minuit, 1943. Pp. 13–29.

———— and Dominique Aury, *La Patrie se fait tous les jours*. Paris, Éditions de Minuit, 1947.

Péri, Gabriel, *Ma Vie*, in *Péguy-Péri*. Paris, Éditions de Minuit, 1944.

Rebatet, Lucien, *Les Décombres*. Paris, Denoël, 1942.

Reverdy, Pierre, *Main d'Oeuvre, poèmes 1913–1949*. Paris, Mercure de France, 1949.

Roy, Claude, *Clair comme le jour* (poems). Paris, Julliard, 1943.

Saint-Exupéry, Antoine de, *Lettre à un ôtage*. New York, Brentano's, 1943.

————, *Pilote de guerre*. New York, Éditions de la Maison française, 1942.

Saint-John Perse (real name Alexis Léger), *Exil*. Buenos Aires, Les Lettres françaises, secret edition of 15 copies. Originally appeared in *Cahiers du Sud*, 1942.

————, *Neiges*. Buenos Aires, Les Lettres françaises, 1945.

————, *Pluies*. Buenos Aires, Les Lettres françaises, 1944.

————, *Vents*. Paris, Nouvelle Revue Française, 1946.

Sartre, Jean-Paul, *Les Mouches*. Paris, Gallimard, 1943.

————, *Huis-clos*. Paris, Gallimard, 1945.

————, "La République du silence," "Paris sous l'occupation," "Qu'est-ce qu'un collaborateur?" "La Fin de la guerre," in *Situations III*. Paris, Gallimard, 1949.

Supervielle, Jules, *Poèmes de la France malheureuse 1939–1941*. Neuchâtel, La Baconnière, 1942.

Talagrand, Jacques (pseud. Thierry Maulnier), *La France, la guerre et la paix*. Lyons, Lardanchet, 1942.

Tardieu, Jean, *Choix de poèmes, 1924–1954*. Paris, Gallimard, 1961.

Thomas, Edith (pseud. Auxois), *Contes d'Auxois (transcrit du réel)*. Paris, Éditions de Minuit, 1943.

Triolet, Elsa, *Le Cheval blanc*. Paris, Denoël, 1942.

————, *Milles Regrets*. Paris, Denoël, 1943.

Trouillé, Pierre, *Journal d'un préfet pendant l'occupation*. Paris, Gallimard, 1964.

Valéry, Paul, *Vues*. Paris, La Table Ronde, 1948.

Weil, Simone (pseud. Emile Novis), "The Iliad, Poem of Force," *Chicago Review*, Vol. XVIII, No. 2 (1965), pp. 5–30. Originally appeared in *Cahiers du Sud*, December 1940 and January 1941.